IEEE Std 602-1996
(Revision of IEEE Std 602-1986)

IEEE Recommended Practice for Electric Systems in Health Care Facilities

Sponsor

**Power Systems Engineering Committee
of the
Industrial and Commercial Power Systems Department
of the
IEEE Industry Applications Society**

Approved 21 March 1996

IEEE Standards Board

Abstract: A recommended practice for the design and operation of electric systems in health care facilities is provided. The term "health care facility," as used here, encompasses buildings or parts of buildings that contain hospitals, nursing homes, residential custodial care facilities, clinics, ambulatory health care centers, and medical and dental offices. Buildings or parts of buildings within an industrial or commercial complex, used as medical facilities, logically fall within the scope of this book.
Keywords: anaesthetizing, clinical, critical branch, emergency system, equipment system, essential electrical system, examination, fire alarm, ground-fault circuit-interrupter, ground-fault protection, grounding, life safety branch, medical, nurse call, patient care, recovery, safety, standby generator, surgical, transfer switch, treatment, wet location

First Printing
January 1997
SH94446

The Institute of Electrical and Electronics Engineers, Inc.
345 East 47th Street, New York, NY 10017-2394, USA

Copyright © 1997 by the Institute of Electrical and Electronics Engineers, Inc.
All rights reserved. Published 1997. Printed in the United States of America

ISBN 1-55937-772-0

Introduction

(This introduction is not a part of IEEE Std 602-1996, IEEE Recommended Practice for Electric Systems in Health Care Facilities.)

IEEE Std 602-1996, IEEE Recommended Practice for Electric Systems in Health Care Facilities, commonly known as the IEEE White Book, is written primarily for the practicing electrical design engineer who may have limited experience with health care facilities and for hospital operating personnel. It will also be useful for those who supply products and services for health care facilities. While the text deals with a broad range of topics relevant to the design and operation of health care facilities, it focuses on those aspects of facility design and operation that are unique to health care facilities. These include patient electrical safety, patient care issues, continuity of electric service, and a reliable source of power to sensitive computer-based clinical and biomedical equipment. The text also touches on communication and alarm systems that are unique to the health care facility.

This IEEE Recommended Practice continues to serve as a companion publication to the following other Recommended Practices prepared by the IEEE Industrial and Commercial Power Systems Department:

— IEEE Std 141-1993, IEEE Recommended Practice for Electric Power Distribution for Industrial Plants (IEEE Red Book).

— IEEE Std 142-1991, IEEE Recommended Practice for Grounding of Industrial and Commercial Power Systems (IEEE Green Book).

— IEEE Std 241-1990, IEEE Recommended Practice for Electric Power Systems in Commercial Buildings (IEEE Gray Book).

— IEEE Std 242-1986, IEEE Recommended Practice for Protection and Coordination of Industrial and Commercial Power Systems (IEEE Buff Book).

— IEEE Std 399-1990, IEEE Recommended Practice for Industrial and Commercial Power Systems Analysis (IEEE Brown Book).

— IEEE Std 446-1995, IEEE Recommended Practice for Emergency and Standby Power Systems for Industrial and Commercial Applications (IEEE Orange Book).

— IEEE Std 493-1990, IEEE Recommended Practice for the Design of Reliable Industrial and Commercial Power Systems (IEEE Gold Book).

— IEEE Std 739-1995, IEEE Recommended Practice for Energy Management in Industrial and Commercial Facilities (IEEE Bronze Book).

— IEEE Std 1100-1992, IEEE Recommended Practice for Powering and Grounding Sensitive Electronic Equipment (IEEE Emerald Book).

The White Book Working Group for the 1996 edition had the following membership:

Hugh O. Nash, Jr., *Chair*

Chapter 1: Overview—**Hugh O. Nash, Jr.,** *Chair*

Chapter 2: Load requirements and energy management—**Lester H. Smith,** *Chair;*
George A. Jackins, Jr., Al Marden, Anthony J. Scalone, Richard H. Wood

Chapter 3: Electrical power distribution systems—**James Harvey,** *Chair;*
Glenn Keates, Mark Martyak, Jack Petro, Vincent Saporita, David W. Stabler

Chapter 4: Planning for patient care—**Richard Nalbert,** *Chair*

Chapter 5: Emergency power systems—**Herb Daugherty,** *Co-Chair;*
Lawrence F. Hogrebe, *Co-Chair;* James R. Harvey, Charles H. Meyer,
James E. Tyson

Chapter 6: Electrical safety and grounding—**Stephen Benesh,** *Co-Chair;* **Jerome Frank,**
Co-Chair; Doug Erickson, Lawrence F. Hogrebe, Steve Kay, Charles H. Meyer,
Gene Schabely, Jeff Steplowski, Clarence Tsung, George Webb

Chapter 7: Lighting—**Walter N. Vernon,** *Chair;*
Ed Hammer, James R. Harvey, L. J. Maloney, David W. Stabler,
John D. Stolshek

Chapter 8: Communication and signal systems—**James R. Duncan,** *Chair;*
Greg S. Batie, Douglas A. Bors, Emanuel M. Furst, James W. Madson,
Maureen Pajerski, David Verner, Walter N. Vernon, Dewey Wilson

Chapter 9: Medical equipment and instrumentation—**Raymond E. Heintel,** *Chair;*
John Credico

Chapter 10: Health care renovations—**Walter N. Vernon,** *Chair;*
Richard Graham, James R. Harvey, Joseph A. Jacke, Stephen J. Schaffer,
John T. VanLandingham

The following persons were on the balloting committee:

Lucas Ananian	A. P. Haggerty	T. David Mills
Robert J. Beaker	James R. Harvey	Daleep Mohla
James Beall	Robert G. Hoerauf	Richard Nalbert
Carl E. Becker	Lawrence F. Hogrebe	Hugh O. Nash, Jr.
Richard W. Becker	Robert W. Ingham	Milton D. Robinson
Rene Castenschiold	R. Gerald Irvine	Vincent Saporita
James M. Daly	Douglas Kanitz	Lynn F. Saunders
James R. Duncan	Suresh C. Kapoor	Stephen Schaffer
Richard A. Evans	C. Grant Keough	Lester H. Smith
Jerry M. Frank	Thomas S. Key	Thomas E. Sparling
Edgar O. Galyon	Steven A. Larson	S. I. Venugopalan
Steven R. Goble	Wei-Jen Lee	Philip A. Zinck
Dan Goldberg	Michael Z. Lowenstein	Donald W. Zipse

When the IEEE Standards Board approved this recommended practice on 21 March 1996, it had the following membership:

Contents

IEEE Recommended Practice for Electric Systems in Health Care Facilities

Chapter 1
Overview

1.1 Scope and general discussion

IEEE Std 602-1996, IEEE Recommended Practice for Electric Systems in Health Care Facilities, commonly known as the IEEE White Book, is published by the Institute of Electrical and Electronics Engineers (IEEE) to provide a recommended practice for the design and operation of electric systems in health care facilities. It has been prepared on a voluntary basis by design engineers, health care end users, as well as electrical and medical manufacturers functioning as the White Book Working Group within the Power Systems Design Subcommittee of the Power Systems Engineering Committee.

This recommended practice will probably be of greatest value to the power oriented engineer with limited health care experience. It can also be an aid to all engineers responsible for the electrical design of health care facilities. However, it is not intended as a replacement for the many excellent engineering texts and handbooks commonly in use, nor is it detailed enough to be a design manual. It should be considered a guide and a general reference on electrical design for health care facilities.

1.2 Health care facilities

The term "health care facility," as used here, encompasses buildings or parts of buildings that contain hospitals, nursing homes, residential custodial care facilities, clinics, and medical and dental offices. Buildings or parts of buildings within an industrial or commercial complex, used as medical facilities, logically fall within the scope of this book. Thus the specific use of the building in question, rather than the nature of the overall development of which it is a part, determines its electrical design category. Today's health care facilities, because of their increasing size and complexity, have become more and more dependent upon safe, adequate, and reliable electrical systems. Every day new types of sophisticated diagnostic and treatment equipment, utilizing microprocessors or computers, come on the market. Many of these items are sensitive to electrical disturbances and some require a very reliable power source. Invasive medical procedures such as cardiac catheterization have become routine in today's hospital. Such procedures make electrical safety extremely important. Moreover, new medical and surgical procedures are constantly being developed. In addition to the special safety and reliability requirements, health care facilities have unique life safety and communication requirements, because patients are generally unable to care for themselves or evacuate themselves in the event of an emergency. For these reasons, perhaps no area of design or construction is changing as fast as health care facilities.

1.3 IEEE publications

The IEEE publishes several standards similar to the IEEE White Book, prepared by the Industrial Power Systems Department of the IEEE Industry Applications Society.[1] The following standards may be useful for anyone designing or operating a health care facility:

IEEE Std 141-1993, IEEE Recommended Practice for Electric Power Distribution for Industrial Plants (IEEE Red Book).

IEEE Std 142-1991, IEEE Recommended Practice for Grounding of Industrial and Commercial Power Systems (IEEE Green Book).

IEEE Std 241-1990, IEEE Recommended Practice for Electric Power Systems in Commercial Buildings (IEEE Gray Book).

IEEE Std 242-1986 (Reaff 1991), IEEE Recommended Practice for Protection and Coordination of Industrial and Commercial Power Systems (IEEE Buff Book).

IEEE Std 399-1990, IEEE Recommended Practice for Industrial and Commercial Power Systems Analysis (IEEE Brown Book).

IEEE Std 446-1987, IEEE Recommended Practice for Emergency and Standby Power Systems for Industrial and Commercial Applications (IEEE Orange Book).

IEEE Std 493-1990, IEEE Recommended Practice for the Design of Reliable Industrial and Commercial Power Systems (IEEE Gold Book).

IEEE Std 739-1995, IEEE Recommended Practice for Energy Management in Industrial and Commercial Facilities (IEEE Bronze Book).

IEEE Std 1100-1992, IEEE Recommended Practice for Powering and Grounding Sensitive Electronic Equipment (IEEE Emerald Book).

IEEE Std 241-1990, commonly known as the IEEE Gray Book, will be of particular importance as a reference book to the hospital designer because of the many similarities between commercial buildings and health care facilities.

---

[1]IEEE publications are available from the Institute of Electrical and Electronics Engineers, 445 Hoes Lane, P.O. Box 1331, Piscataway, NJ 08855-1331.

1.3.1 Industry Applications Society

The IEEE is divided into 35 groups and societies that specialize in various technical areas of electrical engineering. Each group or society conducts meetings and publishes papers on developments within its specialized area. The Industry Applications Society (IAS) presently encompasses 23 technical committees covering electrical engineering in specific areas (petroleum and chemical industry, cement industry, glass industry, industrial and commercial power systems, and others). The Power Systems Engineering Committee, which has balloting authority for the IEEE White Book, is part of the Industrial and Commercial Power Systems Department of the IAS. Papers of interest to electrical engineers and designers involved in the field covered by the IEEE White Book are, for the most part, contained in the *Transactions* of the IAS. Individuals who desire to participate in the activities of the committees or working groups in the preparation or revisions of the White Book or other Color Books should contact the IEEE Standards Department, 445 Hoes Lane, P.O. Box 1331, Piscataway, NJ 08855.

1.3.2 Engineering in medicine and biology society

Another IEEE group of interest to the electrical engineer involved in health care facility design is the Engineering in Medicine and Biology Society (EMBS). The EMBS *Transactions* and the EMBS *Magazine* include articles on the physiological effects of electrical shock and other subjects pertinent to electrical safety. Articles dealing with electrical equipment and instrumentation also appear in the EMBS *Transactions*.

1.4 Professional registration

Most regulatory agencies require that design for public buildings be prepared by state-licensed professional architects or engineers. Information on such registration may be obtained from the appropriate state agency or from the local chapter of the National Council of Examiners for Engineering and Surveying (NCEES).

To facilitate obtaining registration in different states by reciprocity, a national professional certificate is issued by the National Bureau of Engineering Registration[2] to engineers who obtained their home-state license by examination. All engineering graduates are encouraged to start on the path to full registration by taking the engineer-in-training examination as soon after graduation as possible. The final written examination in the field of specialization is usually conducted after four years of progressive professional experience.

Clinical engineering certification is available through an international commission. When available, the hospital's clinical engineer should be involved in the electrical design process.

---

[2]P.O. Box 1686, Clemson, SC 29633-1686.

3

1.5 Codes and standards

1.5.1 National Electrical Code® and other NFPA standards

The electrical wiring and design recommendations in the National Electrical Code® (NEC®) (NFPA 70-1996) are vitally important guidelines for health care facility engineers. Article 517 of the NEC deals exclusively with installation criteria for health care facilities. The NEC is revised every three years, and care should be taken to use the edition that is current and adopted by the authority having jurisdiction of enforcement (AHJ) at the time of construction. The NEC is published and available from the National Fire Protection Association (NFPA).[3] It does not represent a design specification but only identifies minimum requirements for the safe installation and utilization of electricity on the premises. The introduction to the NEC, Article 90, covers purpose and scope, and describes the AHJ's role in interpreting and enforcing the code. The *Handbook of the National Electrical Code®*, sponsored by the NFPA, contains the complete NEC text plus explanations. This book is edited to correspond with each edition of the NEC.

NFPA 99-1996, Health Care Facilities, addresses performance and testing criteria for electric systems in health care facilities as well as requirements for medical gas systems; heating, ventilation, and air conditioning systems; laboratories; and other topics of interest to health care designers. Approximately two thirds of NEC Article 517 is extracted from NFPA 99-1996.

The NFPA publishes the following related documents containing requirements on electrical and medical equipment and systems:

NFPA 20-1993, Installation of Centrifugal Fire Pumps.

NFPA 53-1994, Fire Hazards in Oxygen-Enriched Atmospheres.

NFPA 70B-1994, Electrical Equipment Maintenance.

NFPA 70E-1995, Electrical Safety Requirements for Employee Work Places.

NFPA 72-1993, Protective Signaling Systems.

NFPA 75-1992, Electronic Computer/Data Processing Equipment.

NFPA 77-1993, Static Electricity.

NFPA 101-1994, Life Safety Code.

NFPA 101HB94, Life Safety Code Handbook, 1994 edition.

---

[3]The NEC is available from Publication Sales, National Fire Protection Association, 1 Batterymarch Park, P.O. Box 9101, Quincy, MA 02269-9101.

NFPA 110-1993, Emergency and Standby Power Systems.

NFPA 111-1993, Stored Electrical Energy Emergency and Standby Power Systems.

NFPA 780-1992, Lightning Protection Code.

NFPA FPH1791, Fire Protection Handbook, 1991 edition.

The NEC and other selected NFPA codes are generally adopted by local and state governments for enforcement by electrical and building inspectors and fire marshals.

1.5.2 Health care codes and standards

Additional electrical requirements for health care facilities are included in the Accreditation Manual for Hospitals published by the Joint Commission for the Accreditation of Health Care Organizations (JCAHO). Hospitals seeking JCAHO accreditation must undergo periodic inspection by JCAHO examiners. Accreditation depends on the hospital's conformance with the requirements included in the accreditation manual.

The Department of Health and Human Services formerly published a standard entitled, *Minimum Requirements for Construction and Equipment of Hospitals and Medical Facilities* and enforced it on a national basis. The American Institute of Architects (AIA) obtained the copyright in 1987 and produced a revision called <u>Guidelines for Construction and Equipment of Hospitals and Medical Facilities</u>.[4] AIA revised the document again in 1992–1993. It is still enforced by many state and federal agencies.

Electrical designers working on projects for the Department of Veterans Affairs, Department of Defense, the General Services Administration, Public Buildings Service, and other government agencies must be aware that these agencies generally publish standards for electrical design. These standards or guidelines can be obtained from the appropriate agency.

1.5.3 Local, state, and federal codes and regulations

While most municipalities, counties, and states use the NEC without change, some have their own codes. In some instances the NEC is adopted by local ordinance as part of the building code, with deviations from the NEC listed as addenda. It is important to note that only the code adopted as of a certain date is official, and that governmental bodies may delay adopting the latest code. Federal rulings may require use of the latest NEC regardless of local rulings, so that reference to the enforcing agencies for interpretation on this point may be necessary.

Some city and state codes are almost as extensive as the NEC. It is generally accepted that in the case of conflict, the more stringent or severe interpretation applies. Generally the entity responsible for enforcing the code has the power to interpret it.

---

[4]This publication can be obtained from AIA Press, 1735 New York Avenue, Washington, DC 20006 (tel. 800-365-2724). A 1996 edition is expected to be published shortly.

Failure to comply with NEC or local code requirements can affect the owner's ability to obtain a certificate of occupancy and may have a negative effect on insurance.

In most states, health care construction comes under the jurisdiction of a state health department. In some instances the state will have its own hospital or health care code with specific electrical requirements.

Both state and local authorities may adopt and enforce one of the model building codes written by a regional building officials group. These include the Standard Building Code, the Uniform Building Code™, and the National Building Code.

Legislation by the U.S. federal government has had the effect of giving standards, such as certain ANSI standards, the impact of law. The Occupational Safety and Health Act, administered by the U.S. Department of Labor, permits federal enforcement of codes and standards. The Occupational Safety and Health Administration (OSHA) has adopted the 1971 NEC for new electrical installations and also for major replacements, modifications, or repairs installed after 5 March 1972. A few articles and sections of the NEC have been deemed to apply retroactively by OSHA. The NFPA created the NFPA 70E Committee to prepare a consensus standard for possible use by OSHA in developing their standards. Major portions of NFPA 70E-1988 (Electrical Safety Requirements for Employee Work Places) have been included in OSHA regulations.

OSHA requirements are published in the *Federal Register*.[5] OSHA rules for electric systems are covered in 29 CFR Part 1910 of the *Federal Register*.

The U.S. National Institute of Occupational Safety and Health (NIOSH) publishes *Electrical Alerts* [6] to warn of unsafe practices or hazardous electrical equipment.

The U.S. Department of Energy, by encouraging building energy performance standards, has advanced energy conservation standards. A number of states have enacted energy conservation regulations. These include ASHRAE/IESNA legislation embodying various energy conservation standards such as ASHRAE/IESNA 90.1-1989, Energy Efficient Design of New Buildings Except Low-Rise Residential Buildings. These establish energy or power budgets that materially affect architectural, mechanical, and electrical designs.

1.5.4 Standards and recommended practices

A number of organizations in addition to the NFPA publish documents that affect electrical design. Adherence to these documents can be written into design specifications.

ANSI approves the standards of many other organizations. ANSI coordinates the review of proposed standards among all interested affiliated societies and organizations to ensure a consensus approval. It is in effect a clearinghouse for technical standards of all types.

---

[5]The *Federal Register* is available from the Superintendent of Documents, U.S. Government Printing Office, Washington, DC 20402 (telephone 202-783-3238) on a subscription or individual copy basis.

[6]Copies of this bulletin are available from NIOSH Publications Dissemination, 4676 Columbia Parkway, Cincinnati, OH 45226.

Underwriters Laboratories, Inc. (UL)[7] is a non-profit organization, operating laboratories for investigation with respect to hazards affecting life and property, materials and products, especially electrical appliances and equipment. In so doing, they develop test standards. Equipment that has been tested by UL or another nationally recognized testing organizations (i.e., OSHA), and found to conform to their standards, is known as listed or labeled equipment.

The National Electrical Manufacturers Association (NEMA)[8] represents equipment manufacturers. Their publications serve to standardize the manufacture of, and provide testing and operating standards for electrical equipment. The design engineer should be familiar with any NEMA standard that might affect the application of any equipment to be specified.

1.6 Reference books

The American Hospital Association (AHA) publishes a series of books on topics of interest to hospital engineers. The series is called the *Management and Compliance Series* (MACS). The books are available from the AHA at 840 North Lakeshore Drive, Chicago, IL 60611. Of particular interest to the electrical engineer will be Volume 4, *Fire Warning and Safety Systems* and Volume 7, *Electrical Systems for Health Care Facilities*. Other volumes deal with a wide variety of subjects, including medical gas systems and heating, ventilation, and air conditioning (HVAC) systems.

The Illuminating Engineering Society of North America (IESNA) publishes a *Lighting Handbook* in two volumes. Volume 2, *Applications*, includes a chapter on lighting for health care facilities.

The introduction to the IEEE Gray Book includes a list of additional references and handbooks that may be of interest to the health care electrical designer.

1.7 Periodicals

Spectrum, the basic monthly publication of the IEEE, covers all aspects of electrical and electronic engineering with limited material on health care facilities. This publication, however, does contain references to IEEE books and other publications; technical meetings and conferences; IEEE group, society, and committee activities; abstracts of papers and publications of the IEEE and other organizations, and other material essential to the professional advancement of the electrical engineer. The *Transactions* of the Industrial Applications Society and the Engineers in Medicine and Biology Society of the IEEE can be useful to health care electrical engineers.

Following are some other well-known periodicals:

---

[7]333 Pfingsten Road, Northbrook, IL 60020.
[8]2101 L Street, NW, Washington, DC 20037.

ASHRAE Journal, American Society of Heating, Refrigerating and Air-Conditioning Engineers, 1791 Tullie Circle NE, Atlanta, GA 30329.

Biomedical Engineering, 233 Spring Street, New York, NY 10013.

Consulting-Specifying Engineer, Cahners Publishing Company, 5 South Wabash Avenue, Chicago, IL 60603.

Electrical Construction and Maintenance, McGraw-Hill, 1221 Avenue of the Americas, New York, NY 10020.

Electrical Consultant, One River Road, Cos Cob, CT 06807.

Fire Journal, National Fire Protection Association, Batterymarch Park, Quincy, MA 00269.

Health Care Systems, 1515 Broadway, New York, NY 10036.

Health Facilities Management, American Hospital Publishing, Inc., 737 N. Michigan Avenue, Suite 700, Chicago, IL 60611-2615.

Hospitals, American Hospital Publishing, Inc., 737 N. Michigan Avenue, Suite 700, Chicago, IL 60611-2615.

IAEI News, International Association of Electrical Inspectors, 901 Waterfall Way, Richardson, TX 75080-7702.

Journal of Clinical Engineering, 1351 Titan Way, Brea, CA 92621.

Journal of the Operating Room Research Institute, 100 Campus Road, Totowa, NJ 07512.

Lighting Design and Application, Illuminating Engineering Society of North America, 345 East 47th Street, New York, NY 10017.

Medical Electronics, 2994 West Liberty, Pittsburgh, PA 15216.

Modern Healthcare, 740 N. Rush St., Chicago, IL 60611.

Neta News, published by the International Electrical Testing Association, 231 Red Rocks Vista Drive, P.O. Box 687, Morrison, CO 80465.

Plant Engineering, 1301 South Grove Avenue, Barrington, IL 60010.

Professional Engineer, National Society of Professional Engineers, 1420 King Street, Alexandria, VA 22314.

1.8 Manufacturers' data

The electrical industry through its associations and individual manufacturers of electrical equipment issues many technical bulletins, data books, and magazines. While some of this information is difficult to obtain, copies should be made available to each major design unit. The advertising sections of electrical magazines contain excellent material, usually well illustrated and presented in a clear and readable form, concerning the construction and application of equipment. Such literature may be promotional; it may present the advertiser's equipment or methods in a best light and should be carefully evaluated. Manufacturer's catalogs are a valuable source of equipment information. Some manufacturers' complete catalogs are quite extensive covering several volumes. However, these companies may issue condensed catalogs for general use. A few manufacturers publish regularly scheduled magazines containing news of new products and actual applications. Data sheets referring to specific items are almost always available from the sales offices. Some technical files may be kept in microfilm for use either by projection or by printing at larger design offices. Manufacturers' representatives, both sales and technical, can do much to provide complete information on a product.

Manufacturers of specialized hospital electrical equipment often publish design and installation recommendations and technical updates. This is particularly true of isolation panel, standby system, and transfer switch manufacturers.

1.9 Safety

Safety of life and preservation of property are two of the most important factors in the design of the electrical system. This is especially true in health care facilities because of public occupancy, thoroughfare, high-occupancy density, and patients—some of them critically ill or injured. In some health care facilities the systems operating staff has limited technical capabilities and may not have any specific electrical training.

Various codes provide rules and regulations as minimum safeguards of life and property. The electrical design engineer often needs to provide greater safeguards than outlined in the codes according to his best judgment, while also giving consideration to utilization and economics.

Electrical safety may be divided into the following five categories:

a) Safety for maintenance and operating personnel
b) Safety for the general public
c) Safety for general care patients
d) Safety for critical care patients
e) Safety for patients and staff in wet locations

Safety for maintenance and operating personnel is achieved through proper design and selection of equipment with regard to enclosures, key-interlocking, circuit breaker and fuse interrupting capacity, the use of high-speed fault-detection and circuit-opening devices, clearances from structural members, grounding methods, disconnecting means, and identification of equipment. Adequate lighting in electrical rooms and around electrical equipment is important to personnel safety.

Safety for the general public requires that all circuitmaking and breaking equipment as well as other electrical apparatus be isolated from casual contact. This is achieved by using locked rooms and enclosures, proper grounding, limiting of fault levels, installation of barriers and other isolation, proper clearances, adequate insulation, and other similar provisions outlined in this standard. Only authorized personnel should have access to electrical equipment.

Safety for general patients requires all of the design features used for protecting the general public as well as special provisions to minimize potential differences between any two conducting surfaces likely to come in contact with the patient directly or indirectly. Green ground conductors, installed in metallic conduit with the power conductors, ensure that potential differences are below 20 mV when first installed. Potential differences in general patient care areas are required to be maintained below 500 mV under normal conditions. Potential differences in critical care areas must be kept below 40 mV under normal conditions. However, the designer must be aware that even with properly sized and installed ground conductors, higher potential differences can be generated during fault conditions. Other special protective systems such as ground-fault circuit-interrupter (GFCI) receptacles or isolation transformers are used in wet locations to protect patients and staff and in critical care areas to protect catheterized patients from electric shock through an exposed catheter.

Although flammable anesthetics (like ether) are no longer used in the U.S., they are still popular in some foreign countries. Where flammable anesthesia is used, isolation transformers and a properly grounded conductive floor shall be provided. All wiring in the hazardous area must be installed as required for Class 1 Division 1 locations.

The National Electrical Safety Code® (NESC®) (ANSI C2-1997) is available from the IEEE. It covers outdoor distribution systems, supply and communications systems, overhead lines, high-voltage systems, and other items related to the supply of building power.

Circuit protection is a fundamental safety requirement of all electrical systems. Adequate interrupting capacities are required in services, feeders, and branch circuits. Selective, automatic isolation of faulted circuits represents good engineering. Tripping schemes for the emergency system must be selective, so that faults on adjacent branches or systems or faults on the emergency system itself do not disrupt service to unaffected emergency system circuits—especially if interruption of these circuits can jeopardize the lives or safety of patients. Physical protection of wiring by means of approved raceways under all probable conditions of exposure to electrical, chemical, and mechanical damage is necessary.

Circuits on the emergency system shall be installed in metallic raceway. Circuits to patient care areas shall be installed with a green ground conductor and should be installed in metallic raceway to ensure physical protection and to provide redundant grounding. Such raceways should be of sufficient size for future expansion. Additional raceways and spare conductors for future use may be installed within allowable financial constraints. If the raceways are properly constructed and bonded, they can minimize power interruptions. The design engineer should locate equipment where suitable ambient temperatures exist and ventilation is available. The operation of fault-detection and circuit-interruption devices under conditions of abnormal voltage and frequency should be ensured.

1.9.1 Appliances and equipment

Improperly applied or inferior materials can cause electrical failures. The proper use of appliances and equipment listed by the Underwriters Laboratories, Inc., or other nationally recognized testing laboratories is recommended. The Association of Home Appliance Manufacturers (AHAM)[9] and the Air-Conditioning and Refrigeration Institute (ARI)[10] specify the manufacture, testing, and application of many common appliances and equipment.

High-voltage equipment should be specified to be manufactured in accordance with NEMA, ANSI, and IEEE standards, and the engineer should make sure that the equipment specified conforms to these standards. Properly prepared specifications can prevent the purchase of inferior or unsuitable equipment. The lowest initial purchase price may not result in the lowest cost after taking into consideration operating, maintenance, and owning costs. Value engineering is an organized approach to identification of unnecessary costs; it utilizes such methods as life cycles, cost analyses, and related techniques.

1.9.2 Operational considerations

When the design engineer plans electrical equipment rooms and locates electrical devices, there may be areas accessible to unqualified persons due to limited space. Dead-front construction and ANSI/NEMA Category A type construction should be utilized whenever practical. Where dead-front construction is not available, all exposed electrical equipment should be placed behind locked doors or gates. This will result in a reduction in electrical failures caused by human error, as well as improved safety.

A serious cause of failure, which is attributable to human error, is unintentional grounding or phase-to-phase short-circuiting of equipment that is being worked upon. By careful design such as proper spacing, barriers, and padlocking and by enforcement of published work-safety rules, the engineer can minimize unintentional grounding and phase-to-phase, and ground faults in the distribution equipment. High-quality workmanship is an important factor in the prevention of electrical failures. Therefore, the design should incorporate features that are conducive to good workmanship.

Selective coordination of overcurrent devices is important in health care facilities, especially for critical care areas of hospitals. The system must be studied for both high- and low-level faults. It is therefore important to consider the different levels of available short-circuit current available from utility and standby sources.

Ground-fault protection schemes on large service mains on wye-grounded 480 V systems will help to minimize damage from arcing ground faults. Arcing ground faults or "burn-

---

[9]20 North Wacker Drive, Chicago, IL 60606.
[10]1501 Wilson Boulevard, Arlington, VA 22209.

downs" can cause total destruction of electrical equipment, jeopardizing patient safety by fire and loss of electrical service. By providing one or more additional steps of ground-fault protection downstream, designers can ensure that otherwise harmless ground faults (such as in the powerhouse or kitchen) will not cause an outage of the hospital main or patient care areas of the hospital. Ground-fault systems should be tested for selective tripping to ensure proper and safe operation per the NEC.

1.10 Maintenance

Maintenance is essential to proper operation. The installation should be so designed that building personnel can perform most of the maintenance with a minimum need for specialized services. Design details should provide proper space and accessibility so that equipment can be maintained without difficulty and excessive cost.

The engineer should consider the effects of a failure in the system supplying the building. Generally, the external systems are operated and maintained by the electrical utility, though at times they are a part of the health care facility distribution system.

In health care facilities where continuity of service is essential, suitable emergency and standby equipment should be provided. Such equipment is needed to maintain minimum lighting requirements for passageways, stairways, and to supply power to critical patient care areas and essential loads. These systems are usually installed within the building, and they include automatic or manual equipment for transferring loads on loss of normal supply power or for putting battery- or generator-supplied equipment into service.

Although applicable codes determine the need for standby or emergency generating systems in health care facilities, they are generally required in any facility that keeps acutely ill patients overnight, performs invasive procedures, administers anesthesia, has critical patient care areas, or otherwise treats patients unable to care for themselves during an emergency. High-rise health care facilities, regardless of type, should have on-site emergency or standby generators. Periodic testing and exercising of standby generators is essential to system reliability.

Electrical engineers should consider the installation of bypass/isolation switches in conjunction with automatic transfer switches to permit maintenance on a deenergized transfer switch without jeopardizing patient safety. The isolation/bypass switch permits removal of the transfer switch from the circuit while providing for manual transfer to the normal or emergency source.

Even with isolation/bypass switches, it is possible for a load-side circuit breaker to fail, causing loss of power to all or part of the critical branch. For this reason it is recommended to provide some normal circuits in critical patient care areas per the NEC.

1.11 Design considerations

Electrical equipment usually occupies a relatively small percentage of the total building space, and in design it may be easier to relocate electrical service areas than mechanical areas or structural elements. Allocation of space for electrical areas is often given secondary consideration by architectural and related specialties. In the competing search for space, the electrical engineer is responsible for fulfilling the requirements for a proper electrical installation while at the same time recognizing the flexibility of electrical systems in terms of layout and placement.

Today, architectural considerations and appearances are of paramount importance in the design of a health care facility. Aesthetic considerations may play an important role in the selection of equipment, especially lighting equipment. Provided that the dictates of good practice, code requirements, and environmental considerations are not violated, the electrical engineer may have to compromise the design to accommodate the needs of other members of the design team.

The electrical engineer should work closely with professional associates, such as the architect, the mechanical engineer, the structural engineer, and the civil engineer. There is also concern with the building owner or operator who, as clients, may take an active interest in the design. More often the electrical engineer will work directly with the coordinator of overall design activities, usually the architect. Cooperation with the safety engineer, fire protection engineer, the environmental engineer, and other concerned people, such as interior designers, all of whom have a say in the ultimate design, is essential.

The electrical designer should become familiar with local rules and know the authorities having jurisdiction over the design and construction. The designer should always contact the authorities having jurisdiction and all applicable utilities before beginning design. Local contractors are usually familiar with local ordinances and union work rules and can be of great help. Union work practices may, for reasons of safety or other considerations, discourage the use of certain materials and techniques.

In performing electrical design, it is essential, at the outset, to prepare a checklist of all the design stages that have to be considered. Major items include temporary power, access to the site, and review by others. It is important to note that certain electrical work may appear in nonelectrical sections of the specifications. For example, furnishing and connecting of electric motors and controls may be covered in the mechanical section of the specifications. Another notable example would be elevators, which are usually specified by the architect. The electrical engineer should insist that the proper starter, fireman's recall system, and emergency sequencing of elevators are specified.

Electrical engineers working on health care projects should have a working knowledge of medical gas systems because medical gas outlets often share consoles and headwalls that appear in the electrical specifications. The electrical engineer also should be familiar with medical gas alarm systems.

For administrative control purposes, the electrical work may be divided into a number of contracts, some of which may be under the control of a general contractor and some of which may be awarded to electrical contractors. Among items with which the electrical designer will be concerned are preliminary cost estimates, final cost estimates, plans or drawings, specifications (which are the written presentation of the work), materials, manuals, factory inspections, laboratory tests, and temporary lighting and power. The electrical engineer may well be involved in providing information on how electrical considerations affect financial justification of the project in terms of owning and operating costs, amortization, return on investment, and related items.

1.12 Other considerations

Those involved in the design of health care facilities should understand the process by which drawings are issued for bidding and construction. The designer should also have some knowledge of shop drawing review, estimating, and contract administration. For more information see the Introduction (Chapter 1) to the IEEE Gray Book.

Design and construction of health care facilities are a team process involving engineers, architects, construction managers, general contractors, estimators, subcontractors and equipment vendors. In recent years the contractors and construction managers have become increasingly involved in the design process. In order to successfully complete a health care project, it is important to involve contractors who have a successful track record in health care construction. The larger and more complex the project the more important it is to have contractors who are skilled and experienced in the specialized construction techniques required for medical facilities.

Chapter 2
Load requirements and energy management

2.1 General discussion

As with other building types, the determination of loads to be served by the electrical system is fundamental to health care facility design. Equally important is the economic application of materials, labor, and electrical devices to serve identified loads. As a goal, the completed facility should serve the initial loads, provide a margin for incremental growth, and foster the efficient use of energy.

2.1.1 Loads

One of the purposes of this chapter is to aid the designer in estimating loads usually found in health care facilities and to show the range of power typically required by these loads.

2.1.2 Groups of loads

The cumulative effect of groups of individual loads is one of the determinants of distribution system design. This chapter will provide data from operating health care facilities that will be useful in projecting total load demand. Similarly, a profile for one type of facility will be presented. The reader is cautioned that such data should be viewed within the narrow scope in which it is presented. That is, the data is indicative of a specific building at a specific point in time and cannot be extrapolated necessarily into a typical profile.

2.1.3 Load growth

Patterns of health care have changed rapidly in recent years, and as the biological sciences continue to advance, altering patterns may be expected in the future. Such changes impose on health care facilities the need to adapt to changing demands of many kinds. The designer of electrical systems should plan for inevitable change and should anticipate incremental growth of loads during the useful life of the facility. In fact, the designer's recognition of the dynamic nature of health care facilities may result in extended useful life. Obviously, the type of health care facility affects the level of change that may be anticipated. Teaching hospitals are more prone to change than community general hospitals, and the latter more so than custodial care facilities.

2.1.4 Energy utilization

Electrical system design affects the energy required to operate a facility over its useful life. This consideration should be balanced with the loads to be served as the design is created. Another purpose of this chapter is to present data that will help reduce the unknowns faced by the designer, resulting in a more energy-efficient facility. Additionally, techniques of energy management will be discussed.

2.2 Loads vs. facility type

There are many types of health care facilities, some of which are identified in Chapter 1. Load density for the total building will vary as the type varies.

Teaching and general hospitals may be expected to offer the broadest spectrum of load types and to yield the highest concentration of load per gross square foot. Conversely, minimal care and custodial care facilities will produce generally low concentrations of load.

Outpatient screening clinics and physicians' offices will be similar to commercial office buildings, except that screening clinics sometimes will include extensive laboratory, radiology, and imaging facilities.

Psychiatric hospitals, nursing homes, and minimal care and custodial care facilities share a common bond since large portions of each will be devoted to patient accommodations. While the similarity will stop there in most cases, the load density (watts per gross square foot) will be influenced significantly by their residential character.

Load density is related to other variables in addition to facility type. As an example, choice of fuel for heating and air conditioning will exert considerable influence on loads.

2.3 Lighting loads

Lighting for health care facilities is presented in Chapter 7. Loads imposed by the lighting systems will be a function of several variables, among which are

a)   Tasks to be performed
b)   Quality and quantity of illumination required
c)   Choice of lighting sources

Lighting design for some areas will be similar to that for other commercial buildings. Other spaces will require the application of specialized lighting techniques. Among the latter are patient rooms, intensive care units, nurseries, and surgical and obstetrical suites.

In all cases, task lighting techniques should be applied, in the interest of energy management and of optimum distribution system capacity.

2.3.1 Loads by function

For initial calculations, lighting connected loads may be estimated relying on the designer's previous experience or they may be estimated using the Illuminating Engineering Society of North America (IESNA) lighting power budget technique. Readers should refer to the references and bibliography for this chapter (see 2.7 and 2.8) and to the body of Chapter 7 for more on this subject.

2.3.2 Lighting demand

As with other types of loads, demand factors may be applied to lighting connected load when determining distribution system component capacity. The appropriate factor will depend upon some or all of the following:

a) Function performed in the area served
b) Means of lighting control, i.e., switching, dimming
c) Hours of operation for the area served
d) Local code authority requirements

As an upper limit, the continuous load supplied by a lighting branch circuit should not exceed 80% of the branch circuit rating. For good design practice, the continuous load supplied should not exceed 70% of the branch circuit rating and in some cases should be even lower.

The National Electrical Code® (NEC®) (NFPA 70-1996)[1] permits the use of lighting demand factors in calculating lighting load on feeders. Refer to table 220-11 of the NEC. However, designers should develop their own factors based on the characteristics of a specific project, consistent with restraints imposed by code authorities.

The factors shown in table 2-1 may be used in sizing the distribution system components shown and should result in a conservative design.

Table 2-1—Factors used in sizing distribution system components

Distribution system component	Lighting demand factor
Lighting panelboard bus and main overcurrent device	1.0
Lighting panelboard feeder and feeder overcurrent device	1.0
Distribution panelboard bus and main overcurrent device First 50 000 W or less All over 50 000 W	0.5 0.4
Remaining components	0.4

2.4 Power loads

Power loads may be divided into the following broad categories:

a) Building equipment
1) Heating, ventilating, air conditioning, and refrigeration (HVAC&R)
2) Transportation (elevators, escalators, trolleys)
3) Auxiliary pumps (fire, sump, clinical air and vacuum, pneumatic tube)
b) Functional equipment
1) Kitchen
2) Data processing

---

[1]Information on references can be found in 2.7.

        3)   Communication systems
        4)   Business machines
        5)   Laundry
  c) Medical equipment
        1)   X-ray and imaging systems
        2)   Radiation therapy
        3)   Laboratory
        4)   Surgery
        5)   Intensive care, recovery, emergency
        6)   Physical and occupational therapy
        7)   Inhalation therapy
        8)   Pharmacy
        9)   Materials management
        10) Medical records

NOTE—Major loads occur in the first two categories [a) and b)], and these loads are similar to those in other types of commercial buildings. The third category [c)] is unique to health care.

2.4.1 Building equipment

The types of HVAC&R systems chosen for a specific building will have the greatest single effect on electrical load. First, the choice of fuel will be critical. If natural gas, fuel oil, or coal is chosen, electrical loads will be lower than would be the case if electricity were chosen. Second, the choice of refrigeration cycle will have considerable impact. If absorption chillers are chosen, electrical loads will be lower than those imposed by electric centrifugal or reciprocating chillers. Early discussions between mechanical and electrical designers will be advantageous in planning the electrical distribution system.

For initial estimates, before actual loads are known, the factors shown in table 2-2 may be used to establish the major elements of the electrical system serving HVAC&R systems.

Elevators usually are large loads, but since only a few are required in most health care facilities, elevators do not represent a large portion of total load. For preliminary design of the distribution system in buildings of up to 12 stories, assuming vertical speeds up to 450 ft/min, 4500 lb capacity, the following loads may be used:

Electric traction elevators, each	35–50 hp
Hydraulic elevators, each	40–75 hp

Hydraulic elevators ordinarily will not be employed in buildings higher than seven stories and speeds usually will be limited to 150 ft/min. However, capacities may be higher than 4500 lb. Actual loads should be obtained from the elevator vendor once vertical transportation requirements have been defined sufficiently to permit calculation.

Escalators are not installed frequently in health care facilities but may be employed in a few buildings. For initial estimates, escalator load will approximate 25 hp for each landing served above the first.

Table 2-2—Factors used to establish major elements
of the electrical system serving HVAC&R systems

Item	Unit
Refrigeration machines: Absorption Centrifugal/reciprocating	kVA/ton of chiller capacity 0.10 1.00
Auxiliary pumps and fans: Chilled water pumps Condenser water pumps Absorption Centrifugal/reciprocating Cooling tower fans Absorption Centrifugal/reciprocating	 0.08 0.15 0.07 0.10 0.07
Boilers: Natural gas/fuel oil	kVA/boiler hp 0.07
Boiler auxiliary pumps: Deaerator	kVA/boiler hp 0.10
Auxiliary equipment: Clinical vacuum pumps Clinical air compressors	kVA/bed 0.18 0.10

Horizontal and vertical transportation systems for food, supplies, and materials using automated trolleys or carts are found in a few large health care facilities. Pneumatic tube systems are more common and may be employed as the sole means of transport for small supplies and paper records or as one component in a materials handling system. Automated trolleys or carts impose relatively small loads (less than 10 hp) at numerous locations but will usually be combined with dedicated elevators whose loads will be similar to a service elevator. Pneumatic tube systems are powered by vacuum pumps or exhausters located in a few central locations. Motor drives will vary depending on the extent of the system but are under 10 hp (many, less than 3 hp).

2.4.2 Functional equipment

Equipment of this type usually consists of numerous small loads except that used in kitchens and except for some office copiers. The effect on the electrical system is to require panelboard space and multiple branch circuits but low load density.

The choice of fuel in the kitchen is the major determinant. If natural gas is the primary fuel, electrical loads will be lower on a watts per square foot basis than where electricity is the primary fuel. Preliminary planning should address this question early. For estimating purposes, the following factors may be used. In calculating kitchen floor area include cooking and preparation, dishwashing, storage, walk-in refrigerator/freezer, food serving lines, tray assembly, and offices.

Primary fuel	W/ft^2
Natural gas	25
Electricity	125

Data processing equipment is employed in several areas of the typical hospital. As a minimum, stand-alone systems for patient and general accounting and for laboratory analyses may be anticipated. However, it is common to find these integrated into hospital-wide management information systems today. Such systems use multiple input stations throughout the hospital, all intended to produce a unified patient bill at the time of patient discharge plus inventory control, third party billing, and portions of the patient's medical record.

As in other types of facilities, computer power requirements are usually moderate at the central processor location and low at distributed input stations. For most installations found in hospitals, the total load at the central location will range between 50 kVA and 100 kVA. Data processing facilities in large complexes, especially those associated with university medical schools, may require several hundred kilovoltampere capacity.

At computer workstations or teletype input stations, power demand will not exceed 1 kVA.

Power demand from communication systems, as individual loads and as a whole, is low. Individual loads will not exceed 2 kVA usually, with most less than 1.5 kVA.

As in other commercial structures, there will be a large quantity of office equipment (typewriters, word processors, copiers) but power required will be low, on the order of 0.3–1.2 kVA per item. The exception will be large copy machines. These may be estimated at 3–6 kVA each.

2.4.3 Medical equipment

Types of medical equipment employed in the various departments of health care facilities are discussed in Chapter 9.

Power distribution systems serving multiple x-ray machine installations require special attention. Designers should always be guided by the specific data furnished by vendors supplying equipment for the specific facility. However, an excellent planning guide is available as a NEMA standard (NEMA XR9-1984) and should be consulted.

Quality of voltage supplied is important to x-ray installations. Again, service as direct as possible from the source is desirable. Minimum transient disturbance and voltage drop are essential.

Note that most x-ray machines have two load ratings—continuous and momentary. The continuous load is usually small and poses little problem for either source—utility or standby generator. The momentary demand, however, can be a problem for a standby generator, especially a large x-ray machine served by a small generator. Since x-ray machines have a high power factor, a real power load is imposed on the engine. The effect of this should be evaluated in sizing the engine-generator set.

While momentary demand of x-ray installations will figure prominently in feeder and distribution equipment sizing, it need not be considered in calculating overall power demand imposed on the utility source, provided it is a part of a moderate size system. If the system requires 750 kVA or more, the momentary nature of x-ray operation will not add measurably to the overall demand. For small systems and for additions to existing facilities where service equipment is near capacity, some provision for x-ray demand may be advisable.

Clinical laboratories in hospitals require numerous branch circuits to serve the multitude of electrical devices, but load density is usually low and individual equipment loads are low, most under 1 kVA. A few pieces of equipment in laboratories today perform multiple specialized tests. The loads for these will range between 3 kVA and 8 kVA each. These same items often are sensitive to transient conditions on the power system and may require locally applied surge arrestors.

2.5 Overall demand factors

A tabulation of actual service entrance demand per gross square foot is presented in tables 2-3 and 2-4 for a group of health care facilities. Data used in preparation of these tables was obtained from the Veteran's Administration, now the Department of Veterans Affairs, and the Hospital Corporation of America. Refer to footnotes accompanying the tables for the criteria on which these tables are based. This data was collected during 1977 and 1981.

Table 2-3—Service entrance peak demand (Department of Veterans Affairs)

| Hospital | Floor area (ft^2) | Beds[a] | Degree days[b] | | Principal[c] fuel | W/ft^2 [d] | |
			Cooling	Heating		Maximum	Average
V.A. Hospital #1	821 000	922	234	3536	NG/FO	4.5	3.5
V.A. Hospital #2	334 000	500	863	5713	NG/FO	5.2	3.9
V.A. Hospital #3	645 995	670	3488	1488	NG/FO	3.8	2.8
V.A. Hospital #4	681 000	600	1016	654	NG/FO	6.1	4.0
V.A. Hospital #5	503 500	697	3495	841	NG/FO	7.2	5.5
V.A. Hospital #6	800 000	1050	600	7400	NG/FO	5.9	4.2

[a]Total beds shown. Beds actually occupied could affect values shown for watts per square foot.
[b]Degree days: Normals, Base 65 °F, based on 1941–1970 period. From *Local Climatological Data Series,* 1974, NOAA.
[c]NG/FO = Natural Gas/Fuel Oil. Principal fuel is defined as that used for heating. In all cases, electricity was the fuel used for refrigeration.
[d]Watts per square foot based on measured values at service entrance during metering periods ranging from 9 days to 17 days, during cooling season in all instances, 1981.

Table 2-4—Service entrance peak demand
(Hospital Corporation of America)

Hospital and location	Floor area (ft^2)	Beds[a]	Degree days[b]		Principal[c] fuel	W/ft^2 [d] Maximum
			Cooling	Heating		
#1 – East	273 000	458	1353	3939	NG/FO	6.8
#2 – Southeast	278 000	250	2294	2240	NG/FO	6.3
#3 – Central	123 000	157	—	—	NG/FO	7.5
#4 – Central	36 365	62	2029	3227[e]	E	13.7
#5 – Central	318 000	300	1107	4306	NG/FO	4.6
#6 – Southeast	182 000	225	3786	299[e]	NG/FO	5.3
#7 – East	283 523	320	1030	4307	NG/FO	6.8
#8 – Southwest	135 396	150	2250	2621[e]	NG/FO	6.6
#9 – West	190 000	97	927	5983	NG/FO	2.8
#10 – Southeast	161 000	170	3226	733[e]	NG/FO	6.3
#11 – Southeast	157 639	214	2078	2146	NG/FO	7.3
#12 – Southeast	162 187	222	2143	2378[e]	NG/FO	4.3
#13 – East	109 617	146	1030	4307[e]	NG/FO	5.7
#14 – East	76 000	153	1030	4307[e]	E	8.8
#15 – Southeast	135 150	190	1995	2547[e]	NG/FO	5.9
#16 – Southwest	75 769	131	2587	2382[e]	NG/FO	7.4
#17 – Central	75 769	128	1636	3505[e]	NG/FO	6.3
#18 – Northwest	129 000	150	714	5833[e]	NG/FO	4.4
#19 – Central	54 938	108	1694	3696[e]	E	13.3
#20 – West	144 000	160	2814	1752	NG/FO	4.5
#21 – Southeast	149 000	123	2078	2146[e]	NG/FO	4.5
#22 – Central	89 000	128	2029	3227[e]	E	8.4
#23 – Central	128 500	150	1197	4729[e]	NG/FO	6.2
#24 – West	135 169	170	927	5983[e]	NG/FO	4.7
#25 – Southeast	80 000	124	1722	2975[e]	NG/FO	6.2
#26 – Southeast	83 117	126	3226	733[e]	NG/FO	8.5
#27 – Central	51 000	97	1569	3478	E	8.8
#28 – Southeast	66 528	120	2929	902[e]	E	9.7
#29 – East	112 000	140	1394	3514	NG/FO	4.3
#30 – Central	202 000	223	1636	3505	NG/FO	4.8
#31 – Southeast	56 000	51	3786	299[e]	NG/FO	7.4
#32 – West	47 434	50	927	5983[e]	NG/E	7.0
#33 – Central	23 835	32	1694	3696[e]	E	10.8
#34 – Southeast	105 000	95	2706	1465[e]	NG/FO	8.3
#35 – West	48 575	60	3042	108[e]	NG/E	7.7

Table 2-4—Service entrance peak demand
(Hospital Corporation of America) (*Continued*)

Hospital and location	Floor area (ft^2)	Beds[a]	Degree days[b]		Principal[c] fuel	W/ft^2 [d] Maximum
			Cooling	Heating		
#36 – Southwest	133 000	185	2587	2382[e]	NG/FO	6.3
#37 – Central	42 879	66	1694	3696[e]	E	15.7

[a]Total beds shown. Beds actually occupied could affect values shown for watts per square foot.
[b]Degree days: Normals, Base 65 °F, based on 1941–1970 period. From *Local Climatological Data Series,* 1974, NOAA.
[c]NG/FO = Natural Gas/Fuel Oil; E = Electricity. Principal fuel is defined as that used for heating. In all cases, electricity was the fuel used for refrigeration.
[d]Watts per square foot based on measured values by utility company meter at service entrance, 1977.
[e]Data shown for nearest recorded location.
(Each facility was self-contained, in that refrigeration and air conditioning equipment loads are included in power demands shown.)

The tables show the type of facility, the gross floor area and number of beds for each, the geographic location, and the major fuel type employed for HVAC&R systems in that facility. The derived factors may be used to estimate the anticipated demand for other facilities similar in size, location, and type of fuel. They also may be used to make initial estimates of service entrance capacity, switchgear size, and space required for service entrance equipment. It is important to recognize, however, that they will be useful principally in the schematic design phase. As design proceeds through the preliminary and working drawing phases, these initial estimates should be modified by the actual conditions prevalent in the project.

Figures 2-1 and 2-2 present operating load data for a large general medical and surgical hospital located in the southeastern U.S. It should be useful in visualizing changes in demand over time for a typical operating hospital. Candler General Hospital is a 305-bed facility, 402 000 gross ft^2, situated in Savannah, Georgia. The principal fuel employed for heating is natural gas with fuel oil standby. The chillers are centrifugal. Staff obtained the data during the cooling season, the peak period in this location.

2.6 Energy management

To gain a better perspective of the impact of energy management on the nation's plan to meet future energy goals, an overall view of past, current, and projected energy usage is necessary. Government and independent researchers have developed energy consumption projections to the year 2000 based on historical data on the total domestic energy usage over the past 81 years. Figure 2-3 is a graphic representation of usage from 1900 to 1981. Energy used in "quads" is plotted against years. A quad is one quadrillion Btu (2.93×10^{11} kWh), or more conveniently stated, the approximate amount of energy used by a city of one million people every three years. The distribution of usage by industrial, residential and commercial, and transportation is respectively three-eighths, three-eighths, and one-quarter of the total: 74 quads. An extrapolation of the historical data and a reasonable projection by the National Academy of Sciences to the year 2000 indicates consumption could be 175 quads. By incor-

23

porating the best estimates of the impact of "energy conservation" by the Department of Energy (DOE) and other government and private agencies, the 175 quad projection could be reduced by 65 quads to 110 quads, still 36 quads more per year than used in 1981. Since the current level of usage is better than 15% beyond domestic production capabilities, including nuclear and renewable sources, the truth about the "energy crisis" is apparent.

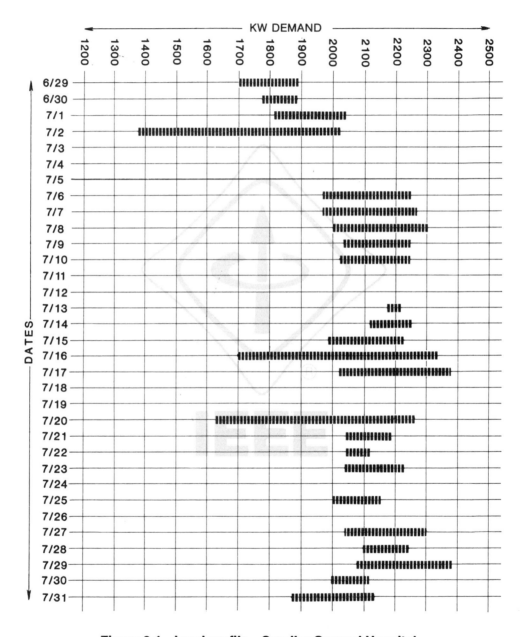

Figure 2-1—Load profile—Candler General Hospital
6/29/81–7/31/81 kilowatt demand

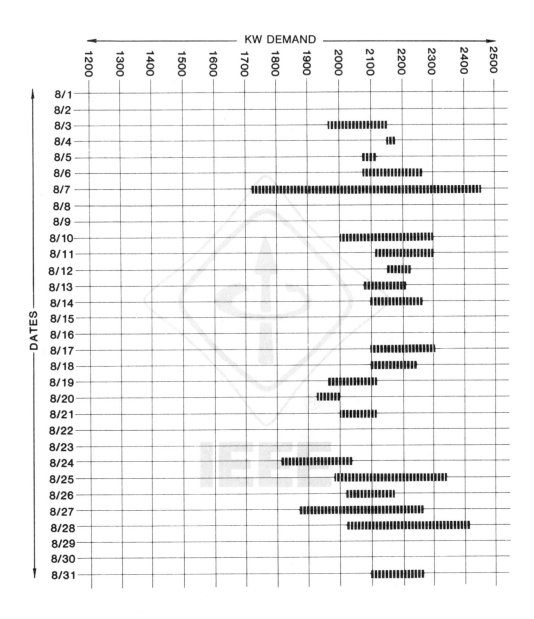

**Figure 2-2—Load profile—Candler General Hospital
8/1/82–8/31/82 kilowatt demand**

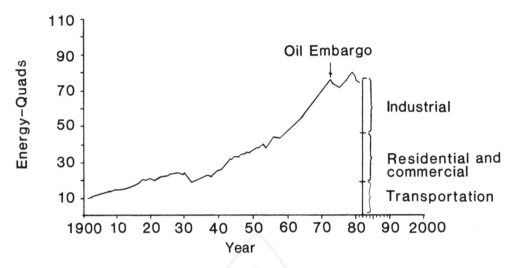

Figure 2-3—U.S. energy consumption

Energy consumption in buildings totaled about 26 quads in 1981, which includes residential and commercial sectors. Total energy consumption of hospitals was 1.1 quads. Assuming fixed percentages for estimating to the year 2000, 2.4 quads will be required without energy conservation measures and 1.5 quads with conservation, a reduction of approximately one-third.

Energy management implies implementation of energy conservation measures and control strategies over operating systems to minimize energy consumed. The designer has a responsibility to examine alternative design approaches and present these to the building owner with their respective cost considerations. This arises not only from the need to conserve fuels but also to control health care costs.

To develop an energy management program for any building, it is necessary to first know its energy using systems and the fuels to most effectively serve them.

The energy input to a hospital can arrive in a number of forms: electricity, natural gas, fuel oil, purchased steam, coal, or other fuels. The size of the stream depends on the rate of fuel consumption and the British thermal units of energy in that fuel. Oil and natural gas, of which the nation faces a limited supply, are important energy inputs in many hospitals. Even when they are not consumed directly, these nonrenewable fossil fuels may have been used to produce other fuels. The total of all energy streams to a hospital is utilized for a number of functions. While the pattern in an individual hospital may vary, the largest single energy usage is usually the heating, ventilation, air conditioning, and refrigeration (HVAC&R) system. Lighting represents the second most important use of energy in hospitals. Since the beginning of efforts to conserve energy, there have been a number of attempts to establish Building Energy Performance Standards. Today, enough data has been accumulated to assist a designer in understanding what constitutes an efficient building. The American Hospital Association with its energy management program is an example.

Energy usage in hospitals usually consists of electric power and a source for heating and process steam needs, such as gas, oil, or more electricity. Table 2-5 shows the typical energy usage for a general, acute care hospital in a moderate climate. The large difference in HVAC&R motor energy usage results from electric chiller energy in the cooling season.

Table 2-5—Typical energy usage

Cooling season	Btu/h/ft^2	%
Lighting	6.8	17
Receptacles	3.4	8
Medical, kitchen equipment	1.8	4
HVAC&R motors	12.0	29
Domestic hot water	8.0	19
Sterilization steam	4.0	11
Miscellaneous	5.0	12
TOTAL	41.0	100

Heating season	Btu/h/ft^2	%
Lights	6.8	10
Receptacles	3.4	5
Medical kitchen equipment	1.8	3
HVAC&R motors	5.0	7
Domestic hot water	8.0	12
Sterilization steam	4.0	6
Heating	40.0	57
TOTAL	69.0	100

2.6.1 Energy economics

Energy codes promulgated since 1975 impose some mandatory requirements for energy conservation and suggest other voluntary opportunities that could be implemented. Incumbent on the building designer is the responsibility to investigate not only the energy conservation opportunities suggested, but also to evaluate nonrenewable fuel sources, energy recovery systems, operating system monitoring and controls, and maintenance management. Beyond the mandated requirements, most owners will require substantiation of the cost effectiveness of implementing energy conservation measures (ECMs).

Several methods exist for determining the cost effectiveness of alternative system designs. Common to all are two basic cost elements: (1) the cost to implement, or first cost, and (2) the net cost savings provided. Two of the methods are simple payback and life cycle costing.

a) *Simple payback.* The simplest method is the payback period. This method for determining the cost effectiveness of added ECMs is calculated by applying the following formula:

$$\text{Payback Period} = \frac{\text{First Cost}}{\text{Annual Savings} - \text{Annual Costs}}$$

The payback period is expressed in years. Annual savings are the first year's savings in energy. Annual costs are the increased maintenance costs due to the measure. First cost is the total installed cost of the improvement.

Generally ignored in this method of analysis are the following:

1) Cost of money—the annual interest on money borrowed
2) Replacement cost—the cost to replace equipment
3) Energy cost inflation—the cost of energy in future years
4) Tax saving—the savings on purchase of equipment generated by federal tax incentives
5) Depreciation

Where the payback period is three years or less, this method is usually accurate enough to facilitate a decision.

b) *Life cycle costing.* Life cycle costing is a means of evaluating the total cost of owning, operating, and maintaining a building or piece of equipment over its useful life. This method involves a systematic comparison of the estimated costs using a discount factor to relate future to present value.

The procedures required to prepare a life cycle cost analysis are

1) Establish nonfuel cost data, both initial investment and recurring cost
2) Establish energy cost data for the time period chosen
3) Determine life cycle costs
4) Determine net savings
5) Calculate savings-to-investment ratio
6) Perform certain sensitivity analyses
7) Measure cost effectiveness

2.6.2 Utility negotiations

In most cases, the selection of a power source will be determined by an analysis made by the design engineers and the utility engineers. With the exception of large high-load factor complexes, economics will dictate the purchase of electricity for prime power requirements. On-site total energy and cogeneration systems should be evaluated on a case-by-case basis considering fuel availability, environmental restrictions, and utility costs. Standby electric generating equipment will be provided in hospitals to produce emergency power for critical loads upon failure of the prime source and may be used to reduce peak demand on the utility source.

The designer of hospital power systems has an important role in selection of the distribution characteristic within the complex, the power source, and subsequently, upon the long-term power costs. To make cost-effective decisions for owners, the designer should have knowledge of utility rate structures, metering, and billing practices.

a) *Electric utility tariffs.* Each electric utility has a series of rate schedules for supplying power to customers under various conditions. To arrive at the most economic choice for obtaining power, a comparison of these rates should be made. The following are factors that usually form the basis for establishing rates and evaluating them:

1) Maximum demand in kilowatts or kilovoltamperes
2) Energy consumption in kilowatthours
3) Adjustment for low power-factor
4) Voltages available
5) Transformer or substation ownership
6) Utility fuel cost adjustments
7) Demand interval
8) Minimum bill stipulations, including ratchet clauses
9) Multiple-metering provisions
10) Auxiliary or standby service charges
11) Seasonal and time-of-day service rates
12) Prompt payment savings
13) Provisions for off-peak loads and interruptible loads
14) Load factor

Since the oil embargo of 1973, and as a direct consequence of the National Energy Act of 1978, electric utilities introduced "rate reform." Essentially, rate reform usually incorporates various forms of

— Inverted rates
— Flat rates
— Lifeline rates
— Marginal cost pricing
— Long-range incremental costing
— Construction work in progress
— Interruptible rates
— Time-of-day pricing
— Reduction in the number of declining blocks
— Modifications of utility fuel cost adjustments
— Deletion of electric discounts

b) *Utility metering.* An understanding of utility metering practices is important for evaluating service arrangements. Practices vary depending upon local utility and regulatory body requirements. The design, usage, and load characteristic for a given application should be carefully weighed before selecting service voltage and metering characteristics. If large momentary demand, highly seasonal, or low power-factor loads are involved, billing penalties may be involved. On the other hand, high load-factor or high power-factor loads may merit a billing allowance or credit.

It is good practice to contact the electric utility supplying service early in the design. Late utility negotiations may result in increased costs and delays in service. A complete discussion of service, metering, and billing is always in order, no matter how preliminary. This should provide time for the consideration of various proposals and the selection of the one best suited to a given application. See [B2][2] for more information.

1) *Metering by type of premises.* Availability of a particular kind of metering and billing often depends upon the type of building and load. A single-occupancy building, such as a hospital, usually will be metered by the utility at the service entrance with a watthour demand meter. Should multiple services be required, and should they be permitted by the electric utility, watthour demand meter reading sometimes may be totalized to take advantage of lower rates.

   In some medical facilities, it may be desirable to submeter portions of the buildings. This could arise where physician offices, separately-owned pharmacies, or other concessionaires lease space within the project. Consent of the utility company should be obtained in such instances.

2) *Metering by service-voltage characteristics.* Metering of the incoming service may be located on the high-voltage or low-voltage side of the transformer, depending on the terms of the contract with the electric utility. When the meter is on the primary side, the transformer losses will be charged to the customer. In some cases, the customer is given a discount to offset this loss. When metering is on the secondary side, utilities may add 1–2% to the bill for transformer losses or may install a device to increase the meter indication to account for transformer losses.

3) *Meter location.* Subject to agreement with the utility, the meter may be installed indoors at the customer's secondary distribution point, in a suitable meter room, or in a separate control building that may also house primary switchgear and associated controls.

   Outdoor installations include pole, exterior wall, and pad mounting. In general, utilities will require accessibility for meter readings and maintenance, and suitable meter protection.

4) *Types of metering.* Tabulated below are types of metering. Utility requirements govern the types available for a given project.

   i)   Master metering
   ii)   Multiple metering
   iii) Primary metering
   iv)   Secondary metering
   v)   Totalized metering
   vi)   Impulse metering
   vii) Compensated metering
   viii) Submetering
   ix)   Subtractive metering

---

[2]The numbers in brackets correspond to those of the bibliography in 2.8.

x) Coincident demand
xi) Telemetering
xii) Power factor metering
xiii) Kilovoltampere metering

c) *Utility billing.* It is customary for utilities to meter and bill each customer individually. Utility rates consider fixed and variable cost requirements to provide services. Hence "rate schedules" generally take the form of a "block" rate, wherein incremental costs usually vary as a function of customer usage. Electric costs generally comprise two components—the demand charge and the energy charge. The demand charge is based upon the maximum rate of energy usage. The energy charge is based upon the total energy consumption. Many utilities have been granted permission to add variable cost factors to their rates. Examples include purchased fuel differential and real estate tax differential costs. Under these provisions, the utility may pass along increased costs; however, the utility must pass along decreased costs as well.

For hospital complexes, the primary metering and attendant billing forms are the following:

1) *Conjunctional billing.* Large institutional customers within the territory served by a given utility should explore the availability of conjunctional billing. This consists of adding the readings of two or more meters for purposes of a single billing. Due to the usual practice of decreasing rates for larger consumption, conjunctional billing may result in a lower energy usage billing than individual meters would produce. Conjunctional billing will generally result in a higher demand charge than a master or totalizing meter because the maximum demand readings on the individual meters are added. Since maximum demands seldom occur simultaneously, the arithmetic sum will be greater than the simultaneous sum, unless a provision is made for coincident demand measurement.

2) *Power factor billing.* If the load to be served will result in a low power-factor, an evaluation should be made to determine if power-factor improvements can be justified to avoid penalties.

3) *Flat billing.* Some applications involve service to loads of a fixed characteristic. For such loads, the utility may offer no-meter or flat-rate service. Billing is based upon time and load characteristics. Examples include area lighting and remote pumping stations.

4) *Off-peak billing.* This is reduced rate billing for service utilized during off-peak periods such as water-heating loads. The utility monitors, and may control, off-peak usage through control equipment or special metering.

5) *Standby service billing.* Also known as breakdown or auxiliary service, this service is applicable to utility customers whose electric requirements are not supplied entirely by the utility. In such cases, billing demand is determined either as a fixed percentage of the connected load or by meter, whichever is higher. This applies to loads that are electrically connected to some other source of supply but for which breakdown or auxiliary service is required.

6) *Backup service billing.* This service is provided through more than one utility circuit, solely for a customer's convenience. The customer often bears the cost of establishing the additional circuit and associated facilities. Usually, each backup service is metered and billed separately.

7) *Demand billing.* Usually this represents a significant part of electric service billing, and a good understanding of kilowatt demand metering and billing is important. An electric demand meter measures the rate of use of electric energy over a given period of time, usually 15 min, 30 min, or 1 h time intervals. The demand register is manually reset periodically when read for billing purposes.

8) *Minimum billing demand.* A utility customer may be subject to minimum demand billing, generally consisting of (a) a fixed amount or (b) a fixed percentage of the maximum demand established over a prior billing period. This type of charge may apply to customers with high instantaneous demands, customers whose operations are seasonal, or those who have contracted for a specific service capacity. Equipment and service requirements should be reviewed carefully to reduce or avoid minimum billing demand charges.

Utility contracts also may include ratchet clauses that establish minimum demand charges based on maximum demand experienced in the previous contract period (e.g., one year's peak demand establishes next year's minimum demand). Designers should advise their clients to control peak demand for several reasons but especially where the utility contract includes a ratchet clause. Clients should be aware that a major decrease in demand may not be reflected in savings for up to 12 months, unless a modification to the ratchet clause is negotiated.

9) *Load factor billing.* The ratio of average kilowatt demand to peak kilowatt demand during a given time period is referred to as the load factor. Many utilities offer a billing allowance or credit for high load factor usage, a qualification usually determined by evaluating how many hours during the billing period the metered peak demand was used. As an example of such credit, the utility may provide a reduced rate for the number of kilowatthours that are in excess of the peak demand multiplied by a given number of hours (after 360 h for a 720 h month or a 50% load factor).

10) *Interruptible service.* A form of peak load shaving used by the utilities is interruptible service. Primarily available for large facilities with well defined loads that can be readily disconnected, the utility offers the customer a billing credit for being able to require a reduction of demand to a specified contract level during a curtailment period. If the customer fails to reduce actual demand during any curtailment period, at least to the contract demand, severe financial penalties are imposed.

2.6.3 Conservation measures

Table 2-5 shows that methods to conserve lighting and HVAC&R energy can have a noticeable impact on a hospital's energy expenditures and, therefore, its operating budget.

a) *Lighting retrofits are a proven method of energy reduction.* Replacing standard watt-age fluorescent lamps with energy-saving lamps reduces energy costs with very little reduction in lumen output. Regular maintenance of luminaires, lamps, and ballasts is essential to energy efficiency regardless of types employed. For even greater savings, it is recommended that incandescent luminaires be replaced with fluorescent or high-intensity discharge (HID) luminaires and that high-efficiency ballasts be specified in all cases.

b) *On-site cogeneration.* On-site cogeneration is the simultaneous production of electric power at the point of use along with the production and use of the heat energy by-product of the electrical generation process. Its economic attraction is that the practice may be more efficient than utility-produced power. The national average for system efficiency of utility-produced power is 30%, whereas on-site cogeneration under ideal conditions can achieve a system efficiency of 80%.

Most cogeneration systems installed in hospitals and other institutional buildings are reciprocating engines (gas or diesel) and gas turbines. The exhaust gases from the engines are passed through a waste heat boiler and can produce 125 psig steam. In addition, the jacket water and lube oil cooling systems of a reciprocating engine can be used to heat hot water. Reciprocating engines have the highest ratio of electrical to thermal energy output and often are the best choice to match the electrical and thermal base loads of a hospital. Ebulliently-cooled reciprocating engines (those in which low pressure steam is produced in the jacket cooling system) can be used where only low-pressure steam (15 psig) or hot water is required (they cannot, however, provide 125 psig steam to laundries or 80 psig steam to sterilizers).

Gas turbines are sometimes applicable, although usually a larger thermal base load, such as a laundry or absorption chillers, is necessary to make them economically attractive. Steam turbines are rarely seen in hospital applications since most hospital boiler systems do not produce the high-pressure steam (300 psig and above) required to justify their costs.

The selection of type and size of equipment depends on many variables, e.g., electri-cal demand, steam quantities and pressures desired, occupancy and load patterns, and electric rate structure. An accurate study should be performed to determine feasibility at a particular hospital site.

Installed costs for engine generators and waste heat recovery systems run approxi-mately $700/kW to $1200/kW.

c) *Peak demand shaving.* Rather than an alternative method of generating one's own power, this is a technique that lowers the monthly demand charge by controlling or scheduling loads so as not to exceed a pre-set limit. Programmable demand control-lers can shed loads automatically, to reduce the peak demand. Generating power from a standby power system is an alternative.

The many arguments, pro and con, for using the existing emergency generators boil down to a single question: will the local building authorities allow it? If not, one many employ conventional load shedding only. If so, an analysis of loads that may be dropped (administrative office areas, medical offices, etc.) will give enough informa-tion to estimate a simple payback. Further, it may be possible to use the same standby emergency generators as required by codes, without adding additional generators.

d) *Thermal storage.* The idea of using cheaper, "off-peak" energy at night for use during "on-peak" daytime hours is becoming more economically feasible, especially as electric utilities increase the demand charge in their rate structure. By making chilled water or ice at night, then melting it during the day, the large electric demand of the water chillers is shifted to the less expensive night time.

Three methods for thermal storage consist of ice storage, eutectic salt systems, and chilled water systems. Ice storage systems produce ice in a tank and then use the building's chilled water system to melt the ice. These systems require the least storage space but require a glycol additive to the circulating water and more energy-intensive low-temperature chillers. Eutectic salt systems utilize a salt solution in sealed containers that freeze at 45–50 °F; thus conventional chillers may be used, but since the latent heat of fusion of the salt solution is less than that of pure water, more storage space is required for the salt containers. Chilled water storage is the simplest system but requires much more storage space.

Installed costs for these systems range from $80/ton-h to $200/ton-h.

e) *Building envelope.* Replacement of clear, single-pane windows with tinted, double-pane insulating glass reduces building heating and cooling requirements, and therefore, energy costs. Weather-stripping and regular building maintenance help to reduce outside air infiltration and its resultant heating/cooling costs.

2.6.4 Design considerations

Energy conservation and capital cost are frequently in conflict with one another. An energy management program should optimize this relationship. Achieving a balance requires consideration of the following topics during design.

a) *Energy value of materials.* Construction materials and equipment possess energy value, built in from mine to construction site. Energy value is added during erection and installation.

Recognition of this helps the designer to avoid over-design. Careful analysis of initial loads to be imposed coupled with allowances for load growth are essential. At the same time, efficient materials and equipment may increase capital costs while lowering operating costs.

b) *Lighting and lighting control.* As noted earlier in this chapter, lighting source choices and lighting control bear directly on energy utilization as well as system load. Principles of task lighting, general lighting, and daylighting are important design considerations for energy management.

c) *Motors.* Selection of motors for efficient use of energy is essential. The use of premium energy-efficient motors can reduce running losses by 25% or more. Induction motors are somewhat less efficient at partial load, but their power factors are considerably poorer. Motors should be chosen to operate at three-quarters load or more. The use of solid-state starters to reduce starting current and the use of variable-speed drives for optimum control of motor loads contribute to energy conservation.

d) *Power factor maintenance.* Prediction of system power factor is difficult during design but more readily determinable in an operating system. Nonetheless, consideration should be given to application of capacitors at three-phase, constant-speed induction motors. In addition, application of power factor correction capacitors or synchronous condensers to the system should be evaluated during design and provisions should be made to install them without major renovations of switchgear. Where nonlinear loads are present, care should be taken when adding capacitors to avoid resonance.

2.6.5 Energy management systems

Use of an energy management system (EMS) is an accepted and frequently recommended way to lower energy and demand costs and to conserve energy. Energy management is a technique for automatically controlling the demand and energy consumption of a facility to a lower and more economical level by implementing operating strategies that optimize system performance to meet building needs more efficiently.

Coordination among owner, architect, and engineers during schematic design may enable use of an EMS for fire and security systems, communication systems, and maintenance management.

An EMS may be simple or complex in design and capability. Controls such as time clocks constitute a simple EMS where an on or off command is give to an item of equipment at predetermined times. Often these simple devices miss the more focused and expanded needs of the energy and maintenance managers. Computerized systems can replace much of the lost time expended by maintenance crews to verify operating status of boilers, fans, and other equipment. It can enable control of HVAC&R functions and lighting from a central unit, performing operations such as start/stop, load shedding, and controlling air mixtures. These functions can be accomplished using mid-range energy controllers.

For maximum energy and manpower saving, the state-of-the-art utilizes direct digital control (DDC) systems. Previous systems had all of the programmable intelligence in the central processing unit (CPU). The remote panels were slaves implementing CPU instructions. They had no stand-alone intelligence. A CPU failure would mean total system shutdown and loss of control and critical data. Today's systems have minicomputers and microprocessors spread throughout the system, including field controllers. The main computer is free to perform sophisticated energy management tasks, while simpler tasks are delegated to the field controller. Each controller can be a stand-alone management center reporting to the central system, and if the main CPU or a transmission link fails, the entire system is not disabled.

Options available today include color graphics on computer workstations, routine operator input/output, conversational English communication, file editing and print-outs, and fire and security functions.

a) Systems for a large building, such as a hospital, should include the following:

    1) Time program control

    2) Optimum start/stop

3) Supply air and water supervisory control
4) Boiler/chiller plant optimization
5) Enthalpy control
6) Load shedding/demand limiting
7) Variable duty cycling
8) Supervisory feedback

b) It should be possible to add features such as

1) Use of light pens for system operation
2) Higher power computers
3) End-user programming
4) Fiber optics transmission

An important consideration in any system is the means by which communication among various pieces of equipment is accomplished. Options include hardwiring, telephone lines, wireless, and carrier current. This is particularly important if the EMS is being designed for application in an existing facility.

Issues that must be faced when starting system design include answers to such questions as how much control does the owner want the system to have over electrical HVAC&R systems? Should the control be distributed to the satellite field panels throughout the project? If the system is to control the emergency power generation, how extensive should the backup be and should the fail-safe switchover be manual or automatic? What is the smallest item to be monitored or controlled by the system?

Refer to NEMA MG10-1983 for techniques to evaluate starting and stopping cycles of electric motors. Some energy management system manufacturers claim no appreciable change in equipment life due to energy management systems. It is advisable that the designer study the technical literature for conclusions of future studies on this subject.

Finally, a critically important consideration in selecting EMS equipment is the service available from the manufacturer for diagnosis and repair of hardware, for modification of system and operating software, and for training of the owner's personnel in utilizing the system.

2.6.6 Energy utilization standards

A uniform standard for energy utilization in various types of facilities does not exist. Several nationally recognized building codes, the 1993 BOCA® National Energy Conservation Code for example, mandate performance for some building components. A number of states have written and adopted energy codes. The Department of Energy is continuing to develop Building Energy Performance Standards (BEPS). Designers may refer to ASHRAE/IESNA 90.1-1989 and ASHRAE/IEEE 90A-1-1988 for general guidance in conserving energy. The IESNA also published a series on Lighting Energy Management (IES LEM-1-1982, IES LEM-2-1984, IES LEM-3-1987, and IES LEM-4-1984) with recommendations for power and energy densities in buildings. However, since 1995, only LEM-3-1987 remains as an active publication. The IEEE Bronze Book (IEEE Std 739-1995) includes recommendations for energy management and conservation.

Other work toward standards has been done by the National Institute for Building Sciences; the American Institute of Architects Research Corporation; the American Society of Heating, Refrigeration and Air Conditioning Engineers; and the American Hospital Association.

In the meantime, designers are obliged to consult legally adopted codes in the jurisdiction where the facility will be constructed and to strive for the lowest energy consumption consistent with the building owner's life-cycle-cost goals.

2.7 References

This chapter shall be used in conjunction with the following publications:

ASHRAE/IEEE 90A-1-1988, Energy Conservation in New Building Design (Sections 1–9).[3]

ASHRAE/IESNA 90.1-1989, Energy Efficient Design of New Buildings Except Low-Rise Residential Buildings.

BOCA® National Energy Conservation Code, 7th ed., 1993.[4]

IEEE Std 739-1995, IEEE Recommended Practice for Energy Management in Industrial and Commercial Facilities (IEEE Bronze Book) (ANSI).[5]

IES LEM-3-1987, Design Considerations for Effective Building Lighting Energy Utilization.[6]

NEMA MG 10-1983 (Revised 1988), Energy Management Guidelines for Selection and Use of Polyphase Motors.[7]

NEMA XR9-1984 (R 1989), Power Supply Guidelines for X-Ray Machines.

NFPA 70-1996, National Electrical Code® (NEC®).[8]

NFPA 99-1996, Health Care Facilities.

---

[3]ASHRAE publications are available from the Customer Service Dept., American Society of Heating, Refrigerating, and Air Conditioning Engineers, 1791 Tullie Circle NE, Atlanta, GA 30329.

[4]The BOCA® National Energy Conservation Code is available from the Building Officials and Code Administrators (BOCA) International, Inc., 4051 West Flossmoor Road, Country Club Hills, IL 60478-5795, tel. (708) 799-2300.

[5]IEEE publications are available from the Institute of Electrical and Electronics Engineers, 445 Hoes Lane, P.O. Box 1331, Piscataway, NJ 08855-1331.

[6]IES publications are available from the Illuminating Engineering Society of North America , 120 Wall Street, Fl 17, New York, NY 10005-4001.

[7]NEMA publications are available from the National Electrical Manufacturers Association, 1300 N. 17th St., Ste. 1847, Rosslyn, VA 22209.

[8]NFPA publications are available from Publications Sales, National Fire Protection Association, 1 Batterymarch Park, P.O. Box 9101, Quincy, MA 02269-9101.

2.8 Bibliography

Additional information may be found in the following sources:

[B1] Crook, E. D., *Determination of Electrical Demand for V.A. Medical Buildings.* Washington, DC: Veteran's Administration, Office of Construction, 1982.

[B2] Edison Electric Institute, Handbook of Electricity Metering, 9th ed.

[B3] Harold, R. M., et. al. *Lighting Power Budget Determination by the Unit Power Density Procedure,* Illuminating Engineering Society (IES), Publication No. EMS-6, 1979.

Chapter 3
Electrical power distribution systems

3.1 General discussion

As the medical profession is increasingly more dependent upon complex electrical equipment and instrumentation for patient care and facility operation, the proper design of electrical power distribution systems in health care facilities is most important. The proper selection of the system components, and their arrangement, is critical to providing the health care facility with reliable, safe, and economical electric power.

Total or partial loss of electric power in a health care facility can cause acute operational problems (i.e., power loss to the lighting systems makes it impossible to perform vital medical tasks such as dispensing medicine, performing surgical procedures, or performing precise medical laboratory work). The loss of power to tissue, bone, or blood bank refrigerators can leave the health care facility without these vital resources. Power loss to electrical life support equipment such as heart pumps, medical vacuum pumps, dialysis machines, and ventilators can be fatal. Clearly, continuity of high-quality electric power should be the most important factor in the design of the electrical distribution systems for health care facilities.

Safety is another particularly important design criteria for health care facilities because

a) Medical personnel frequently come into contact with electrical apparatus in their daily routines.

b) Patients often are very vulnerable to electrical shock hazard because of their weakened condition, because of drugs or anesthesia administered, and/or because of their unconscious state. Electrical shocks that would not severely affect a healthy person could be fatal to a patient.

c) It is necessary for maintenance personnel in health care facilities to come in daily or weekly contact with electrical distribution equipment for routine maintenance or minor system additions and renovations.

Maintainability, expandability, and flexibility are also very important design criteria. The designed system shall allow needed preventive and failure maintenance to be done with little disruption to the operations of the hospital. New technologies are always being presented to the medical profession. These new technologies may require additional power, additional support systems, and often new building areas. The ability to expand, and the flexibility to change, the distribution system to meet these new technologies are also very important design criteria.

Another design criteria is economy. Public and political pressure is always present to reduce the cost of health care and to develop a more competitive market place for health care. Therefore, facility designs, including electrical distribution system designs, should consider economics. The designer shall consider both the initial cost and the operating expense of the electrical system.

This chapter will develop these basic design criteria as they relate to system planning, electrical power systems, voltage considerations, current considerations, grounding, overcurrent protection and coordination, electrical equipment, and installation and system arrangements.

3.2 Systems planning

Basic overall systems planning is the first, and probably one of the most important, phases in the overall design of an electrical power distribution system for a health care facility. During this phase, preliminary design data is gathered from administrators and staff of the health care facility, the local utility, and authorities having jurisdiction over electrical construction. All relevant national, state, and local codes, and facility design guidelines, should be reviewed. Two national codes having a major affect on health care power distribution design are

— The National Electrical Code® (NEC®) (NFPA 70-1996)[1]
— NFPA 99-1996, Health Care Facilities

In addition, the architectural plans and existing site conditions should be examined from an electrical system perspective to determine potential problems and needs. The following subclauses will discuss some of the issues that should be addressed during the system planning phase of the design.

3.2.1 Consult with the project architect

A vital step in systems planning is early and ongoing coordination with the project architect. A first step is giving input to, and providing review of, the preliminary floor plan and schematics from an electrical design perspective. The architect needs the electrical designer's input as early as possible in order to avoid potential problems due to building limitations and electrical requirements such as

a) Inadequate electrical and communication equipment room sizes

b) Inadequate space in other certain areas having significant electrical equipment such as radiology suites or computer rooms

c) Electrical rooms that have poor accessibility to the electrical equipment and devices, or that restrict or prohibit easy equipment removals and installations after initial construction is complete

d) "Wet areas" that are located near or above electrical or communication rooms, which could be potentially hazardous

e) Telephone/communications/data room size and location requirements, which do not provide needed working or maintenance clearances

f) Ventilation, cooling, and/or exhaust needs of electrical/communication rooms, which is not provided, or is inadequate

---

[1]Information on references can be found in 3.10.

g) Space for needed raceways, busways, and trays that is not provided

h) Space for the temporary installations and use of large electrical testing apparatus that is not present

It is a good practice to have all electrical equipment in rooms dedicated to such equipment. Piping, ductwork, or any architectural appurtenances that do not serve that room or space (and only those rooms) are not permitted to penetrate the walls of electrical spaces (with minor exceptions). Accordingly, the designer should work closely with the architect and mechanical engineer to ensure proper placement and utilization of electrical spaces. A problem often seen is the location of toilet rooms or mechanical equipment rooms directly over electrical spaces. Those room placements often force the installation of "forbidden" equipment in the electrical rooms.

3.2.2 Consult with the health care facility administrators, nursing and medical staff, and maintenance/operation staff, and other personnel as required

The following consultations provide information on the specific needs, requirements, constraints, and limitations of the planned facility:

a) *The facility function.* The designer must know the specific functions to be performed in the facility. This information is needed in order to apply the proper Codes and to weigh the importance of reliability, quality of electrical power, safety, and economy. For example, the reliability designed into a distribution system serving a hospital that specializes in open heart surgery would not be justified in an outpatient clinic. Also, a facility that extensively utilizes computerized diagnostic, patient records, and accounting systems would require a higher quality of electric power than a hospital that does not use such computerized equipment. The system designer is the one charged with determining the functions of the facility.

b) *Financial and budget information.* The designer must know the financial expectations of the administrators before beginning to develop an electrical system. The administrators typically have a fixed budget (in dollars) or have a "variable" budget (in dollars per square foot of facility). This budget must be considered in all phases of design in order to assure satisfaction. Such economic constraints, however, do not allow critical needs to be ignored simply to meet a budget. If the budget is unrealistic, the designer shall call this to the attention of the hospital administrator as soon as possible.

The administrators are concerned not only at the one-time capital costs of the projects, but also at the yearly operating costs of the installed systems. The designer should provide information on the relative operating expenses of different possible design options. The administration may decide it is better to increase the capital outlay to reduce the facility's ongoing expenses.

c) *Preferences on systems or equipment.* The maintenance/operational staff often have preferences on the types of systems or equipment to be installed in their building(s). The reasons for these preferences are many and varied. Whatever the reason, the designer should keep these preferences in mind throughout the system design. If the

41

designer feels that these preferences are unjustified, they should be reviewed with the staff during the design process; and if necessary, discussed and documented with the administrators as to the cost, safety, and/or code implications of the staff's "preference."

d) *The skill of maintenance and operations personnel.* The skill and 24-hour availability of the facility's maintenance and operations personnel is an important design consideration. For example, if the maintenance personnel for a particular facility does not include skilled electricians, the designer may consider specifying a system that requires minimum maintenance, and is automated, or supervised from a competently staffed remote location (in real time), compared to a system that requires much more maintenance and/or more ongoing operator involvement. Where the skill level of the maintenance staff may compromise the necessary design of the electrical systems to meet the other goals, then this should be brought to the attention of the hospital administrator.

e) *Future expansion of the facility.* The administrator of the facility will usually have some plans for the future of the facility. These plans could be in the form of preliminary ideas or may be well-documented. It is essential that these plans be analyzed and well incorporated into the electrical system design. Depending on budget constraints, additional capacity should at least "set up" the distribution system for future expansion(s).

3.2.3 Determine the basic loads and demand data

The designer should begin to tabulate preliminary load data. The preliminary architectural floor plans can be used effectively by superimposing load data on them. The floor plans should show major equipment loads, block loads based on square footage, and any future loads or buildings that the power system should be designed to accommodate. Always allow for load growth even beyond the defined plans for future expansions.

In the initial stages of planning, exact load data will seldom be known. However, the designer can estimate probable loads based on existing, similar, health care facilities. Helpful data is listed in Chapter 2 of this recommended practice and IEEE Std 241-1990 (Chapters 2 and 16). Also refer to the electrical load data in the Handbooks of the American Society of Heating, Refrigerating, and Air-Conditioning Engineers (ASHRAE). The sum of the electrical ratings of each piece of equipment will provide a total "connected load." Since most equipment will operate at less than full load, and some intermittently, the "connected demand" on the power source is always less than, or equal to, the "connected load." Standard definitions for these load combinations have been devised and defined in Chapter 2 of this recommended practice, IEEE Std 141-1993, and the NEC (Article 220). The projected electrical system's heat loads should always be reviewed with the mechanical engineer to ensure that the air-conditioning system is sized properly for that load.

3.2.4 Consult with the local electric power company

The designer shall discuss the proposed health care facility with the power company to determine their specific requirements and limitations. The power company will be interested in the size of the load demand, the projected power factor, the load factor, and the need for backup service. They will also be interested in the plans for on-site generation, the size of the largest motors and the method of starting (for voltage drop reasons), and any unusual demands or service requirements.

The designer should clearly determine the following issues:

a) Are there any limitations on the size of load the utility can service?

b) Will there be any "up front" charges for supplying power to the facility?

c) What type of service does the utility plan to provide? What are their requirements? What is the service history?

   1) Single phase (two or three wire), or three phase (three or four wire)
   2) Voltage level
   3) One circuit or two circuits
   4) Overhead or underground services
   5) Termination details for their cables and/or overhead lines (phase rotation, circuit labeling, etc.)
   6) Space requirements for their equipment (including landscaping, set backs, roadways, etc.)
   7) Metering requirements, details, and space requirements. Also are there any loads needing separate meters, etc.?
   8) Outage histories of proposed services to evaluate reliability (also confirm "outage" definitions as used in those histories)

d) What components of the electrical service will the owner be required to furnish?

   1) Primary conduit(s)
   2) Primary trenching, backfill, and "markers"
   3) Primary cables
   4) Transformer(s)
   5) Transformer vault(s)
   6) Concrete pad(s)
   7) Metering and metering conduit
   8) Surge arresters and transient voltage surge suppression
   9) Environmental protection (noise abatement from transformers, oil spill systems, fire protection, etc.)

   What is the physical "breakline" between utility-supplied and owner-supplied equipment (e.g., property line, last pole, underground vault, etc.)?

e) What are the utility's billing rates and rate structure? Below are some general considerations (see Chapter 2 for more details).

   1) Are there penalties for low power factor?
   2) Are there penalties for multiple services and/or meters?
   3) Is it economical to purchase power at primary (or higher) voltage levels rather than lower voltage levels?
   4) What limits or penalties are there for harmonic distortion?

    5)   What are (voltage) flicker limits (maximum variations and maximum occurrences per day)?

    6)   Determine the utility's definitions for power quality terms such as "outage," "voltage sag," etc.

f)   How reliable will the power source be? (Obtain a copy of the utility outage record for the past several years.)

g)   What will be the maximum and minimum voltage to be expected at their power supply point? (Will voltage regulating equipment be required?) If possible, get a copy of voltage meter chart.

h)   May internal generation, if it will exist in the proposed system, be allowed to operate in parallel with the utility? If yes, what are their requirements on relaying, control, metering, and communications?

i)   What is the maximum short-circuit current available? Ask them to supply three-phase, and the single-phase-to-ground duties (with the respective X/R ratios) for today's system, and as expected five years into the future.

j)   What are their protective device coordination requirements?

Please note that the utility is not required to follow the NEC in providing an electrical service. The utility does normally, however, follow the National Electrical Safety Code® (NESC®) (Accredited Standards Committee C2-1997). The designer in any case should stress the utility's responsibility to work with the designer in order to provide the health care facility with a safe, reliable service.

3.2.5 Reliability issues

Life support and high-value continuity uses may merit the redundancy offered by secondary-selective systems, radial systems with secondary voltage transfer switches, and other similar systems. The system designer should plan to perform the increased engineering analysis that accompanies these higher reliability systems, and compare the value of improved continuity of service, reduction in false outages, and the improved level of equipment protection—all balanced against cost. IEEE Std 493-1990 describes the reliability of radial systems and other systems.

3.2.6 Consult with the local authorities having jurisdiction over new electrical construction

The designer should meet with the local authorities having jurisdiction over electrical construction, and discuss their special requirements and interpretations of the relevant Codes. The designer should incorporate the effects of these interpretations during the system planning stage. The local authorities can also provide input on any local natural phenomena that may affect the electrical design, such as the presence of frequent violent electrical storms, seismic conditions, or a corrosive environment. These authorities include the electrical inspector, fire marshall (chief), Department of Health (city, state, and/or federal), Occupational Safety and Health Administration (OSHA), Insurance Underwriters, etc.

3.2.7 Summary

This subclause reviews many of the system planning issues that should be addressed during this phase of design. It is important that all information gathered be well-documented for ease of reference throughout the project. The designer should continually update this planning information as changes or new developments occur.

Once the system planning phase is complete, the designer will have the necessary information to begin the actual design of the electrical distribution system for the health care facility.

3.3 Electrical power systems basics

Power systems for health care facilities require a high degree of safety, maintainability, expandability, flexibility, and reliability. Some areas of health care facilities require electrical design similar to that documented in IEEE Std 241-1990 (Chapters 2 and 16). However, most areas will require additional considerations as dictated by

a) The numerous governing codes and standards.
b) The use of complex and electrically sensitive medical equipment.
c) Most importantly, the fact that patients and medical personnel must be guarded against electrical hazards.

While it is now uncommon, the designer should ask if flammable anesthetics are still being used. If this is the case, extreme care should be exercised to prevent fire and explosion. These areas are deemed very hazardous, and the designer should refer to the NEC (Articles 500-503 and 517), NFPA 99-1996, and all other national and local codes that may be applicable. In operating rooms, special attention shall be given to power distribution. For example, general-purpose overhead luminaires are usually powered from the normal grounded distribution system, provided the fixtures cannot be touched by personnel during the course of surgical procedures. However, surgical luminaires that may be adjusted during surgery, outlets for electrical surgical instruments, monitoring equipment, portable x-ray, etc., should be powered through an isolation transformer with a line-isolation monitor as outlined in Chapter 6. (Refer to Chapter 4 for power distribution requirements in other specific areas.)

3.3.1 Power sources

Generally, the normal power source is furnished by the electric utility and the required alternate power source by an on-site power source such as a generator set, uninterruptible power supply (UPS), or battery/inverter system. However, when the normal source consists of an on-site power generator(s), the alternate power source required can be another power generator unit or the electric utility. A battery/inverter system can be applied as the principal alternate power source for nursing homes, residential custodial care facilities, and other health care facilities provided they meet the conditions outlined in NFPA 99-1996. A UPS may be justifiable for large computing centers or other critical, sensitive loads.

Please note that a generator set is required as the alternate power source for hospitals. Additional data pertaining to generator units and batteries can be found in Chapter 5 of this recommended practice, as well as the NEC (Articles 517 and 700), NFPA 99-1996 (Chapter 8), NFPA 110-1993, NFPA 111-1993, and IEEE Std 446-1995.

3.3.2 Distribution circuits

Distribution systems for health care facilities are basically divided into two categories—the normal electrical system (non-essential) and the essential electrical system. Both systems are supplied by the normal power source; however, the essential electrical system can be transferred to the alternate power supply whenever the normal power source experiences a power failure.

a) *Non-essential electrical system.* The non-essential electrical system consists of distribution equipment and circuits that supply electrical power from the normal power supply to loads that are not deemed essential to life safety, or the effective, and essential operation of the health care facility.

b) *Essential electrical system.* The essential electrical system consists of the alternate power supply (or supplies), transfer equipment, distribution equipment, and the circuits required to assure continuity of electrical service to those loads deemed as essential to life safety, critical patient care, and the effective operation of the health care facility. NFPA 99-1996 and the NEC cover these topics in great detail and should be carefully reviewed. The information given here summarizes much of that data.

For hospitals, the essential electrical system can be subdivided into two systems—the emergency system and the equipment system. The emergency system itself is comprised of two branches defined as the life safety branch and the critical branch. These branches include distribution equipment and circuitry, including automatic transfer devices required to enable emergency loads to be transferred from normal to emergency power sources automatically. To increase the reliability of the system, circuits from each of these two branches are required to be installed separately from each other and from all other types of circuits. NFPA 99-1996 and the NEC require that the emergency system automatically restore electrical power within 10 s of power interruption. The NEC also defines the types of electrical loads to be served by the life safety branch and the critical branch (Articles 517-32 and 517-33). Article 517-33 of the NEC allows the designer to install "other equipment and devices necessary for the effective operation of the hospital" on the critical branch of the emergency system. This gives some flexibility in tailoring the design to the specific needs of the health care facility. The designer should use his/her experience, hospital staff input, and good engineering judgment in applying this Article to the design.

The equipment system consists primarily of three-phase distribution equipment and circuits, including automatic, delayed-automatic, or manual transfer devices to serve equipment loads essential to the effective operation of the facility as defined by NFPA 99-1996 (Chapter 8). In addition, the Joint Commission on Accreditation of Health Organization (JCAHO) requires that if a hospital has a fire pump it shall be connected to the equipment system via an automatic transfer switch.

For nursing homes and residential custodial care facilities, which provide care requiring electromechanical sustenance and/or surgical treatment requiring general anesthesia, the essential electrical system is subdivided into two systems—the emergency system and the critical system. The emergency system in these cases is limited to those loads defined for the life safety branch for hospitals, plus sufficient illumination to exit ways in dining and recreation areas. These emergency system circuits are required to be installed separately and independently of non-emergency circuits and equipment. The NFPA standards require that this emergency system branch be designed to permit automatic restoration of electrical power within 10 s of power interruption. The critical system is limited to critical receptacles, task illumination, and equipment necessary for the effective operation of the facility.

For other health care facilities (excluding hospitals, nursing homes, and residential custodial care facilities where the facility administers inhalation anesthetics or requires electromechanical life support devices), the essential electrical system consists of one system supplying a limited amount of lighting and power considered essential for life safety and orderly cessation of procedure whenever normal electrical service is interrupted for any reason. The type of system selected should be appropriate for the medical procedures performed in the facility.

The design for emergency power generators, in the above noted facilities, shall meet the requirements defined for Type I, Type II, and Type III installations as noted in NFPA 99-1996, Section 3-5.1.2.1. These "Type" designations define maximum start times, maximum run times, etc., as noted in NFPA 110-1993.

3.4 Voltage considerations

The proper selection, regulation, and quality of utilization voltages is extremely important because of the extensive use of sensitive medical equipment that is available in many different voltage ratings. This equipment shall not be jeopardized by misapplied or poorly regulated voltages or voltages with high harmonic content. The dynamic characteristics of the overall system should be recognized and the proper principles of voltage control should be applied so that satisfactory voltage will be supplied to all utilization equipment under all conditions of operation (i.e., including large motor starting, etc.). The reader is referred to IEEE Std 141-1993 and IEEE Std 241-1990 for a detailed discussion of voltage.

3.4.1 Select system voltages

The voltage levels selected will depend on the utility voltage available, the size of the health care facility, the loads served, expansion requirements, the building layout, voltage regulation requirements, and cost.

Typically, a large health care facility will be supplied power at a medium voltage level from the utility and it will be stepped-down to either 480Y/277 V or 208Y/120 V for utilization. Either 480 V or 208 V can be used to supply mechanical equipment (chillers, fans, pumps, etc.), medical equipment (radiology, medical air pumps, etc.), and other support equipment such as laboratory equipment and kitchen equipment. If 480 V is present, however, it is preferred. From initial cost considerations, ongoing operating cost reasons, and isolation from sensitive 120 loads, the 480 V level is the better choice for these equipments.

The use of 277 V lighting in lieu of 120 V in large health care facilities is common. The application of 277 V lighting in hospitals, however, differs from other commercial facilities because of the requirement for the four divisions of the electrical system (normal, critical branch, life safety branch, and the equipment system). Depending on other equipment requirements, applying 277 V lighting may increase the number of 480Y/277V panels on each floor and/or in each electrical room. There is no general rule on when to apply 277 V lighting. Each individual application should be analyzed to determine its feasibility. Typical benefits of 277 V lighting include reduced system losses, reduced number of branch circuits for lighting, reduced sizes of power conductors, reduced heat gains on the air conditioning system due to power losses, and segregation of the harmonics of the electronic ballasts in luminaires from the medical equipment operating at 208Y/120 V.

3.4.2 Nominal voltage

Once the nominal utilization voltages have been selected, the voltage of all medical equipment to be installed in the facility should be carefully checked to assure proper application. If the equipment is new, it should be ordered to one of the planned utilization voltages. If this is not possible, then "buck"/"boost," autotransformer, or standard two-winding transformers should be considered to supply rated voltage to the equipment. A common misapplication includes the use of nominally rated 230 V motors installed on a 208 V system.

Carefully consider the design of the distribution system to supply equipment obtained from international sources. These are often designed for use on 415Y/240V, 400Y/230V, or 380Y/220 V, and/or 50 Hz systems. Carefully check the frequency rating of the equipment from international sources to ensure satisfactory operations at 60 Hz. Also check the equipment's tolerance to the ±5%, or ±10% tolerances (voltage range A or B) that are found on U.S. utility services. (Note that Europe, in 2003, will be standardizing on a 400 Y/230V standard voltage that has a tolerance of ±10% of nominal.)

Radiology equipment is available in a variety of single-phase and three-phase voltages. It is necessary to know the exact voltage requirements and tolerances of the equipment from the manufacturer's data to properly plan for its installation. Because of their operating characteristics (low load factor, low power factor, and/or high surges) x-ray systems are often supplied by dedicated power distribution systems.

In general the engineer should be aware that transformer regulation may result in a voltage drop of 2.5–5%. Therefore, to maintain acceptable voltage at the utilization equipment, the voltage drop in the wiring should be limited to less than 2.5%.

3.4.3 Voltage variation and disturbances

Variations in the sinusoidal voltage waveform can be caused by many different types of power system disturbances. Transient overvoltages are caused by lightning, capacitor switching, fault switching, welding, arcing grounds, brush-type motors, or switching of inductive loads, such as motors, radiology equipment, etc. Nonlinear loads such as switch-mode power supplies, ballasts, and adjustable speed drives are generators of harmonics which can cause serious neutral overloading, transformer overloading, and interference problems. See IEEE Std 1100-1992. Momentary total loss of voltage can be the result of utility switching, fault clearing operations, some transient voltage arrester operations, or equipment failure. Transient voltage suppression is dealt with in IEEE Std 141-1993, IEEE Std 142-1991, and IEEE Std 241-1990, and the IEEE Surge Protection (C62) Standards Collection. See also the requirements of NFPA 780-1995.

There is a variety of voltage protection, regulating, and conditioning equipment available on the market. Surge arresters, voltage regulators, transient voltage surge suppressors, shielded isolation transformers, voltage regulators, power conditioners, UPSs, or combinations of this equipment can be applied to solve voltage variation problems. The choice of which equipment to apply depends on the nature of the voltage variations and the characteristics of the equipment to be protected.

a) Surge arresters, voltage regulators, and transient voltage surge suppressors are designed to remove temporary overvoltages from the power system for protection of distribution and utilization equipment.

b) Shielded isolation transformers are effective in rejecting certain types of transients. They will, however, not provide a clean, noise-free ground. IEEE Std 142-1991 and IEEE Std 1100-1992 are excellent references on transformer and sensitive load grounding.

c) Voltage regulators or constant voltage transformers are designed to tightly control output voltage (for many cycles) regardless of variations of input voltage. The range of input voltage for which the output voltage will remain regulated is generally −10% to +20%, or −15% to +15% of nominal. In addition to input voltage range, other considerations in applying a voltage regulator are regulator load sensitivity, load compatibility, power factor, energy efficiency, and electrical isolation.

d) Power conditioners generally combine regulation, isolation, and/or transient suppression into one package.

e) Static (electronic) UPSs provide a constant voltage with standby battery capacity for power failures, and short outages. Static UPSs may, however, be a source of electrical noise/harmonics themselves, and may not always deliver a clean sinusoidal waveform unless they are specified carefully.

   Rotary (mechanical/electrical) UPSs are available to provide a pure sinusoidal waveform. Further, there is a rotary UPS configuration that is always on-line, and that relies on a diesel engine for backup. This type of UPS does not require large battery banks.

Harmonic currents can be controlled or suppressed through the use of delta-connected transformers, harmonic filters, isolation transformers, etc. IEEE Std 141-1993 deals with this subject in great detail.

The first step toward properly solving a voltage variation problem is to properly diagnose the problem. Only when the problem is properly defined is it possible to select the proper voltage regulating, protection, or conditioning equipment. Unless the exact problem is known, an engineer may specify equipment that amplifies the problem, rather than reduces or eliminates the problem.

3.4.4 Voltage problem diagnosis

In an existing facility, a high-accuracy power analyzer can be an effective tool in diagnosing voltage problems. A portion of the electrical system can be observed over a period of time with voltage variations and quality recorded including magnitude, duration of the variation, the per-unit harmonic content, and the time it occurred. This data can then be matched with medical equipment operational logs, problem logs, and/or maintenance trouble reports to determine any possible correlations.

Variations in the voltage in a health care facility commonly will be noticed first in the operation or output of computerized equipment. The designer should calculate voltage variations from motor starting, etc., on all of the various available circuits. Select the arrangement that best provides stable voltages within acceptable limits, at the lowest cost. High electrical energy losses may result if equipment operates with voltages that are unbalanced, or high in harmonic content. If the load being served is on the essential electrical system, both normal and emergency power sources need to be analyzed in this manner.

3.4.5 High transient loads

Radiology machines draw very high momentary currents during an exposure. Therefore, a low-impedance source is necessary to assure that the voltage drop is within acceptable limits, usually 3–5%. The x-ray tube will experience loss of life and equipment malfunction if proper voltage regulation is not maintained. Please note, however, that standard voltage regulators applied on radiology equipment feeders may not improve regulation because the pulse width of the equipment may be less than the response time of the regulator.

Voltage fluctuations and dips caused by motor starting, within the hospital, should be maintained within the limits dictated by the utility and by industry standards for computerized equipment. This can normally be accomplished by providing reduced voltage starters or "soft starters" on large motors or installing large motors on a separate transformer from the "sensitive" loads. The designer should carefully study the application of these starters, or separate transformers, to minimize system voltage drops at reasonable costs.

3.5 Current considerations

The full-load current requirements in a health care power system are determined by the load equipment. However, the short-circuit current requirements are determined principally by the power sources, and to a lesser degree, by the possible contributions from rotating equipment such as motors.

The short-circuit duty, during a fault, at any point in a system, is limited by the impedance of circuits and equipment from the source (or sources) to the point of fault; to the size and type of rotating equipment; and to the X/R ratio of the system. It is not directly related to the kilowatt load on the system. Additions to the system that increase its capacity to handle a growing load (while not affecting the then external load) may drastically increase the fault currents, however.

In most health care facilities, the fault-current contribution will differ in magnitude and decay rate between the normal and the alternate power sources. This can occur when

a)   The normal power source is from a utility having a high-fault current capability, and the service entrance point is removed by several transformations and transmission circuits, from the utility generation sources.

b)   The alternate power supply consists of a relatively low kilovoltampere on-site generator, or generators, and relatively short-distribution circuits between the alternate power supply and essential electrical power circuitry.

Thus, for a fault occurring within the essential electrical power system, the fault-current magnitude from the normal power source would be relatively large and have a slow decay rate. A fault under the same fault conditions when served by the alternate power source would be relatively small and have a fast decay rate. These factors should be taken into account when selecting and setting protective devices since the essential electrical system can be supplied power from either source.

Short-circuit calculations must be understood to correctly apply protective equipment, choose adequately rated equipment, choose protective devices settings, determine degree of coordination achieved, and calculate the voltage dips of impact loads such as motor starting, etc. The reader is referred to IEEE Std 141-1993 (Chapter 5), IEEE Std 241-1990 (Chapter 9), IEEE Std 242-1986, and IEEE Std 393-1991 (Table 12) to obtain information on these fundamentals.

3.6 Grounding

The word *grounding* is commonly used in electrical power work to cover both "equipment grounding" and "system grounding." These and other terms used when discussing this topic are defined in the NEC and IEEE Std 142-1991. These definitions should be quite familiar to obtain a better understanding of grounding principles.

In health care facilities, both the system and equipment are grounded. In addition, special grounding requirements shall be applied to those subsystems and equipment involved in patient care areas, operating rooms, anesthetizing locations, and special environments as presented in Chapter 6 of this recommended practice, the NEC (Article 517), and NFPA 99-1996.

3.6.1 Equipment grounding

Equipment grounding is the interconnection and bonding (grounding) of non-electrical conducting material that either encloses, or is adjacent to, electrical power conducting components. Its purpose is to reduce electrical shock hazards and provide freedom from fire hazards and to minimize damage to equipment from component overheating caused by over-currents, arcs, or bolted faults. To attain this, the grounding conductor circuit shall be designed, and be properly installed, to present a sufficiently low impedance path to ground-fault currents. For ac systems, the (return) ground current will flow through the lowest imped-ance path, not the lowest resistance path as in dc systems. The lowest ground-impedance path will be a path close to the power conductors, such as a ground conductor installed with the power conductors and/or the metal raceway enclosing the power conductors (i.e., the conduit, housing of busway, etc.).

Furthermore, to maintain the lowest ground-current impedance, junctions and terminations should be properly installed. Metal joints should make good contact to avoid sparking during fault conditions. Adequate connections between equipment ground buses and/or housings and metal raceways shall be provided. In addition, the ground return circuit components (conductors, terminations, etc.), shall be sized to carry the available ground-fault current for all types of fault conditions and durations "permitted" by the overcurrent protection system (i.e., the ground-fault current may be 12 000 A or more).

3.6.2 System grounding

The term *system grounding* relates to the type of grounding applied to the electrical system. The basic reasons for system grounding are the following:

— To limit the differences of electrical potential between all non-insulated conducting objects in a local area.

— To provide for isolation of faulty equipment and circuits where a fault occurs.

— To limit overvoltages appearing on the system under various fault conditions.

It should be noted that in an ungrounded system, a fault condition can, in certain instances, lead to system resonance that causes an extreme overvoltage to be imposed on the system. This overvoltage can be sufficient in magnitude to create severe shock hazard as well as cause electrical equipment failure due to insulation breakdown. For these and other reasons, system grounding is required for all health care facilities.

There are several methods available to ground a system such as "line grounding," "neutral grounding," etc. The preferred method for health care facilities is solid neutral grounding, since the system neutral is generally readily available. This will avoid the special system operating precautions required when employing other grounding methods. See also IEEE Std 142-1991.

a) *Selection of system grounding points.* It is necessary to solidly ground at each voltage level to achieve the advantages of neutral grounding in all parts of the system. Each voltage level may be grounded at the neutral lead of a generator; power transformer bank; or, in rare instances, neutral deriving grounding transformer provided they meet the requirements of the NEC (Article 250-5).

When there are two or more sources at a given point, each source should have a grounded neutral point since the bus-tie circuit may be open. Refer to IEEE Std 242-1986 and to NEMA PB 2.2-1988 for special techniques of system neutral grounding of double-ended substations.

b) *Neutral circuit arrangements.* When the method of grounding the neutral has been selected, the next question to consider is how many source generator(s) or transformer neutral(s), or both, will be used for grounding, and whether

   1) Each neutral will be connected independently to ground, or
   2) A neutral bus with single ground connection will be established.

c) *Medium-voltage source neutral(s).* The medium-voltage portion of the power system is usually a three-phase, three-wire system where the neutral is not used as a circuit conductor. The advantages and disadvantages of various medium-voltage grounding methods as well as design conditions for each method are covered extensively in IEEE Std 141-1993. The reader should use this reference if medium-voltage grounding is an issue.

d) *Low-voltage source neutral(s).* The low-voltage system for health care facilities is usually a three-phase, four-wire system where the neutral is used as a circuit conductor. Thus, the source's neutral should be solidly grounded to permit neutral loading as well as meet the requirements of the NEC (Article 250-5).

Where the power supply consists of services that are dual-fed in a common enclosure or grouped together in separate enclosures and employ a nonswitched (solid) secondary tie, the common neutral conductor can be effectively grounded at one point. Where the power supply for the health care facility consists of a normal, and alternate power supply, at least one of the power supplies, usually normal, is considered the service and its neutral(s) are effectively grounded. If the normal and alternate power supply are not electrically connected, then both power supply neutrals need to be effectively grounded.

3.6.3 System and load characteristics

The type of system grounding that is employed, and the arrangement of system and equipment grounding conductors, will affect the service continuity. Grounding conductors and connections shall be arranged so that objectionable stray neutral currents will not exist and ground-fault currents will flow in low-impedance, predictable paths that will protect personnel from electrical shock and assure proper operation of the circuit protective equipment.

Where phase-to-neutral loads shall be served, systems are required to be solidly grounded. However, 600 V and 480 V systems supplying only phase-to-phase loads may be solidly grounded, high-resistance grounded, or ungrounded. High-resistance grounded systems may provide a higher degree of service continuity than solidly grounded systems and might be useful in serving phase-to-phase loads requiring very high reliability. Any such system, however, needs to be carefully monitored to detect phase-to-ground faults early enough so that the fault(s) can be isolated and repaired promptly. Ungrounded systems are not recommended, however, since they may experience overvoltages due to resonance conditions, or "neutral" shifts occurring during a ground fault condition.

When the alternate power supply [generator(s) or separate utility service] and its wiring system are electrically interconnected with the normal power supply, either by the neutral or phase conductors, or both, then the alternate power supply, per the NEC [Article 250-5(d)], is not a separately derived system, and thus, its neutral is not permitted to be grounded. Only the normal power supply neutral is permitted to be effectively grounded as shown in figure 3-1. This is to prevent objectionable neutral load currents from flowing in the system ground conductors. Note that the equipment grounding conductor defined as "EGC" in figure 3-1 is still required; thus, the generator neutral must be insulated from the machine frame.

When the alternate power supply [generator(s) or separate utility service] and its wiring system are not electrically interconnected with the normal power supply wiring system either by the neutral or phase conductors, or both, then the alternate power supply, as in the NEC [Article 259-5(d)], is a separately derived system and its neutral is grounded at the alternate power supply [in addition to the neutral(s) of the normal power supply]. Figure 3-2 depicts a system where the neutral and phase conductors between the alternate and normal power supply wiring systems are not electrically interconnected by the use of a four-pole transfer device. Thus, the on-site generator is defined as a separately derived system and its neutral is solidly grounded. Since the neutral conductors are isolated between the two power systems, grounding of the generator neutral will not provide an alternate path (to ground) for load currents on the normal power source.

The choice of whether or not to switch the neutral should be carefully considered. See Chapter 5 in this recommended practice, IEEE Std 446-1995, and IEEE Std 242-1986 for more details on these issues.

3.7 System protection and coordination

The system and equipment protective devices guard the health care facility power system from the ever present threat of damage caused by overcurrents that can result in equipment loss, system failure, and hazards to patients and personnel. To achieve this protective function, protective equipment such as fuses, circuit breakers, surge arresters, or current limiting reactors, and ground fault protective devices are applied. All protective devices should be applied within their ratings of voltage, frequency and current interrupting rating, and current withstand rating. In addition, the site where they are to be applied needs to be taken into account (i.e., if it is at a higher altitude, if seismic activity is common, if temperatures are extreme, if humidity is high, etc.). Many references and standards provide guidelines as to the various device descriptions, their ratings and application limits, and rating factors if required. These requirements are best documented in IEEE Std 141-1993 (Chapter 4), IEEE Std 241-1990 (Chapter 9), and the other ANSI, NEMA, and IEEE standards listed in 3.10. The reader should refer to these for details. The following summarizes some of the information in those references.

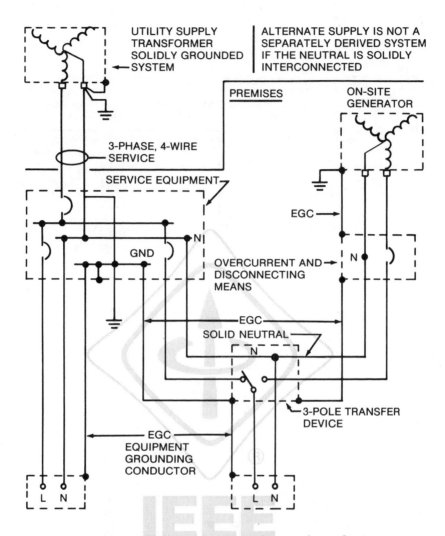

**Figure 3-1—Solidly interconnected neutral conductor
grounded at service equipment**

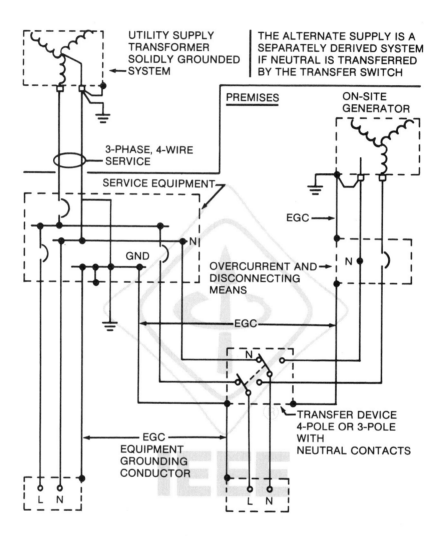

**Figure 3-2—Transferred neutral conductor grounded at service equipment
and at sources of an alternate power supply**

3.7.1 Protection system basics

Protection, in an electric system, is designed to minimize hazards due to the high energy released during short-circuit conditions. The protective features built into a system are on standby until called upon to clear a fault or some other unplanned or unintentional disturbance. They are designed to reduce the extent and duration of the power interruptions, and the hazards of property damage and personnel injury.

It is not possible to build a practical, fault-proof, power system. Consequently, modern systems are designed to provide reasonable insulation, physical and electrical clearances, etc., to minimize the possibility of faults. However, even with the best designs, materials will deteriorate and the likelihood of faults will increase with age. Every system is subject to short circuits and ground faults. A knowledge of the effects of those faults on system voltages and currents is necessary to design suitable protection. See IEEE Std 141-1993 (Chapter 4) and IEEE Std 241-1990 (Chapter 9).

3.7.1.1 Protection requirements

The design of a protective system involves the following two separate, although interrelated, steps:

a)   Selecting the proper device to protect the intended system or device

b)   Selecting the correct ampere rating and setting so they will operate selectively with other devices (i.e., to disconnect only that portion of the system that is in trouble, or faulted, and with as little effect on the remainder of the system as possible)

Protective devices should be selected to ignore normal operating conditions such as full-load current, permissible overload current, and starting (or inrush) currents. They should, however, be chosen to detect abnormal currents and to operate quickly. Often they are chosen to operate in an inverse-time manner on sustained overloads or short circuits (i.e., the higher the fault current level, the shorter the operating time to open the circuit). Further, the devices should be "coordinated" so that the protective device closest to the fault opens before "line-side" devices open.

Determining the ratings and settings for protective devices requires familiarity with the NEC requirements for the protection of cables and motors; and with IEEE Std C57.12.59-1989 and IEEE Std C57.12.00-1993 for transformer magnetizing inrush current and transformer thermal and magnetic stress damage limits. Determining the size or setting for the overcurrent protective device in a power system can be a formidable task that is often said to require as much art as technical skill. Continuity of health care facility electrical service requires that interrupting equipment operates selectively as stated in NFPA 99-1996 (Chapter 8) and the NEC (Article 517). NEMA PB 2.2-1988 provides information on the overcurrent tolerances of various classes of equipment. It is a valuable resource when overcurrent protection levels are being selected to prevent serious equipment damage.

As total selectivity and maximum safety to personnel are critical, a total short-circuit, coordination, and component protection study shall be performed. This work should normally only be done by someone who is qualified and experienced in such work. This study first determines the available short-circuit currents at each major component throughout the system. Then time vs. current coordination curves are drawn and coordination time intervals (CTIs) are established to determine if the overcurrent devices are selectively coordinated at the various available fault currents. Then the component withstand ratings are checked to see if the device actually protects the "load-side" equipment at the fault current levels that may be present during a fault. This method of analysis is useful when designing the protection for a new power system, when analyzing protection and coordination conditions in an existing system, or as a valuable maintenance reference when checking the calibration of protective devices. The coordination curves provide a permanent record of the time-current operating relationship of the entire protection system.

For information on fault studies and plotting time-current curves, see the references noted in 3.10. For information on the special requirements regarding arcing ground faults, see IEEE Std 242-1986 or NEMA PB 2.2-1988.

3.7.1.2 Current sensing protectors

The current sensing (overcurrent and short-circuit) detectors in the circuit protectors (circuit breakers, fuses, etc.) shall detect all types of faults that may be present in the distribution system. The current magnitude of those faults depend upon the system's overall impedance (from the utility) and upon the method of system grounding.

3.7.1.3 Types of faults

For the bolted or arcing fault, the solution involves a two-step approach.

First, minimize the probability of fault initiation by

— Selecting equipment that is isolated by compartments within grounded metal enclosures.

— Selecting equipment with drawout, rack-out, or stab-in features, where available, thereby reducing the necessity of working on energized components. Such equipment should have "shutters" that automatically cover the energized bus when the device is withdrawn.

— Providing isolated bus.

— Providing insulated bus. This alternative should be considered to prevent the occurrence of ground faults, especially on the line side of mains where the utility does not provide ground-fault protection.

— Providing proper installation practices and supervision.

— Protecting equipment from unusual operating or environmental conditions.

— Insisting on a thorough clean-up and survey of tools and instruments immediately before initial energization of equipment.

— Executing regular and thorough maintenance procedures.

— Maintaining daily good housekeeping practices.

Second, sense and remove the defective circuit quickly so that damage will be minimized.

— Pay careful attention to system design, monitoring equipment, and to the settings of protective devices.

— Pay careful attention to component withstand ratings and fault clearing capabilities.

3.7.1.4 Ground-fault protection

Phase overcurrent devices ratings, or settings, are normally determined by the load requirements. They are set to be insensitive to full-load and inrush currents as well as provide selectivity between load-side and line-side devices. Accordingly, the phase overcurrent device cannot distinguish between normal load currents and low-magnitude, ground-fault short-circuit currents of the same magnitude. Therefore, ground-fault detection is added to supplement the phase overcurrent devices to provide arcing ground-fault protection.

The application of ground-fault protection requires additional careful attention (i.e., the fault currents from the generator normally are much lower than from the utility).

3.7.1.4.1 Equipment selection

When choosing ground-fault protective devices, the system ground currents and system wiring configuration shall be considered.

3.7.1.4.2 Types of ground currents

Several types of ground currents can exist in any power system as follows:

a) Insulation leakage current from appliances, portable cleaning equipment and/or tools, etc. Normally, the magnitude of this current is very low (in the order of microamperes in small systems to several amperes in extensive systems). Line-isolating power supplies, or ground-fault circuit interrupters (GFCIs) (serving patient or staff functions) are designed for these lower current values.

b) Bolted-fault ground current commonly caused by improper connections or metallic objects wedged between phase and ground. For this type of fault, the current magnitude may even be greater than the three-phase fault current.

c) Arcing fault ground current commonly caused by broken phase conductors touching earth, insulation failure, loose connections, construction accidents, rodents, dirt, debris, etc. The current magnitude may be very low in relation to the three-phase fault current. The expected level is 35–40% of the single-phase-to-ground fault current, but may be only one half of this magnitude.

d) Lightning discharge through a surge arrester to ground. The magnitude of current could be quite large depending on the energy in the lightning stroke; however, the duration is extremely short, measured in microseconds. Protective overcurrent devices within a building's distribution system are not ordinarily affected by direct lightning strokes.

e) Static discharge.

f) Capacitive charging current, etc.

3.7.1.4.3 Preventing ground currents

Solutions to equipping the electrical system to handle or prevent these currents are varied such as

a) Insulation leakage—higher order of insulation and monitoring for same at low level and removing power promptly. Refer to Chapter 6, which further discusses monitoring equipment utilized in health care facilities.

b) Lightning discharges—proper grounding, and surge or lightning arresters.

3.7.1.5 Cost vs. equipment safety

The system designer should balance economics against cost of equipment damage to arrive at a practical ground-fault protection system, keeping in mind that the extent of equipment damage can increase the extent of power service loss, thus increasing risk to patients and ensuing liabilities.

There is no single solution for all power systems; each should be analyzed individually. In this analysis, the important factors to be considered are

a) *Power system selection.* The type of ground-fault detection scheme applied is a function of voltage level and system arrangement. Most health care facility applications are low voltage with a radial arrangement, which is the easiest to analyze and lends itself to a straight-forward protection system design. The problem becomes more difficult with secondary-selective and spot-network circuit arrangements.

b) *Neutral circuit.*

1) A three-phase, three-wire or three-phase, four-wire power system with radial feeders (and associated neutrals) presents few problems.

2) For a power system with neutrals that are used as a load conductor; where those neutrals are looped, or continuous, between alternate power sources; and are grounded only at the sources, or grounded "on the load side;" extreme care should be taken in applying ground-fault protection.

An experienced and qualified person should study such a system to confirm the proper design and operation of a ground-fault system. That study should also confirm full compliance to the NEC and other applicable codes. See IEEE Std 242-1986 and 3.6.3 of this recommended practice for more information.

c) *Ground return path.* The ground return path should be designed to present a low-impedance path and provide adequate ground-fault current-carrying capability to hold the voltage gradients along its path to less than shock hazard threshold values.

This design will also permit sensitive detection of ground-fault currents. IEEE Std 142-1991 provides details on the design of low-impedance, higher current grounding systems.

3.7.1.6 Summary of protective system design basics

An orderly approach to performing the above noted protective device coordination study is as follows:

a) Construct a single-line diagram of the system.

b) Record pertinent data on the single-line diagram:

    1) Distribution equipment ratings, continuous amperes, amperes interrupting current (AIC), etc.

    2) Equipment load ratings

    3) Impedance data on cables, transformers, source, etc.

    4) Pressure relief ratings of surge arresters

c) Perform calculations to determine short-circuit currents.

d) Determine equipment operating and protection ratings as defined by the NEC, equipment nameplates, the Insulated Cable Engineers Association (ICEA), texts or handbooks, manufacturers' bulletins, etc. List these ratings on the single-line diagram.

e) Determine the protective device ratings required to meet the system voltage, frequency, continuous current, momentary withstands, and short-circuit duty, as well as any unusual conditions due to site application such as altitude, vibration, shock, temperature, etc. Estimate neutral current loadings caused by nonlinear loads and single-phase loads. Also, take into account any Underwriters Laboratories (UL), NEC, or local code requirements. List the ratings chosen on the single-line diagram.

f) Choose a tentative protection device full-load rating based on load conditions. List the choice on the single-line diagram.

g) Obtain characteristic time-current curves of all protective device detectors involved in the system under study.

h) Develop time-current plots to determine device settings and be able to analyze degree of coordination and protection achieved.

i) Determine if zone selective interlocking is required to obtain selective coordination (or enhanced coordination).

Please note that these calculations and plottings can often be done by computer using one of the many commercially available programs.

3.7.2 Ground-fault detection schemes

The following are two basic methods of applying ground-fault sensing devices to detect ground faults:

a) *Ground return method.* The ground-fault sensing device is placed to detect the total ground current flowing in the grounding electrical conductor and the main bonding jumper. This method can only be used at the main disconnect point of services or for separately derived systems.

b) *Outgoing current method.* The ground-fault sensing device is placed to detect the vectorial summation of the phase and neutral (if present) currents. The sensing device is located load side (downstream) from the point at which the distribution system is grounded. This is the only method that can be used for feeders. It can also be used for the incoming main disconnect, for multiple mains, and for ties.

The ground-fault relay pickup level is adjustable and may be equipped with an adjustable time-delay feature. Operation of the relay releases the stored energy (spring) holding mechanism on the interrupting device. Selectivity in substations can be achieved either through a time delay, and/or current setting or blocking function/ zone selectivity. The "blocking function" or "zone selective interlocking" are systems that restrain main breaker tripping when the same fault is also seen on a feeder breaker. In these cases the main breaker should only trip if the feeder breaker failed to trip properly.

Care should be taken to selectively coordinate load-side levels at ground-fault protection with line-side levels and also to coordinate ground-fault protection with both line-side and load-side phase overcurrent devices. (Unwisely many systems have been designed with ground-fault devices that coordinate with one another, but do not coordinate with the phase overcurrent devices.) A carefully designed and coordinated ground-fault detection system is an important component of a reliable, safe, and economic power distribution system.

Electronic ground-fault trip devices may have a "memory circuit." Consult with the manufacturer of the device to determine if adjustments must be made to avoid "memory-circuit," nuisance-trips for cycle loads, pulsating loads, loads generating non-sinusoidal waveshapes, or other "unusual" loads.

3.7.3 Medium-voltage systems

As previously discussed in 3.6.2 item c), medium-voltage systems for health care facilities are generally three-phase, three-wire systems with the neutrals solidly grounded or resistance grounded.

When the neutral is solidly grounded, the ground-fault current magnitude is relatively high and a residual connected ground-fault relay is usually applied. This residually connected ground-fault relay, shown in figure 3-3, monitors the outgoing ground-fault current.

When the neutral is resistance grounded, the ground-fault current magnitude is relatively low, 1200 A or less, and a ground sensor with a secondary connected ground-fault relay is usually applied. This ground-fault sensor, with ground-fault relay, shown in figure 3-4, monitors the outgoing ground-fault current.

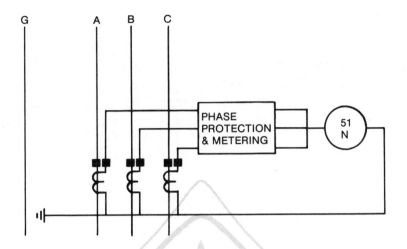

Figure 3-3—Residually connected ground-fault relay

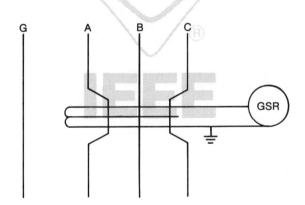

Figure 3-4—Ground-fault sensor and ground-fault relay

The ground sensor relay shown in figure 3-5 monitors the returning ground-fault current.

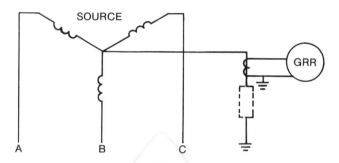

Figure 3-5—Ground-fault sensor and ground-fault relay with ground resistor

3.7.4 Low-voltage systems

As previously discussed in 3.6.2 item d), low-voltage systems for health care facilities are generally three-phase, four-wire systems. The normal power source neutral is effectively grounded. The alternate power source neutral may, or may not be, effectively grounded at the alternate source. The ground-fault schemes applicable will depend on how the alternate power supply is grounded.

For feeder circuits having no neutral conductor requirements (three-phase, three-wire loads), or for three-phase, four-wire loads where the neutral conductors are not electrically interconnected between power source on the load side of the feeder breaker, residually connected, ground-fault relay, or integral ground-fault relays (see figures 3-6, 3-7, and 3-8) may be applicable for the feeder overcurrent device.

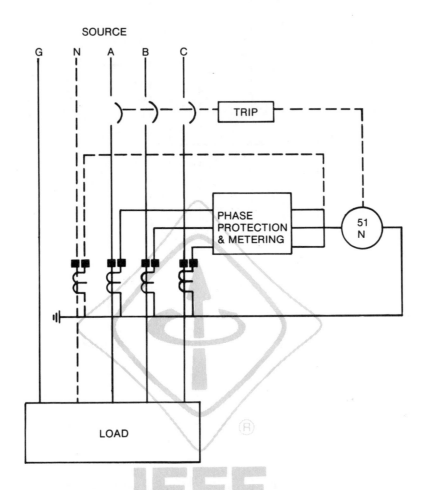

**Figure 3-6—Residually connected ground-fault relay
with shunt trip circuit breaker**

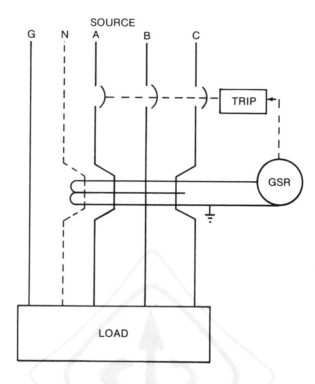

Figure 3-7—Ground sensor fault relay

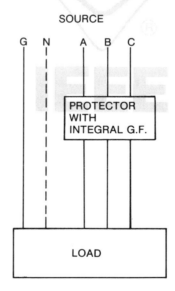

Figure 3-8—Integral ground-fault relay

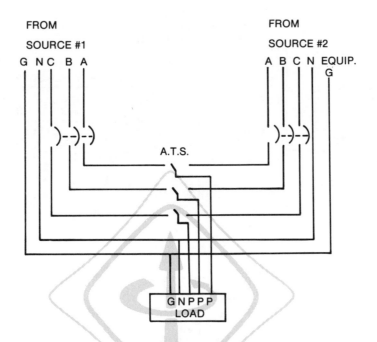

Figure 3-9—Dual source electrically interconnected

For feeder circuits with neutral conductor requirements where the neutral conductors are electrically interconnected between power sources on the load side of the overcurrent device, "outgoing current method" schemes will be applicable. Figure 3-9 is an example of such a circuit.

Typical ground-fault relaying systems are shown (see figures 3-10 and 3-11) for a health care facility power system that consists of normal and alternate power supplies. The power systems shown in figure 3-10 have an electrical power conductor interconnection between power supplies. Note the vectorial summation of ground-fault currents (outgoing current method) in the relaying scheme required for the power system shown in figure 3-10. In both figures 3-10 and 3-11, ground-fault relay R2 is optional.

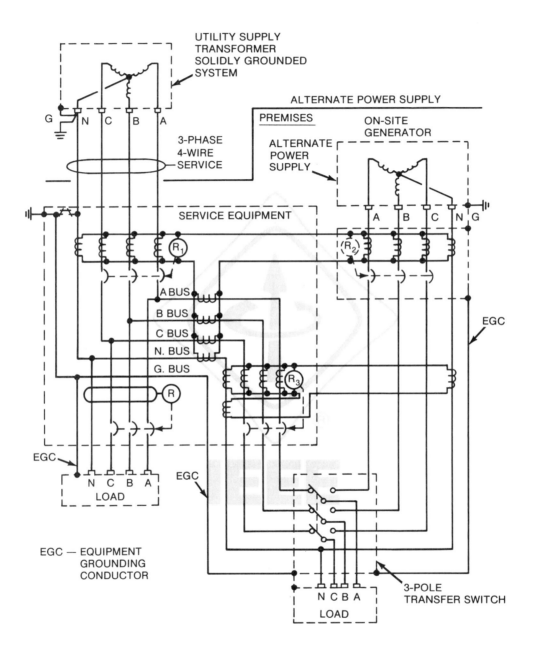

**Figure 3-10—Ground-fault scheme for a normal and alternate power supply
having an electrical power conductor (neutral) interconnection
between supplies**

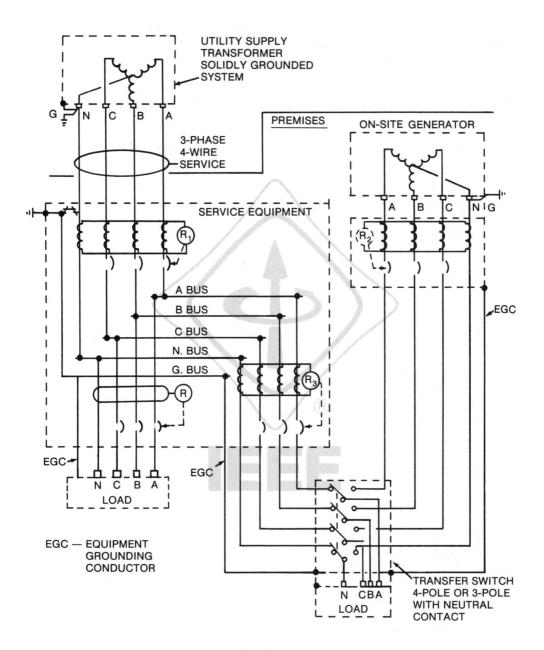

Figure 3-11—Ground-fault scheme for a normal and alternate power supply with no electrical power conductor interconnection between supplies

3.8 Electrical equipment selection, installation, and testing

3.8.1 Equipment selection

Electrical power distribution equipment is described in detail in IEEE Std 141-1993 and IEEE Std 241-1990. When used in health care facilities, there are more criteria involved in the selection of equipment. Some of the factors influencing the engineers' choice of equipment are

  a)   Reliability, protection, and coordination requirements, and how rapidly vital service can be replaced following an outage.

  b)   Initial cost including installation, maintenance facilities, maintenance cost, availability, and cost of space.

  c)   Listing and labeling of equipment according to recognized standards by a nationally recognized testing laboratory (NRTL).

The engineer should remember that not just revenues or production will be lost should the system fail, but possibly human lives. The system should therefore provide the most reliable power possible (within economic feasibility) to patients and procedures that require electrical power. All the components used in the electrical system for health care facilities should provide a reliable and safe electrical system. Careful consideration during the design and installation should be given to the location of the electrical components to minimize exposure to hazards such as lightning, storm, floods, earthquakes, fires, or toxic and/or environmental hazards created by adjoining structures or activities.

3.8.2 Working space

Ample working space around electrical components should be provided to allow and permit all tasks, installation, maintenance, testing, operating, etc., to be performed in a safe manner. See the NEC, NFPA 70B-1994, and NFPA 70E-1995.

3.8.3 Labeling

Proper permanent labeling should be applied to all components where power is initiated and terminated. Equipment such as switchgear, switchboards, motor control centers, panelboards, automatic transfer switches, etc., should all have engraved plastic nameplates (that designate source, purpose, and loads served) applied on incoming sections, tie sections, and feeder sections. All cables, busways, and buses should also be identified as to phase, to assist in maintaining proper phase sequence. Also apply a consistent and unique method of labeling electrical rooms so they can be easily found.

3.8.4 Acceptance testing

Upon completing installation and before energizing, the electrical components should be thoroughly cleaned. A visual inspection should be performed to assure that all components are installed properly, and protective devices are set properly. After these steps are completed, the system is ready for acceptance testing. All components including protective devices and circuitry, control circuitry, etc., should be acceptance tested to assure proper operation before energization. The acceptance testing should be performed by an organization specializing in this work. Refer to NFPA 70B-1994 and the NETA Electrical Acceptance Testing Specifications (ATS).

3.8.5 Segregation of services

In selecting and installing the electrical distribution components for the essential electrical system, high priority should be given to achieving maximum continuity of the electrical supply to the load. To achieve this high reliability, the components (distribution circuitry, electrical equipment, etc.) for the essential electrical system should be installed so that they are physically separated from the non-essential power system components. Furthermore, as in NFPA 99-1996 (Chapters 8 and 9), each branch of the emergency system should be installed so as to be physically separate and independent of each other and all other wiring. An exception is allowed only where the electrical components require two separate services such as in a transfer switch. Separate panelboards and raceways for the emergency systems are required to achieve this high level of redundancy.

3.8.6 Equipment selection

The following subclauses discuss the equipment commonly applied in health care facilities. Considerations mentioned here are those of specific concern in a health care facility. The in-depth considerations as outlined in IEEE Std 141-1993 and IEEE Std 241-1990 should be understood to assist in choosing proper equipment.

3.8.7 Transformers

While transformer operating cost is an important factor when selecting a transformer, consideration should also be given to initial cost, operating costs of no-load and load losses, reliability, sound level, thermal life, overload capability, ability to supply nonlinear loads, installation costs, size, weight, availability of application, and servicing resources. The goal would be to balance the no-load losses and load losses to a minimum point at the normal loading point of the transformer [i.e., a transformer whose load losses are four times as large as the no-load losses would be most efficient at approximately 50% of its nameplate (base) rating].

3.8.8 Switchgear, switchboards, and motor control centers

This equipment (as well as the transformers) should be located as close as possible to their loads to shorten cable runs, reduce losses in the cables, and minimize voltage drops. These pieces of equipment should not be located near electronic monitoring equipment that is sensitive to electromagnetic interference (EMI). If this is unavoidable, consideration should be given to shielding the electronic equipment, or specifying the electronic equipment to be compatible with the EMI that may be present. Adequate clearances and ventilation should be planned for present equipment and possible future expansions.

Adequate metering equipment should be incorporated in the switchgear, switchboard, or motor control center to permit proper monitoring of the (quantity and quality) current and voltage, electrical demand, and consumption conditions of the power system.

Additional metering precautions are also required, or recommended, at switchboards and panelboards by [B2].[2] Thus metering would allow better monitoring of energy consumption. Also refer to IEEE Std 739-1995.

3.8.9 Protective devices

Overcurrent protective devices should be chosen to provide complete coordination of the system. Circuit interrupting devices have two basic elements that provide a detecting function and a switching function. They may generally be divided into the following four categories:

— Circuit breakers equipped with protective relays or direct acting trips
— Contactors equipped with overload relays
— Transfer switches equipped with voltage and frequency sensing relays
— Switches equipped with fuses

When applied within their ratings, the switching devices are generally capable of performing the following:

— *Contactors and transfer switches.* Repetitively closing, carrying and interrupting normal load currents; interrupting overload currents; withstanding but not interrupting any abnormal currents resulting from short-circuits (unless circuit breakers or fuses are built-in).

— *Switches.* Closing; carrying and interrupting load current; and when properly coordinated with a fuse, withstanding but not interrupting any abnormal current resulting from overloads and short circuits. The fuse provides detection and interruption feature for overloads and short-circuits within its design characteristics.

   NOTE—When switches are equipped with "shunt trip coils" they can be electrically tripped by ground-fault relaying equipment, or other controls.

— *Circuit breakers.* Closing; carrying and interrupting load current; withstanding and interrupting overload and short-circuit currents, and arrange ground-fault currents. Of these devices, only circuit breakers and fused switches are generally applied as overcurrent protective devices that interrupt overload, short-circuit currents, and arcing ground-fault currents. Transfer switches are applied to transfer loads from one source of power to another by monitoring power source voltage. Contactors are applied as load powering devices such as motor starters, lighting, etc.

There are basically three types of detectors used with the protective devices—fuses, relays, and direct acting trips.

— Low-voltage fuses detect and interrupt the abnormal current in one non-adjustable element. They are thermal-type devices, which are sensitive to ambient temperature

---

[2]The numbers in brackets correspond to those of the bibliography in 3.11.

and the current flowing through them. The continuous current ratings typically are based in open air, and when applied inside equipment, may need to be derated to account for increased ambient temperature. Normally, an 80% derating factor is applied. Fuses are single-phase devices and are installed in each phase of a three-phase circuit fusible switch. The application of fuses as overcurrent protective devices is similar to applying circuit breakers.

High-voltage fuses operate in a similar manner except that they are more often used to only interrupt short circuits. Also, their fuse size (e.g., 25E) does not directly relate to the current at which they operate.

— Protective relays are designed to be responsive to electrical quantities, which change during normal and abnormal conditions. The basic quantities that may change are the magnitude and/or direction of current, voltage, power, phase-angle, and frequency. Protective relays are designed to be responsive to one or more of these quantities instantaneously or at a time rate dependent on magnitude. Figure 3-12 shows a typical relay response curve. Generally, these relays are field adjustable, have a wide operating ambient temperature range, and have a drawout construction. They can be obtained with special features such as sensitivity to directional quantities only, etc. Relays, although not limited to, are normally applied in conjunction with, high and medium-voltage circuit breakers. Upon pickup, at the selected current setting, and after any time delay selected, the relay trip contacts close to energize the trip circuit of the circuit breaker, which releases the stored energy (spring) holding mechanism that then opens all circuit breaker poles. Electronic (solid state) and microprocessor based tripping units for low-voltage circuit breakers operate similarly to other protective relays; however, the circuit breaker tripping devices are often integral with the removable circuit breaker element. Figure 3-13 shows several typical, lower voltage response curves.

— Direct acting trips are responsive to current either instantaneously or at a time rate dependent on the current magnitude. They are mounted inside low-voltage circuit breakers in series with the breaker trip mechanism, which opens all circuit breaker poles. They are of a thermal-magnetic, magnetic, or electronic design. As for fuses, the thermal type requires a derating factor consideration. Some units are ambient compensated. The electromagnetic, electromechanical, or electronic (static) types are generally field adjustable.

Trip units are generally designed to be nonresponsive to load or circuit conditions that generate minor harmonic distortions. Where the harmonic content will be high, or the loads are pulsating, the circuit breaker manufacturer should be contacted. Nuisance trip signals from electronic trip units, may result when the trip unit has a "memory circuit." (See 3.7 and Chapter 6 for more information on memory circuits.)

Ground-fault detection in medium-voltage systems is generally accomplished by electromagnetic overcurrent relays and toroidal or bar-type current transformers. Generally, in low-voltage systems, microprocessor relays and matching current sensors, whether integral or external to the protective device, provide the ground-fault protection.

A word of caution is that ground-fault detection requires additional attention as outlined in 3.7.1.4 if nuisance power outage is to be avoided.

For further protective device description and application, the reader is referred to IEEE Std 141-1993 (Chapter 4), IEEE Std 241-1990 (Chapter 9), NEMA PB 2.2-1988, NEMA AB 3-1991, manufacturers' publications, and engineering handbooks listed under 3.10 and 3.11.

3.8.10 Transfer switches—Automatic and manual

Transfer switches are applied to transfer from one power source to another to maintain service to the emergency power system and designated equipment. Due to their important function in the health care facility power system, they are required to be listed for emergency electrical service and have adequate capacity of the loads being served, as well as be properly located and installed to provide reliable service. Furthermore, they must have adequate withstand ratings to prevent contact welding due to load, overload, or short-circuit currents.

Automatic transfer switches are required to be electrically operated and mechanically latched to prevent change of state, open or closed, whenever control power is unavailable.

An ATS permits the transfer and re-transfer of the load automatically when required. Manual or non-automatic transfer switches are also required to have a mechanical latching feature. Other requirements such as switch position indication, interlocking, voltage sensing, time delay, etc., are outlined in NFPA 99-1996 (Chapter 8), the NEC, NFPA 110-1993, and NFPA 111-1993.

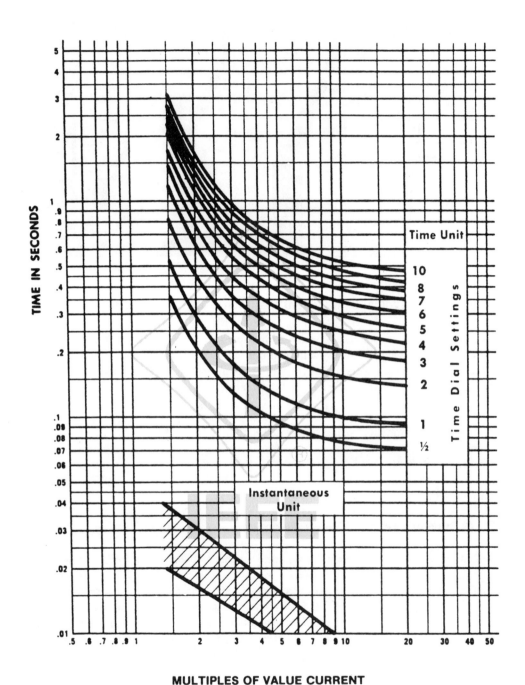

Figure 3-12—Time-current characteristics of a typical inverse-time overcurrent relay

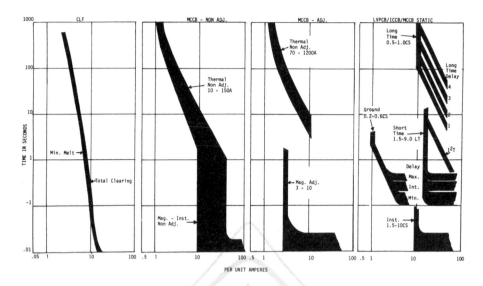

Figure 3-13—Typical time-current characteristics for low-voltage protection

To permit ease of maintenance, consideration should be given to providing bypass/isolation switches. These switches will allow normal preventive maintenance and breakdown maintenance to be performed when required with minimal, or no, disruption to patient services. (Order the bypass/isolation switches to allow maintenance transfers with no loss of power to loads.)

For additional information on transfer switches, refer to Chapter 5.

3.8.11 Generators

See Chapter 5.

3.8.12 Special wire, cable, and busway

In addition to meeting the general code requirements as noted in the NEC (Chapters 1–4), certain hospital/health care occupancies require special attention (i.e., wire and cable installed in areas classified as hazardous must meet certain installation requirements of Class 1, Division 1). One such hazardous area would include any remaining areas where flammable anesthetizing agents are used. These areas shall have wire and cable installed in approved rigid metal raceways utilizing threaded connections that are properly sealed. All boxes, fittings, and joints shall be suitable for hazardous locations.

Wiring supplying the primary of isolation transformers is restricted to having not more than 600 V between conductors. Furthermore, the conductors shall have a dielectric constant of 3.5 or less and be color coded as in the NEC (Article 517). Caution is required when installing the conductors in the isolation secondary circuits so as to not increase the conductors' dielectric constant.

3.8.13 Panelboards

Electrical panelboards should be located as close to the load as possible. Lighting and receptacle panelboards should be located to minimize circuit length to approximately 75 ft (22.9 m) between the panelboard and load. This close placement reduces voltage drops on the circuits. Panelboards should be located in electrical rooms, and should have a sufficient number of spare circuits to accommodate future expansion.

Good design and code requirements includes a low-resistance ground path, from all panelboard ground buses back to the source of power. This will limit shock hazards and provide a low-impedance path for ground-fault currents in a grounded system.

3.8.14 Isolated power supplies

Isolated power supplies consist of an isolating transformer, motor-generator sets, or batteries, a line isolation monitor, and the ungrounded circuit conductors and overcurrent protectors. Refer to Chapter 6 for more on this topic.

3.9 System arrangements

In the design and installation of the electrical power system, careful attention should be devoted to selecting the proper electrical system arrangement to provide a reliable power system. A power service consisting of two or more separate dedicated utility service feeders, fed from separate substations or from separate distribution buses, provide a much higher degree of reliability than one utility service feeder. Furthermore, the reliability is enhanced even more if each service feeder is installed separately (i.e., on separate pole lines) so that a fault in one feeder circuit will not affect the other feeder. This "two feeder" type of installation will improve the reliability compared to a single-line service.

Distribution system arrangements should be designed and installed to minimize interruptions to the electrical systems due to internal failures. Among the factors to be considered as outlined in NFPA 99-1996 are

a)   Abnormal current sensing devices, both phase current and ground current, should be selected and set to quickly disconnect any portion of the system that is overloaded or faulted.

b)   Abnormal voltage conditions such as single-phasing of three-phase utilization equipment, switching and/or lightning surges, voltage reductions, etc., should be anticipated.

c)   Capability to quickly restore any given circuit after clearing a fault or overload.

d)   Ability of system to be modified for accepting increasing loads in the facility and/or changes in supply capacity.

e)   Stability and power capability of the alternate power systems' prime mover during and after abnormal conditions.

f) Sequence reconnecting of loads to avoid large transient currents that could trip over-current devices or overload the emergency generator(s).

g) Feeder and branch circuits should be adequately rated to power their electrical loads and sufficient in number to allow load distribution that will minimize the effect of a feeder or branch circuit outage.

h) Separate nonlinear loads or high harmonic current loads [such as UPSs and adjustable frequency drives (AFDs)] from loads requiring higher quality power.

Most panelboards, motor control centers, busways, and switchboards of the electrical distribution system are installed in electrical rooms. The space requirements and location of these rooms should be identified early in the preliminary phases of a health care facility development. The ideal location for electrical rooms is in the center core of the facility, or in the middle of large wings, so that branch circuits can be run in many directions, but not to exceed typically 75 ft (22.9 m) in length. Electrical rooms on adjacent floors should be vertically aligned so that electrical power circuit risers can be installed without excessive bends and/or inaccessible taps.

The electrical rooms should be large enough to accommodate the existing and future electrical panels, switchboards, and transformers, and permit working space for access and maintainability in accordance with the NEC, NFPA 70B-1994, and NFPA 70E-1995. Rooms, especially those containing dry-type transformers, shall be ventilated to prevent heat buildup per the NEC (Article 450). Sprinkler heads should not be located in electrical rooms since their operation could cause loss of normal and emergency power service. However, where local jurisdictions insist upon installing sprinkler heads in electrical rooms, the highest permissible temperature head should be considered for installation, or a "pre-action" sprinkler system should be installed. (In a pre-action system, the sprinkler lines are normally dry. They are charged with water only after several detection devices have operated and/or been confirmed by other devices such as smoke detectors.)

Large motors have high inrush current characteristics. When supplied from the same power source that supplies voltage-sensitive equipment, precautions should be taken to prevent these inrush currents from adversely affecting the voltage-sensitive equipment. In facilities with one utility service, one method is to provide a separate feeder for supplying the voltage-sensitive equipment. Another method is to design systems with motor feeders separated from the general lighting and power feeders on double-ended switchgears or switchboards, to reduce the effects of motor starting on other electrical loads.

The motors in a health care facility that might cause voltage dip problems include elevators, air compressors, vacuum pumps, and large chiller motors. However, due to their infrequent starting (once or twice a day), the chiller motors will seldom present a severe problem if their starts are carefully scheduled and/or sequenced. The voltage drop problems of all of these loads can be minimized by electronic ("soft start" motor starters/controllers) or "reduced voltage" starters (such as autotransformer starters with closed transitions).

The electric power supply for radiology also needs special attention. The system should be installed to provide a low-voltage spread (usually 3% or less) to prevent malfunction on the x-ray equipment. Also, the x-ray system equipment should also be segregated from other voltage-sensitive equipment.

3.9.1 Radial system arrangement

3.9.1.1 Smaller facilities

For small facilities, small nursing homes and residential custodial care facilities, a single service-entrance switchboard, and a small generator can be the major components of the electrical system (see figure 3-14). These facilities usually have several normal power panelboards fed from the normal power system. If motor loads are to be energized by the generator, their restoration under emergency conditions can be delayed by using a time-delay relay in the automatic transfer switch (see Chapter 5) or by adding a time-delay relay in the motor starter, which is energized by auxiliary contacts within the transfer switch as shown in figure 3-15.

Where there will be significant emergency power requirements, several transfer switches may be used to increase reliability. The transfer switches used for the equipment system can be adjusted to transfer sequentially, thus minimizing generator inrush requirements. However, the transfer switch(es) serving the life safety system shall transfer within 10 s.

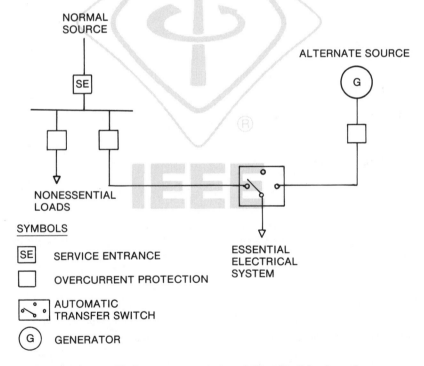

Figure 3-14—Major components of the electrical system

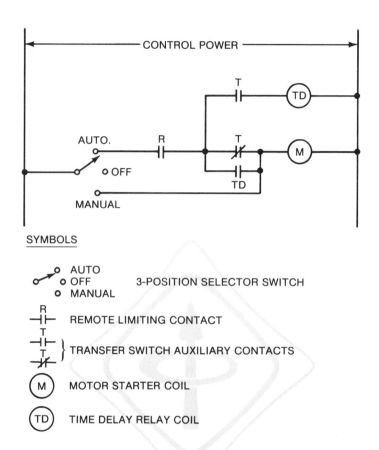

Figure 3-15—Time-delay relay in transfer switch of motor starter

3.9.1.2 Larger facilities

As health care facilities become larger, additional feeders for normal power loads and essential electrical power systems will be required. The essential electrical system will thus require three or more transfer switches, some of which could be non-automatic. Using several smaller transfer switches, in lieu of a large switch, will contribute to system stability and reliability. Further, reliability can be obtained by placing the transfer switches as close to the ultimate load as possible.

For example, figure 3-16 shows two schemes for distributing power through vertical risers. When an outage occurs in the normal power supply, the transfer switches will direct an alternate power supply to the essential electrical system panelboards. However, if a specific normal feeder outage occurs, only Scheme A can sense the specific outage and restore power to the affected panel via the alternate power supply. Scheme A is more reliable than Scheme B, but is a more costly arrangement. Loss of normal power is sensed at the transfer device to initiate start-up of the emergency generator via auxiliary contacts. When the voltage and frequency of the emergency power is in proper limits, and stable, then relays initiate switching to the alternate power source. Finally, restoration of normal power causes the automatic transfer switches to return to the normal power source while initiating a shut-down of the emergency generator. Note that time requirements between switching events are documented in NFPA 99-1996 (Chapter 8).

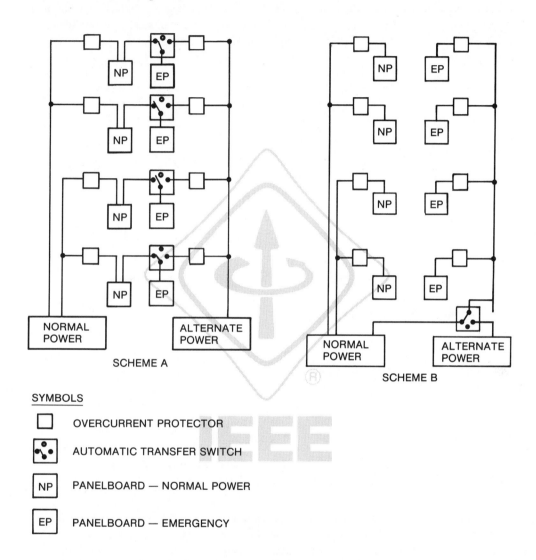

Figure 3-16—Two schemes for distributing power through vertical risers

3.9.2 Double-ended system arrangement

A double-ended substation should be considered where transformation will exceed 750 kVA. This is especially true if two utility sources are present.

For example, figure 3-17 utilizes a normally-open circuit breaker that is interlocked with the main circuit breaker so that all three circuit breakers cannot be closed simultaneously. Upon loss of a single transformer or its feeder, the tie circuit breaker can be automatically (or manually) closed and its load can be added to the remaining transformer. Additional benefits of the double-ended substation are lower fault currents than with a single larger transformer. There is the ability to normally separate motor loads, from lighting and x-ray loads that require a higher degree of voltage regulation. The design, however, should ensure adequate voltage regulation when the substation is single-ended.

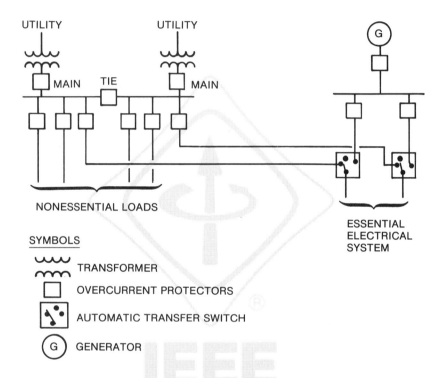

**Figure 3-17—Normally-open tie protector interlocked
with the main protectors**

When double-ended substations are installed, each transformer must safely carry the full load of the entire substation. Since core losses are a continuous power cost, it is important to minimize the "spare" capacity as long as safety, reliability, and good practice are maintained. During the time of outage of a single transformer, the increased voltage drop, the increased transformer losses, and the possible loss of transformer life (if overloaded) must be taken into account. Usually the outage time is minimal, but in the event of a transformer failure, replacement time may be in the order of weeks. Transformers can be safely overloaded in accordance with ANSI C57 standards with little or no loss of life; fans can be added to increase the emergency load capability of the transformer; and, when transformers are purchased they can be specified with a higher temperature insulation rating than is required for the normal full-load rating. "Oversized" transformers not only increase core-loss costs, but also usually increase the available fault current at their secondary, and possibly require increased switchgear sizes.

Liquid-immersed power transformers rated 55/65 °C rise have a higher overload rating than units rated 55 °C rise. Dry-type power transformers rated 80 °C rise and with 220 °C insulation have a higher overload rating than 115 °C rise units with 220 °C insulation. For example, dry-type power transformers 500 kVA and over should be specified with a temperature rise of 80 °C (preferred) or 115 °C (alternate).

Liquid-immersed power transformers should be specified to include controls to start the auxiliary cooling system (fans and pumps) when the temperature at the bottom of the tank reaches the predetermined temperature.

If the double-ended substation scheme uses a normally open electrically operated tie circuit breaker that will automatically close upon loss of an incoming feeder, then additional control and protective relaying shall be added to prevent the bus tie protector for closing when a main protector has tripped due to overload or short-circuit conditions.

In rare instances, a utility may permit a double-ended substation to be operated with a closed tie and main protectors. The advantages of using a double-ended substation with mains and tie normally-closed are better voltage regulation, and flickerless transfer upon loss of one power source. The disadvantages are greater complexity, greater fault current, greater cost, and loss of isolation between sensitive loads and high inrush loads. Also, reliability can be less since one failure, a bus fault, may cause loss of both buses. The greater complexity requires that the design engineer carefully coordinates and specifies the required additional protection to assure proper operation. Also refer to the NEC (Article 450) for reverse current relaying requirements.

3.9.3 Network system arrangement

A network service consists of two or more transformers with their secondary bused together through network protectors as shown in figure 3-18.

The advantages of network service are high reliability, no service interruption when one feeder is removed from service, and good voltage regulation. The disadvantages are high cost, high-fault currents, and may include an inability to expand the network service without increasing the interrupting ratings and sizes of existing components. In metropolitan areas, a service supplied from the utility-owned network may be available. The utility's network in cities consists of many network transformers with their secondary tied into a grid of secondary cables covering a large area. This network usually allows one primary feeder to be removed from service at any time, or two primary feeders to be removed from service during lightly loaded periods without causing undue low-voltage on the secondary grid. Where demand is over 500 kVA, utilities may opt for a "spot network" consisting of two to four network transformers in close proximity with their secondary bused together, but not connected to the general urban network.

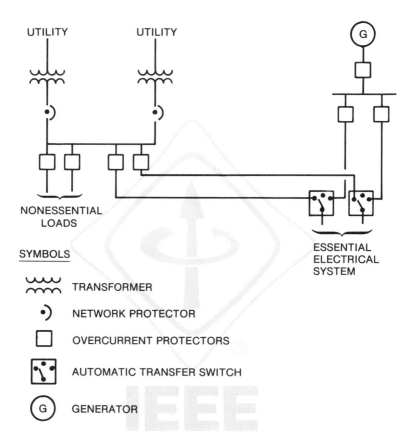

Figure 3-18—Network service

The network service is considered the most reliable, but also the most expensive type of electrical service. Life cycle costs may be reduced somewhat by having the hospital, rather than the utility, own and maintain the network transformers in order to qualify for the lower primary service rate.

The network would be used for very large loads where multiple feeders are required for each service; no interruptions are permitted on switching of feeders, and the system is fully automatic. The open-ended double-ended substation does not do this.

3.9.4 Medium-voltage system arrangements

One of the most commonly used medium-voltage systems for hospitals is the primary selective system. For facilities with very experienced staffs, the loop system may be considered also. Both of these systems allow a single cable section or feeder to be removed from service without a prolonged outage. The use of pre-formed separable connectors in manholes and at transformers can expedite the isolation, but not the switching, of a faulted cable section. (As a safety consideration, only dead-front switchgear should be used for switching.) Also, fault current detectors can be attached to cables, in manholes and certain enclosures, to aid in locating cable faults. More detailed descriptions of the loop and selective primary systems can be obtained from IEEE Std 141-1993 (Chapter 1).

3.9.5 Existing system arrangement

Where extensive new load is added to a hospital having an existing substation, it is often more convenient to add a new transformer to the distribution system, rather than to change the existing substation unless the existing unit is still adequately rated as shown in figure 3-19. Adding a new substation might provide an excellent way to introduce 480 V distribution, if the older substation is operating at a lower voltage.

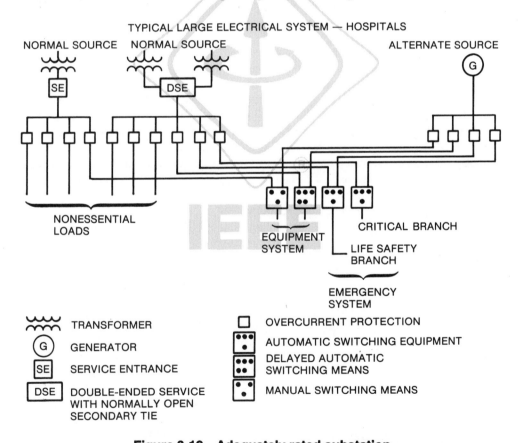

Figure 3-19—Adequately rated substation

3.9.6 Metering arrangement

Where more than one service entrance exists, the utility may bill each service independently. Since most utility rate structures are of a declining cost per block type for both power (kW) and energy (kWh), the total utility bill for all service will be more than if a single meter were used. The utility may add the demands (kW) and add the energy (kWh) consumptions and then calculate the bill as though one meter existed. This combined or additive bill will be less than the sum of the individual bills and is often referred to as conjunctional billing.

Even with just an additive bill for both kilowatts and kilowatt hours, the advantage of diversity of loads for the demand will still not be realized. This can be obtained by providing features such as interwiring of demand meters to provide a totalized demand. This is often called conjuctional billing with coincident demand.

Modern electronic power consumption meters permit various combinations of types of metering including conjunctional and coincidence features, time-of-day metering, off-peak or shoulder period metering. It is important that the engineer become familiar with the rate structures and options available, including special rate structures for certain categories of users (perhaps public buildings including health care facilities) before beginning negotiations with regard to electric service.

The design engineer should carefully evaluate the economics, maintenance, and operations associated with the purchase of medium-voltage vs. low-voltage power. If medium-voltage power is purchased, then the utility customer usually purchases all of the transformers and low-voltage equipment and is responsible for maintaining and operating this equipment. The utility usually will provide lower rates to compensate for the additional purchase and operating costs that the customer incurs. There may be technical design advantages to having a customer-owned, medium-voltage system such as distribution over large areas and for various switching schemes or even economic advantages in cost of power. However, maintenance of the medium-voltage system may introduce a level of (owner) responsibility (for safety), require a trained and experienced staff, and/or incur additional transformer losses and installation costs, any or all of which may not be justified.

3.10 References

This chapter shall be used in conjunction with the following publications:

ANSI C37.16-1988 (Reaff 1995), Preferred Ratings, Related Requirements and Application Recommendations for Low-Voltage Power Circuit Breakers and AC Power Circuit Protectors.[3]

---

[3]ANSI publications are available from the Sales Department, American National Standards Institute, 11 West 42nd Street, 13th Floor, New York, NY 10036.

ANSI C57.12.10-1987, Requirements for Transformers 230 kV and Below, 833/958 Through 8333/10 417 kVA Single Phase, and 750/862 Through 60 000/80 000/100 000 kVA, Three Phase.

ANSI C57.12.20-1994, Requirements for Overhead-Type Distribution Transformers, 500 kVA and Smaller: High Voltage, 34 500 Volts and Below; Low Voltage, 7970/13 800Y Volts and Below.

ANSI C57.12.21-1995, Requirements for Pad-Mounted Compartmental-Type Self-Cooled Single-Phase Distribution Transformers with High-Voltage Bushings (High-Voltage 34 500 Grd Y/19 920 Volts and Below; Low-Voltage, 240/120; 167 kVA and Smaller).

ANSI C84.1-1995, Voltage Ratings for Electric Power Systems and Equipment (60 Hz).

IEEE Std 141-1993, IEEE Recommended Practice for Electric Power Distribution for Industrial Plants (IEEE Red Book) (ANSI).[4]

IEEE Std 142-1991, IEEE Recommended Practice for Grounding of Industrial and Commercial Power Systems (IEEE Green Book) (ANSI).

IEEE Std 241-1990, IEEE Recommended Practice for Electric Power Systems in Commercial Buildings (IEEE Gray Book) (ANSI).

IEEE Std 242-1986 (Reaff 1991), IEEE Recommended Practice for Protection and Coordination of Industrial and Commercial Power Systems (IEEE Buff Book) (ANSI).

IEEE Std 393-1991, IEEE Standard Test Procedures for Magnetic Cores (ANSI).

IEEE Std 399-1990, IEEE Recommended Practice for Industrial and Commercial Power Systems Analysis (IEEE Brown Book) (ANSI).

IEEE Std 446-1995, IEEE Recommended Practice for Emergency and Standby Power Systems for Industrial and Commercial Applications (IEEE Orange Book) (ANSI).

IEEE Std 493-1990, IEEE Recommended Practice for the Design of Reliable Industrial and Commercial Power Systems (IEEE Gold Book) (ANSI).

IEEE Std 739-1995, IEEE Recommended Practice for Energy Management in Industrial and Commercial Facilities (IEEE Bronze Book) (ANSI).

IEEE Std 1100-1992, IEEE Recommended Practice for Powering and Grounding Sensitive Electronic Equipment (IEEE Emerald Book) (ANSI).

---

[4]IEEE publications are available from the Institute of Electrical and Electronics Engineers, 445 Hoes Lane, P.O. Box 1331, Piscataway, NJ 08855-1331.

IEEE Std C37.010-1979 (Reaff 1988), IEEE Application Guide for AC High-Voltage Circuit Breakers Rated on a Symmetrical Current Basis (ANSI).

IEEE Std C37.13-1990, IEEE Standard for Low-Voltage AC Power Circuit Breakers Used in Enclosures (ANSI).

IEEE Std C37.41-1994, IEEE Standard Design Tests for High-Voltage Fuses, Distribution Enclosed Single-Pole Air Switches, Fuse Disconnecting Switches, and Accessories (ANSI).

IEEE Std C57.12.00-1993, IEEE Standard General Requirements for Liquid-Immersed Distribution, Power, and Regulating Transformers (ANSI).

IEEE Std C57.12.59-1989, IEEE Guide for Dry-Type Transformer Through-Fault Current Duration (ANSI).

NEMA AB 1-1993, Molded Case Circuit Breakers and Molded Case Switches.[5]

NEMA AB 3-1991, Molded Case Circuit Breakers and Their Application.

NEMA PB 2.2-1988, Application Guide for Ground Fault Protection Devices for Equipment.

NEMA SG 2 -1993, High-Voltage Fuses.

NETA Electrical Acceptance Testing Specifications.[6]

NFPA 70-1996, National Electrical Code® (NEC®).[7]

NFPA 70B-1994, Electrical Equipment Maintenance.

NFPA 70E-1995, Electrical Safety Requirements for Employee Workplaces.

NFPA 99-1996, Health Care Facilities.

3.11 Bibliography

Additional information may be found in the following sources:

[B1] Accredited Standards Committee C2-1997, National Electrical Safety Code® (NESC®) (ANSI).

---

[5]NEMA publications are available from the National Electrical Manufacturers Association, 1300 N. 17th St., Ste. 1847, Rosslyn, VA 22209.

[6]NETA publications are available from the International Electrical Testing Association, P.O. Box 687, Morrison, CO 80465, tel. (303) 697-8441.

[7]NFPA publications are available from Publications Sales, National Fire Protection Association, 1 Batterymarch Park, P.O. Box 9101, Quincy, MA 02269-9101.

[B2] ASHRAE/IESNA 90.1-1989, Energy Efficient Design of New Buildings Except Low-Rise Residential Buildings.

[B3] Beeman, D. L., ed., *Industrial Power Systems Handbook*. New York: McGraw-Hill, 1955.

[B4] Blackburn, J. L., ed., *Applied Protective Relaying*. Trafford, PA: Westinghouse Electric Corporation, Printing Division, 1976.

[B5] Fischer, M. J., "Designing Electrical Systems for Hospitals," vol. 5 of *Techniques of Electrical Construction and Design*. New York: McGraw-Hill, 1979.

[B6] IEEE Std 446-1995, IEEE Recommended Practice for Emergency and Standby Power Systems for Industrial and Commercial Applications (IEEE Orange Book) (ANSI).

[B7] IEEE Surge Protection (C62) Collection, 1995 Edition.

[B8] Mason, C. R., *The Art and Science of Protective Relaying*. New York: John Wiley and Sons, 1956.

[B9] NFPA 110-1993, Emergency and Standby Power Systems.

[B10] NFPA 111-1993, Stored Electrical Energy Emergency and Standby Power Systems.

[B11] NFPA 780-1995, Lightning Protection Code.

[B12] Parsons, Robert A., *1993 ASHRAE Handbook—Fundamentals* (Chapter 28, Energy Estimating Methods). Atlanta, GA: American Society of Heating, Refrigerating, and Air-Conditioning Engineers, 1993.

Chapter 4
Planning for patient care

4.1 General discussion

Electrical power is of ever-increasing importance in the planning and design of health care facilities and hospitals. Because of this, it is important that the electrical engineer designing a hospital locate the correct device in the correct location. This arrangement should optimize patient care, as electrical power can dictate the patient's comfort and even affect life-and-death situations. This chapter is divided into four clauses. The typical wiring devices utilized in a hospital are discussed in 4.2, while some suggested "good practice" in laying out patient areas are discussed in 4.3. The devices described in 4.2 are shown in 4.3. Information on references can be found in 4.4.

4.2 Wiring devices

4.2.1 General

In general, hospitals have two sources of power available, normal and emergency. It is vital that the wiring devices on emergency power be easily identified. This reduces the time wasted locating receptacles to power life-support equipment when even seconds are critical. There are two ways to identify devices: (1) by a distinctive color, such as red, or (2) by labeling. Marking with a distinctive color is not only easier and less costly than labeling but can prevent confusion later. For instance, when painters remove the lettered emergency and normal cover-plates, there is no longer a distinction between devices. Also, since emergency receptacles in critical care areas must have panelboard and circuit number labels, the device cover-plates tend to become cluttered. The distinctive color is also easily spread into other portions of the emergency systems (such as lighting control) to maintain uniformity. Consideration should be given to using lighted emergency power receptacles in any patient areas that do not have emergency lighting, thus making the receptacle easier to find in the near-darkness of a power outage. Devices in a hospital need to be mounted for easy use by staff and patients. Since a large number of hospital patients spend time in wheelchairs, special attention should be given to "handicapped" requirements. These requirements are typical of occupational therapy areas [aids to daily living (ADL)] and are described in 4.3.9 b). It is to the advantage of all patients and staff if all receptacles are mounted 24 in (610 mm) above the floor [see 4.3 and 4.3.9 b) 2)]. This mounting height will reduce the fatigue caused when staff members must repeatedly bend down to connect or disconnect a plug.

4.2.2 Hospital grade receptacles

Application. In accordance with the National Electrical Code® (NEC®) (NFPA 70-1996)[1], hospital grade receptacles are listed as suitable for use in health care facilities. Health care

---

[1]Information on references can be found in 4.4.

facilities are defined in NEC Article 517 as: "Buildings or parts of buildings that contain, but are not limited to, hospitals, nursing homes, residential custodial care facilities, clinics, medical and dental offices, and ambulatory health care facilities, whether fixed or mobile."

The receptacles, plugs, and cable connectors should be UL listed "Hospital Grade" (see UL 498-1993). The "Hospital Grade" receptacle meets UL's additional test criteria for grounding path integrity through superior mechanical and electrical characteristics. Among these criteria, and perhaps of primary importance to the health care facility, are stringent minimum retention and ground resistance specifications. While it is true that some "Spec Grade" receptacles are of high quality and are similar to those UL listed as "Hospital Grade," no formalized standards exist for a "Spec Grade" receptacle. Consequently, it is very difficult to control the desired quality level and minimum standards when a project or purchase order specification lists "Spec Grade" as its only requirement. "Hospital Grade" receptacles are presently required in critical care areas per the NEC and have been mandatory in general care area patient bed locations since 1 January 1993 under postponed implementation of NEC Article 517-18(b). However, it should be noted that most engineers have been specifying and most hospitals have been using "Hospital Grade" receptacles in all patient care areas since they have become available.

Parallel blade devices should be mounted ground pin or neutral blade up. In this configuration any metal that drops between the plug and the wall will most likely contact a nonenergized blade.

While either 15 A or 20 A receptacles are permitted, it is highly desirable to use only 20 A within a health care facility. This allows for greater flexibility in equipment usage, and simplifies stocking of replacement receptacles. Additionally, it should be noted that where only a single receptacle is used on a 20 A circuit, it must be rated 20 A.

4.2.3 Hospital grade isolated ground receptacles

Application. These receptacles are used where separation of the device equipment ground and the building ground is desired in order to protect sensitive equipment from malfunction due to transient currents (electrical noise) on the equipment grounding path. This is normally when digital electronic equipment is used, including microprocessor-based instrumentation, computer cash registers, computer peripherals, and digital processing equipment. NEC Articles 517-16 FPN and 517-1(c) require careful planning of isolated grounding systems in patient locations to avoid compromising either low ground path impedance or effectiveness of the isolated ground system.

4.2.4 Hospital grade tamper-resistant receptacles

Application. Tamper-resistant receptacles prevent contact with an energized contact in the receptacle unless a plug is inserted. Pediatric locations and psychiatric locations (only if the receptacle manufacturer specifically indicates suitability for psychiatric locations) should use these receptacles exclusively to comply with NEC Article 517-18(c). When selecting tamper-resistant receptacles, the type that makes and breaks internal switching contacts is not generally recommended where life support equipment may be needed. While it is not a requirement, consideration should be given to the use of tamper-resistant mounting screws for switch and receptacle wall plates in pediatric and psychiatric locations.

It should be noted that certain dedicated psychiatric isolation rooms might be better served by not having any receptacles. In these cases flush tamper-resistant ceiling lights with the switch located outside the room would be indicated.

4.2.5 Hospital grade ground-fault circuit interrupter receptacles and ground-fault circuit interrupter circuit breakers

Application. Ground-fault circuit interruption (GFCI) can be provided by either GFCI circuit breakers or GFCI receptacles. GFCI protection is mandated by the NEC for wet locations, where interruption of power is acceptable. If interruption of power is not acceptable (e.g., in areas where life support equipment may be used), an isolated power system should be used.

GFCI receptacles offer the advantage of local trip indication and reset, at least where they are not used in the feed-through mode. This can be an important consideration when selecting between the circuit breaker or receptacle integrated GFCI device.

4.2.6 Anesthetizing location receptacles

Application. Certain UL listed "Hospital Only" configurations are manufactured as both hazardous location and nonhazardous location devices. Hazardous location receptacles are interlocked with an internal switch. Hazardous location plugs will close the switch, whereas nonhazardous location plugs will not.

The use of explosive anesthetizing agents is virtually nonexistent and therefore the need for operating rooms designed for their use no longer exists. The NEC permits the use of "Hospital Grade" receptacles within anesthetizing locations so long as they are within nonhazardous areas. The current trend is to equip anesthetizing locations with these lower-cost receptacles. Additions to existing surgical suites must be reviewed carefully before receptacles are specified, since generally a mix of "Hospital Only" and "Hospital Grade" receptacles is not desirable. Changing the plugs on dedicated equipment used in the operating room suite or changing out existing "Hospital Only" receptacles may prove more costly than providing the addition with "Hospital Only" type receptacles.

4.2.7 Mobile x-ray plugs and receptacles

Application. X-ray plugs and receptacles should be noninterchangeable with any other equipment plugs. This prevents high-impulse loads on branches and feeders that were not designed for such service. X-ray devices come in 50 A and 60 A models; 50 A plugs can be connected to either a 50 A or 60 A receptacle, while a 60 A plug can only be connected to a 60 A receptacle. When locating these receptacles, the force required to insert the plug must be considered. These receptacles have a spring-eject type feature that guarantees that the plug will be fully inserted. Because of the insertion pressure required, they should be mounted at a minimum of 30 in (735 mm) above the floor.

4.2.8 Wallplates

Application. Any UL listed wallplate is suitable for health care facilities. Stainless steel wallplates are the most durable but plastic wallplates provide color matching. Wallplates should be made of impact-resistant construction, and manufactured of high-impact plastics, stainless steel (type 304 or better), or anodized aluminum. All plates should hold up under frequent cleaning with hospital cleaning chemicals. Tamper-resistant mounting screws should be used with switch and receptacle wallplates in pediatric and psychiatric locations.

4.2.9 Headwall units

The use of prefabricated patient care units (headwall units) is now so prevalent as to be almost standard in both renovation and retrofit projects, as well as in new construction projects. Headwall units can and are used in all patient care areas of the hospital. It should be pointed out that the term "headwall" is general and applies to many units that are not even remotely similar to "walls" (see figure 4-7).

Headwalls normally contain electrical power distribution systems. While headwall units do contain some mechanical equipment and could be considered architectural, they are considered more of an electrical device than anything else and, consequently, they are typically specified by the electrical engineer.

a) *Considerations.* Several basic reasons for using headwall units are: future flexibility, serviceability, shortened construction schedule, superior appearance, expenditure deferral, cost savings, etc. Perhaps the reason for the rapid rise in popularity of headwall units is that the advantages of using them can be appreciated by the nurse, patient, administrator, maintenance department, architect, engineer, and contractor.

Nursing personnel will find the pre-planned component locations accessible and convenient, resulting in fast, efficient patient service, thereby maximizing the patient's comfort. Hospital maintenance personnel find the quality headwall both durable and easily serviced. Hospital administrators find that they can defer the cost of the headwall along with all of the equipment it contains until just shortly before the hospital is scheduled to open. Architects and engineers find that both design and coordination of services are greatly simplified for both new or remodeling construction. Contractors find that their jobsite labor costs are significantly reduced and their coordination of service problems at the patient location also can be greatly reduced.

b) *Selection.* While the selection and specification of headwall units is far simpler than locating and specifying the individual services within the structural wall, time, thought, and some study are necessary in order to ensure that everyone's needs as well as the needs of the area served are satisfied. Whenever possible, the medical team responsible for that area of the hospital to be served by the headwall in question should be consulted as to quantity, location, and type of equipment required to serve the patients in that area. After a design has been selected, it is helpful to review the choice through the use of a full-size mock-up or full-size drawing. Confirming locations and dimensions in this fashion can eliminate some undesirable surprises after the unit is installed. The architect should be consulted on color selection.

Due at least in part to the widespread acceptance of the headwall concept, many styles of headwalls are available for the specifier's choice. Oftentimes, several types are available from a single manufacturer. The style or type selected will often be dictated by the medical team requirements. Figure 4-1 illustrates what is commonly referred to as a short wall designed for use in a general care patient area. This construction is generally used where space is at a premium and the area below the wall is required for placement of a bedside table or similar equipment. As shown in figure 4-2, the junction boxes for the various services are located within the wall. A wall mounting bracket becomes the top of the wall and a suitable termination point for services before the wall is in place. Note the drawing of the wall in figure 4-3, which shows the junction box located as an integral part of the wall mounting bracket above the ceiling. This section can be scheduled to arrive at the jobsite during the

Figure 4-1—Short wall designed for use in a general care patient area

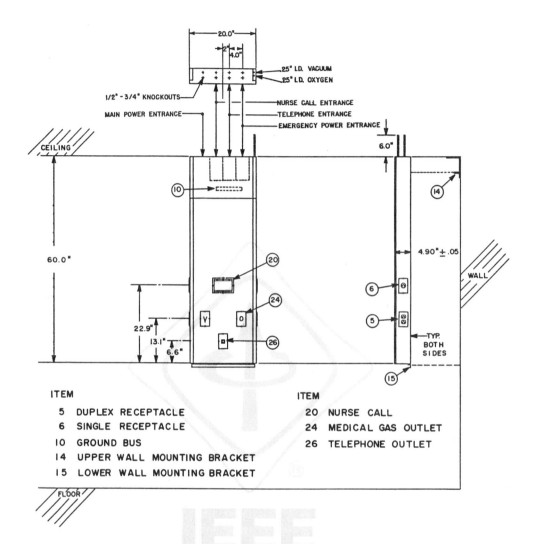

Figure 4-2—Junction boxes located within the wall

rough-in stages and becomes the termination point for the services. Either method is acceptable; the important thing is to have a method of terminating services without having to install the headwall unit. Figure 4-4 is an illustration of a full, single-section general care wall. This type of unit, as well as the single-section short wall, can be designed for a location with either a single bed or two patient beds.

The headwall, by necessity, contains considerably more equipment when it is designed to serve an intensive care or coronary care patient. Figures 4-5 and 4-6 illustrate a three-section and a single-section wall, both of which are designed to serve an intensive care unit/coronary care unit (ICU/CCU) environment. The three-section wall allows the luxury of dividing the equipment on both sides of the patient. Better segregation of medical gases and electrical receptacles is maintained. If a

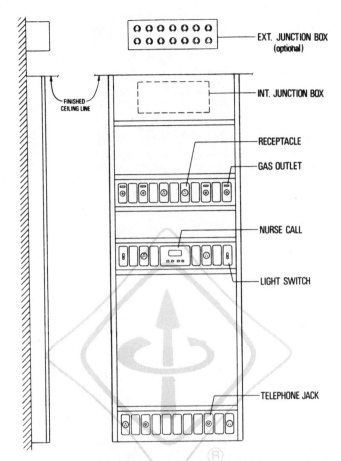

**Figure 4-3—Junction box located as integral part of
wall mounting bracket above ceiling**

single-section wall is used for an ICU/CCU area for economical reasons, it is recommended that at least one duplex receptacle be placed on the side of the bed opposite the headwall unit. This should also be considered in general care areas. Another difference between the walls shown in figure 4-5 and figure 4-6 is that the unit in figure 4-5 uses both vertical and horizontal placement of the equipment, whereas the unit in figure 4-6 is an illustration of the unit using horizontal placement only. Each of the design methods has its benefits and advocates. It is an area in which personal preference often plays an important role. It should be pointed out that many times manufacturers will make both design versions to meet the individual requirements of their customers.

One other popular variation of the ICU/CCU wall, although it is not illustrated here, should be noted, that is, the use of a single-section module on each side of the bed without the use of a center section. This variation provides the advantages of greater equipment placement flexibility at somewhat less expense than the full three-section wall.

Figure 4-4—Full single-section general care wall

The unit illustrated in figure 4-7 would perhaps more appropriately be called a neonatal service console, rather than a headwall unit. However, it does fall under this general category and units of this type are being used extensively. The unit pictured here is intended for a neonatal intensive care area and can be used as an island unit or installed against a structure wall. It often provides storage facilities and work areas as well as the normal electrical and mechanical patient services. Variations of this unit have also been used in adult intensive care areas.

Figures 4-8 and 4-9 show another variation of the headwall that has recently been finding great favor among hospitals. These are free-standing service columns that offer the advantage of greater access to the patient. The head of the patient bed is generally located 2–3 ft from the closest wall, thereby allowing medical personnel an immediate access to that area behind the patient's head. These service columns do require more floor space per patient than the flat column concept in order to fully utilize all the advantages that they offer. Careful consideration should also be given to traffic patterns as well as patient visibility.

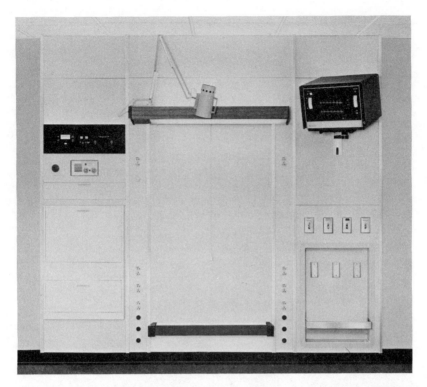

Figure 4-5—Both vertical and horizontal placement of equipment

It can readily be seen that firm recommendations on the selection of headwall units are not practical due to the many variables from project to project. Consideration should be given to medical team practices and preferences, available space, hospital specialties, and hospital budget.

c) *Medical gas services.* The specification for medical headwall units should clearly state the type and style of desired medical gas outlet. The outlets can be furnished by the headwall manufacturer, or the mechanical contractor can be requested to furnish these devices to the headwall manufacturer. The former is the most desirable since it allows the headwall manufacturer to coordinate delivery times directly with the manufacturer. Additionally, there is often more than one mounting method available within a given style of outlet, and allowing the headwall manufacturer to do the ordering diminishes many of the coordination problems that could otherwise be encountered.

The medical gas outlets are most commonly located on one side of the patient even within an intensive care environment. However, there are times when the medical team will request outlets on both sides of the patient, and this is of course possible when multisection headwalls are used. The medical gas outlets should be maintained within the headwall and the piping should be brought out to an area that would be convenient for the mechanical contractor to make the final connections. This is

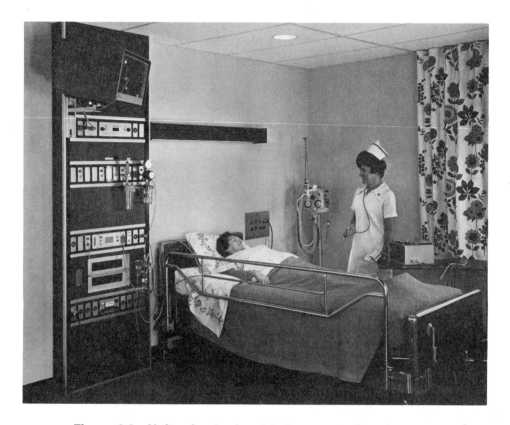

Figure 4-6—Unit using horizontal placement of equipment

generally at the top of the unit and the connections are made above the lay-in ceiling. Where the medical gas outlets are all located on one side of the patient, a single pipe for each service is extended to the top of the headwall. An approximately 6 in stub is allowed for final connection. Where gas outlets are furnished on each side of the patient in a multisection wall, it is not practical to manifold the piping from both sides within the headwall. The specification should clearly show that the contractor will have to make the final connections to each set of gas outlets external to the headwall.

It is important that the headwall manufacturer install and test the mechanical gas outlets and associated piping in accordance with the specification in NFPA 99-1996. It should be pointed out that this testing does not excuse the mechanical contractor from performing a final system test that would include the piping and outlets contained within the medical headwall unit. These test requirements are also contained within NFPA 99-1996.

The spacing of medical gas outlets is critical since in use they will have collection containers and pressure-regulating devices extending both above and below the outlet. There will also be tubing running between these devices and the patient.

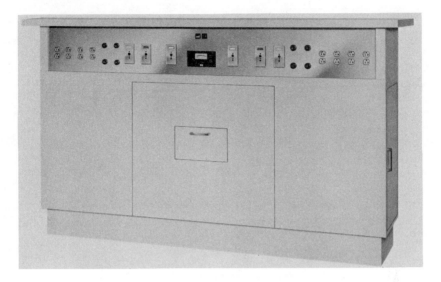

Figure 4-7—Neonatal service console

Coordination with the hospital team responsible for these services to determine the exact size of the equipment to be used is essential. The general rule for spacing is to leave a minimum of 4.5 in centerline-to-centerline, between outlets horizontally, and 12–14 in between outlets vertically. While these are the general minimums, the specific use to which the outlets will be placed and the equipment they will accommodate will sometimes allow some reduction in these numbers; however, careful consultation with the hospital personnel and the gas equipment manufacturer before such reductions are undertaken is required.

The accepted manifold pipe sizing is shown table 4-1.

Table 4-1—Medical gas manifold pipe size

No. of outlets	Gas service type		
	Oxygen	Air	Vacuum
1	1/4 in ID	1/4 in ID	1/4 in ID
2	1/4 in ID	1/4 in ID	1/2 in ID
3	1/4 in ID	1/4 in ID	3/4 in ID
4	1/4 in ID	1/4 in ID	3/4 in ID

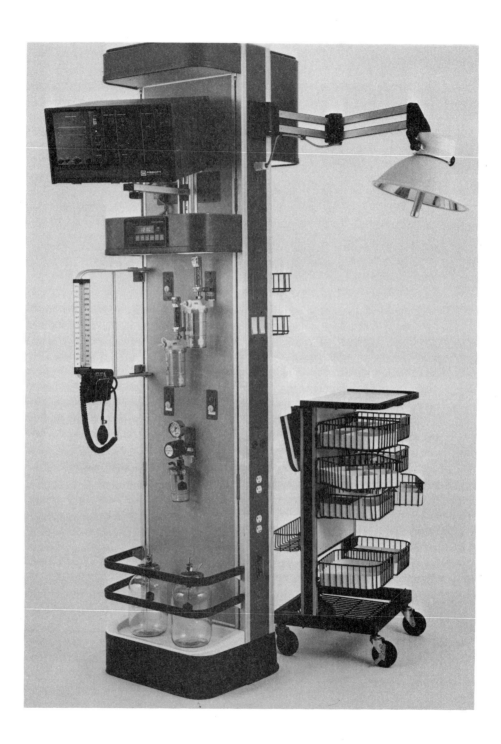

Figure 4-8—Free-standing service column

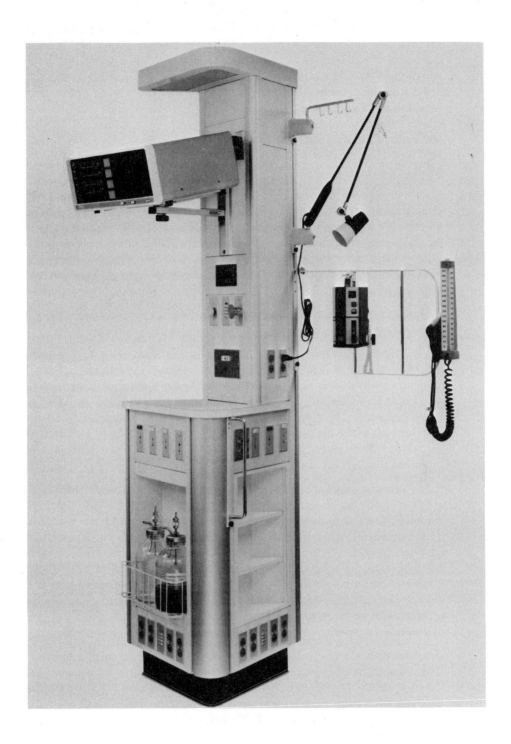

Figure 4-9—Triangular free-standing service column

Generally, some type of storage facility in the headwall or hanging facility is required for vacuum collection receptacles. Reusable bottles, disposable bottles, and disposable plastic bags are all used for this purpose. While a hospital may use only one of these types of receptacles, at the moment there is no assurance that they will not expand their usage to other types. Therefore, vacuum bottle slides should be furnished as an absolute minimum, and if it is known that bottles will be used, the convenience of a vacuum bottle storage tray or tub is recommended. The vacuum bottle tub provides an easily cleaned and protected location for vacuum bottles, and also allows for storage of an empty bottle for immediate use. As an alternative to the bottle tub, a long (36 in) vacuum bottle slide may be incorporated.

d) *Electrical services.* The headwall unit can, and usually does, contain all of the electrical services required to serve the patient. The minimum services required are described in 4.2. Equipment that can be accommodated within the headwall would include patient and general lighting, examination lighting, power receptacles, ground jacks, isolated and grounded electrical distribution systems, clocks and timers, portable x-ray outlets, night lighting, low-voltage electrical lighting systems, emergency electrical services, etc.

Typically, a general care wall would contain four duplex receptacles per patient. Intensive care walls would contain six to nine duplex receptacles per patient.

Normal lighting in a headwall unit would consist of an overbed fluorescent fixture providing two 30 W lamps for up lighting or general illumination, and one 30 W lamp for patient reading light or bed light use. At a minimum the down light should be controllable by the patient. A night light should be provided and should be located below the bed level so as to minimize patient disturbance. Low-level chart lights are best provided within the fluorescent overbed fixture. These lighting specifications are applicable to both general care and intensive care areas. For additional information on patient area lighting, see Chapter 7.

Examination lights are generally required in all areas and they are available in a large range of styles and prices. They can, for instance, be high-intensity lighting units mounted in the ceiling over the bed and controlled by switching in the headwall unit. The most universally accepted are of the adjustable arm type, which are attached to the headwall or the overbed light fixture. General care areas require only an incandescent-type exam light, which can also double as an over-the-shoulder reading light. Intensive care usually calls for some type of high-intensity lighting with a better color balance. The extended arm type of lighting can create some obstruction problems and, therefore, location of these lights should be given careful thought so as to preclude interference with other equipment.

e) *Communication services.* The headwall should contain minimal communication services as described in other areas of this chapter. However, it is recommended that this equipment not be furnished by the headwall manufacturer. For best coordination, the headwall should contain provisions for the nurse call, emergency call, and telephone services. These provisions should include a backbox of sufficient size to accept the equipment and raceways from that backbox to an appropriate junction box located at the top of the headwall. Installation should be possible without disassembly of the headwall other than that necessary to expose the entrance junction box at the top of the headwall. Conduit size should be carefully specified so that it will accommodate the necessary cable and connectors.

f) *Miscellaneous services.* A number of services that can be provided in a headwall unit could fall under the category of miscellaneous. Almost any patient service item can be incorporated into a medical headwall. Some are so commonly used as to be almost standard. For example, physiological monitor provisions are almost always furnished on a headwall intended to be used in an intensive care area. The physiological monitor is commonly supplied by the headwall manufacturer. The manufacturer must be furnished with the correct brand and catalog number of physiological monitor that the hospital intends to use. Sometimes this information is not available until after shipment of the headwalls is required. In that event, provisions for the monitor bracket can be made and shipment of the actual bracket is delayed until the hospital has made its choice of monitor. One duplex power receptacle should be located immediately behind the bracket for convenient connection of the equipment. The physiological monitor outlet (electronic signal) is handled in the same manner as the nurse call. That is, the box size should be specified (generally a two-gang electrical box) and this box is connected to an entrance compartment at the top of the headwall with its own raceway or conduit. If a patient physiological outlet provision is desired, another box near the patient level is provided and connected to the physiological outlet junction box by separate conduit. Care should be taken in specifying the correct size conduit so that it will accommodate the necessary cable and connectors.

Services not so commonly found are hyperthermia provisions and renal dialysis provisions. In the case of hyperthermia, the headwall unit may contain the necessary plumbing and a portable hyperthermia unit can be plugged into the headwall by quick disconnects. In other cases, the entire hyperthermia unit may be permanently housed within the headwall. The provisions provided in the headwall for renal dialysis would be the correct electrical services as well as pressure water connections and drain connections. These connection points would be of the quick-disconnect variety.

Various mechanical devices can be provided in or on the headwall unit. As an example, sphygmomanometers of various types can be furnished by the headwall manufacturer, or provisions for mounting them can be specified. Mechanical rail systems for hanging medical instrumentation can be supplied by many of the headwall manufacturers and accommodate equipment such as profusion pumps, respirators, etc.

It becomes apparent that neither the electrical engineer nor the architect can specify the proper equipment without a great deal of guidance from the hospital medical team. Communication and coordination with this group is absolutely mandatory in order to obtain satisfactory headwall design.

g) *Specifications.* It is virtually impossible to write a general specification that would cover the wide variety of headwall units available in the marketplace today. These specifications should be tailored to the specific designs that are finally selected. In selecting the equipment within a headwall unit, care should be taken to comply with all applicable standards. Aside from local and state standards, those of importance to hospital design are the NEC and NFPA 99-1996.

The specification for any headwall unit should clearly demand that the entire unit be UL listed and labeled. This should include all accessory equipment that is provided with the headwall, such as vacuum bottle tubs. This assures both the electrical engineer and the user, as well as the local code authorities, that all currently recognized standards are being followed in the construction of the headwall, and that the materials used will pass stringent flamespread and smoke emission regulations for this occupancy. Clients should be discouraged from using a design that cannot be UL labeled. They may have to sacrifice some feature or material that they desire, but they must be convinced that such sacrifice will yield a safer installation.

4.2.10 Patient consoles

A patient console is a strip of outlets and equipment. The console can be part of a headwall unit or self-contained. It provides a rigid, aligned mounting system, which consolidates many varied outlets into a homogeneous unit. It can also provide spaces for future expansion. When the console is self-contained, future additions of outlets will require some cutting and patching. This device can be difficult to mount in the headwall—steel studs, double studs, etc., must be designed into the wall. However, all the outlets will have a consistent appearance. These units are not designed for easy future flexibility.

4.3 Typical patient care areas

In all patient areas, several items should always be kept in mind. Outlets of all types are installed for someone to use. As simple as this sounds, receptacles are still installed too close to the floor and often behind beds and equipment. In patient care areas, the ability to obtain the function desired quickly (respiration, cardiac level, etc.) could save a life or prevent permanent damage to a patient. It is for this reason that elevations of equipment and outlets should be checked. Medical gas outlets should never be mounted directly above electrical outlets, as the regulators will obstruct the receptacles. If receptacles and ground jacks are to be mounted in an over-under configuration, the ground jack should be installed below the receptacles. This is due to the logical order of insertion of plugs (that is, if the ground jack were installed above the receptacle, once the ground cable is connected it will hamper the insertion of the power plug since the hanging cable obstructs the receptacle). Receptacles should be mounted 24–48 in (588–1176 mm) above the floor, to make them accessible to a visitor or to a patient in a wheelchair and also to lessen the fatigue on staff members who must constantly bend over to connect and disconnect equipment [see 4.3.9 b) 2)]. Any area that uses life support devices should have an alternate power system available that can be reached with a 50 ft (14.7 m) extension cord. Consideration should be given to making the entire area a dual power source area, having one alternate (emergency or normal) power receptacle at each bed. Outlets should always be located so that cords connected to them provide the minimum amount of hindrance to the staff.

Each vacuum outlet needs space not only for a regulator on the outlet but also for a vacuum collection bottle either on the outlet, on a slide, in a rack, or on the floor. If patients from one area can overflow into another, these overflow beds should be designed to the most stringent requirements. As an example, if general care beds are sometimes used as acute care beds they should be designed as acute care beds.

4.3.1 Patient rooms

a) *Light care bed locations.* Patients in these areas are normally ambulatory, hospitalized for diagnostic testing, physical therapy, or for post-operative and pre-operative observation. They could be undergoing ultrasound, thermography, or radiological examinations. This class of patient requires little nursing care. However, as the age of the patient increases, the care required could approach that of acute care. In some facilities these spaces are listed as hospice or long-term care.

   1) *Medical gases.* One vacuum outlet between two beds is required for oral suction or sump drains (drains placed in an incision to drain fluid while under slight vacuum). One oxygen outlet at each bed is required for oxygen therapy or intermittent positive pressure breathing (IPPB). IPPB can be administered pre- and post-operatively.

   2) *Electrical power outlets.* An electrical outlet located on the headwall or headwall column is required for each of the following:

      i)   Electric bed

      ii)   Portable suction

      iii) Treatment use (e.g., K-pad)

      iv)   Electrocardiograph (EKG) machine for inpatient test or for an additional K-pad

      v)   Television set

      vi)   Patient equipment, shaver, etc.

      vii) Respiratory therapy equipment

      When K-pads (hospital heating pads) are used to treat phlebitis, normally both arms or both legs are treated. In the case of an obese person, two K-pads may be required for each leg. K-pads are also used to treat blood clots and ulcer patients.

   3) *Communications.* A system should be available at each bedside for both patient and staff to summon help.

b) *Acute care bed locations.* Acute care represents about 80–85% of the inpatients in a hospital. These patients usually rely on machines of some type and require more nursing care than the light care patient. They may have stomach disorders or require oxygen treatment or suction bags. Post-operative patients, accident victims, and people with medical disorders can usually be found in acute care beds. The vast majority of hospitals being built today are acute care hospitals since more procedures every year are being done at clinics and on an outpatient basis.

   1) *Medical gases.* Two vacuum outlets should be provided at each bed. One vacuum outlet is for oral suction, while the other is for a sump drain. Increasingly, surgeons are using two sump drains on one patient; this requires both vacuum outlets. One oxygen outlet should be provided at each bed as most acute care patients require either oxygen or oxygen-related therapy. It is suggested that one medical air outlet be provided for the respiratory therapy equipment.

2) *Electrical power outlets.* A typical acute care patient may be a post-operative surgical patient, who is classified stable. The patient's electrical requirements include outlets for the following:

    i)   Electric bed

    ii)   Chest pump

    iii) Portable suction

    iv) K-pad

    v)   IVAC machine (used to monitor intravenous solution drips)

    vi) Patient appliance (e.g., shaver) or other portable suction (i.e., if the patient has two sump drains); this could also be used for monitoring or test equipment

    vii) Television set

    viii) Respiratory therapy equipment

Depending on the intensity of the care offered in the area, emergency power is recommended for at least one duplex outlet. These should be in the headwall. It is recommended that six outlets (three duplex receptacles) be installed.

3) *Communications.* A system should be available at each bedside for both patient and staff to summon help.

4.3.2 Coronary care areas

Coronary care patients vary from electrically susceptible critical list patients to patients ready for release. Depending on the size and operating procedures of the hospital, noncritical patients may be transferred to stepdown and later to acute care.

a) *Medical gases.* Each patient bed should be equipped with two vacuum outlets for suction. Also, each bed should have three oxygen outlets and one medical air outlet for respiratory care. Each oxygen outlet can supply approximately 10 L/min, while a patient on 100% oxygen can breathe 30 L/min.

b) *Electrical power outlets.* The NEC permits the use of single-phase grounded power circuits for this area. There are some states that still require the use of ungrounded, isolated power, and some hospitals who prefer to use them. This is permitted by the NEC. Where this is the case, specifications for isolation systems are the same as those found in Chapter 6 for use in flammable anesthetizing areas. It is recognized that isolation systems do contribute to overall electrical safety and continuity of power in the event of a line-to-ground fault.

Eight electrical outlets or four duplex outlets should be provided, as cardiac patients can use many pieces of electrical equipment at one time, including the following:

1) Heating water in respirator

2) Suction for nasal gastric tube

3) Swan ganz line

4) Chest pump

5) Electrical bed (if the patient is transferred to the unit from another part of the hospital in "distress," the bed is not usually switched until the patient's condition is stable)

6) Rotating tourniquet

7) IVAC machine (used to monitor intravenous solution drips)

8) Respiratory therapy equipment

The lights over the bed should have both a high and a low level.

Each bed shall have at least one dedicated outlet. Emergency power shall be supplied for use with a respirator in coronary care. Circuit breakers should be near the bed and clearly labeled. Consideration should be given to placing a circuit breaker panel in the room.

c) *Communications.* A system should be available at each bed for both patient and staff to summon help. In these coronary care beds, special consideration should be given to the increased chance of cardiac arrest. Also, a cardiac arrest alarm should be provided with an automatic trip from the monitor and an elapsed time clock to start upon cardiac arrest.

4.3.3 Intensive care areas

The intensive care bed may be used for:

— Surgical post-operative patients
— Artificial ventilation of patients
— Treating for shock
— Cardiac monitoring of post-operative patients
— Pacemaking
— Peritoneal or haemodialysis
— Biochemical correction of severe metabolic disorders

Facilities for portable x-ray use should always be provided. The ICU isolation room can be used to perform tracheotomy or haemodialysis. ICU special patient treatments may include the following:

— Maximum care (breathing and tetanus insufficiency)
— Hyperbaric oxygen treatment
— Induced hypothermy (-12 °C)

a) *Medical gases.* Three vacuum outlets, two oxygen outlets, and one medical air outlet for respiratory care should be provided at each bed. The vacuum outlets are most often used for post-operative patient drains.

b) *Electrical power outlets.* The NEC permits the use of single-phase grounded power circuits for this area. There are numerous hospitals that prefer to use ungrounded, isolated power in these areas and this is specifically permitted by the NEC. Where this is the case, specifications for isolation systems are the same as those found in Chapter 6 for use in flammable anesthetizing areas. It is recognized that isolation systems do contribute to overall electrical safety and continuity of power in the event of a line-to-ground fault.

At least eight outlets or four duplex electrical outlets should be provided, as cardiac patients can use a lot of electrical equipment at one time, including:

1) Heating water in respirator

2) Suction for nasal gastric tube

3) Swan ganz line

4) Chest pump

5) Electrical bed (if the patient is transferred to the unit from another part of the hospital in "distress," the patient is not usually moved from the electric bed until the patient's condition is stable)

6) Rotating tourniquet

7) IVAC machine (used to monitor intravenous solution drips)

8) Respiratory therapy equipment

The lights over the bed should have both a high and a low level.

Each bed must have at least one dedicated outlet. Emergency power must be supplied for use with a respirator in intensive care. Circuit breakers should be near the bed and clearly labeled. Consideration should be given to placing a circuit breaker panel in the room.

c) *Communications.* A choice should be available for music or quiet in the bed—quiet for ulcer patients, and music to calm or entertain other patients. A nurse call system should be available at each bed for both patient and staff to summon help. Also, a cardiac arrest alarm should be provided with an automatic trip from the monitor and an elapsed time clock to start upon cardiac arrest.

4.3.4 Emergency suites

An emergency department may consist of trauma, treatment, and minor operating and exam rooms, where a variety of medical procedures takes place. These procedures range from treating accident victims to delivering babies and to typical outpatient work during off-hours. A minor operating room (OR) should be treated as a small surgery room. One class above the minor OR is the trauma room where somewhat similar operations take place without the inhalation anesthetic. General anesthetics are not normally used in the emergency room. Both these rooms can involve invasive procedures, and special care should be used as these patients can be electrically susceptible. In some hospitals, babies will be delivered in an obstetrics/gynecology (OB/GYN) room on an emergency basis. This is most apt to happen when a hospital closes its maternity wing or when it is near a poverty-stricken urban area and does not have a maternity wing. The rooms in any emergency department must be analyzed by the governing body of the hospital as to their probable use. The patient holding rooms should be treated as acute care beds as these are used to watch developments. Typically, various emergency department rooms should be designed like the same type of room as found elsewhere in the hospital (i.e., a cardiac room is much like a CCU treatment room). Some emergency suites have surgery rooms while others have a less intense treatment philosophy. The hospital must be contacted for the usage.

4.3.5 Surgical room

There are many types of surgical procedures, each with its own set of criteria. The most important point in surgery room layout is how the room will function. Description of function, typical procedures, and traffic patterns can be obtained from the hospital planner(s) who planned the suite. Care should be exercised in equipment layout to prevent obstruction to traffic in the surgery room.

a) *Medical gases.* Medical gases need to be determined by both the medical procedures to be performed and the surgical staff operating procedures.

b) *Electric power outlets.* Emergency isolated power is required. Due to the large quantities of equipment used in surgery, 16 electrical outlets (8 duplexes, if straight blade devices are used) are recommended. The distribution and placement of these receptacles throughout the room should be determined after consultation with the surgical staff. This will minimize interference with planned procedures. Provisions for portable x-ray and/or fluoroscopy machines are also generally required; the electrical requirements of this equipment vary greatly. Consideration should be given not only to existing equipment but also to equipment planned in the near future.

4.3.6 Pediatrics

The pediatrics area is used to treat juveniles. It is important not to alienate any children by sending them to other areas. The pediatrics area should be at least as well equipped as a general care area.

a) *Pediatric patient rooms.* These rooms should be designed similar to general care rooms, with some rooms equipped similar to acute care rooms and intensive care rooms.

　　1) *Medical gases.* The following medical gas outlets should be provided: one vacuum outlet and one oxygen outlet between each two beds.

　　2) *Electrical power outlets.* Four electrical outlets or two duplex outlets per bed are recommended. All outlets should be safety-type with tamperproof screws.

　　3) *Communications.* Similar to other areas.

b) *Playrooms.*

　　1) *Medical gases.* For emergency use, playrooms should have one vacuum outlet and one oxygen outlet.

2) *Electrical power outlets*. All electrical outlets should be safety-type with tamperproof screws.

3) *Communications*. Both staff communications and emergency-help functions should be provided.

c) *Pediatric (Critical Care)*. These beds are similar to ICU and CCU: one critical care bed per 20 regular pediatric beds is suggested, with three oxygen outlets, and two vacuum outlets. These beds should be located in the pediatrics wing to prevent alienation of children. The medical gases, electrical power outlets, and communications equipment installed in these areas should be similar to those in 4.3.3, except that they should be tamperproof.

4.3.7 Nurseries

a) *General nurseries*. These nurseries are where normal newborns are housed. The baby normally sleeps in a bassinet. Nursing care is minimal, while observation is important.

1) *Medical gases*. Each bassinet should be equipped with one oxygen outlet and one vacuum outlet. This arrangement permits typical care if minor complications develop.

2) *Electrical power outlets*. Two duplex electrical outlets should be located at each bassinet, one on each side. These should be supplied from emergency power. Normal power should be located outside the bassinet area but within reach of a 50 ft cord as in 4.3.7 c) 2). It is recommended that one normal power duplex receptacle be placed in each room.

3) *Communications*. Each bassinet should be equipped with a staff help/call station, to summon help from the nursing station. At a minimum, place a staff help/call station between the bassinets. In nurseries with limited nighttime staffing, each nursery should be equipped with an emergency help/call system to an adjoining department such as labor-delivery.

b) *Special care nurseries*. Newborns requiring specialized care are kept in the special care nursery. These are babies who have developed complications. The isolette is larger than a typical bassinet; therefore, outlet spacing and height should be checked.

1) *Medical gases*. Due to the length of care anticipated, each incubator or isolette location should be equipped with two vacuum outlets, two oxygen outlets, and two medical compressed air outlets.

2) *Electrical power outlets*. Due to the increased care in this area, each isolette should be provided with at least 12 electrical outlets or 6 duplex outlets. One should be a dedicated outlet for the incubator or isolette. All outlets should be on emergency power. Normal power should be located outside the isolette area but within reach of a 50 ft cord as in 4.3.7 c) 2). It is recommended that one normal power duplex receptacle be placed in each room.

3) *Communications*. Communication requirements are the same as in general care nurseries [4.3.7 a) 3)].

c) *Neonatal nursery.* Premature babies can be housed in a neonatal or a special care nursery. A large percentage of the babies requiring special care are premature. Premature babies are kept in incubators or isolettes.

  1) *Medical gases.* Medical gas requirements are the same as in special care nurseries [4.3.7 b) 1)].

  2) *Electrical power outlets.* Each incubator should be provided with 12 electrical outlets or 6 duplex outlets and a dedicated incubator outlet, all powered by emergency power. Normal power should be available outside the isolette area within reach of a 50 ft extension cord. It is recommended that one normal power duplex receptacle be placed in each room. This will provide power in the event of a failure in the emergency power distribution system.

  3) *Communications.* Communication requirements are the same as in general care nurseries [4.3.7 a) 3)].

4.3.8 Psychiatric care areas

Psychiatric care areas are occupied by basically two types of patients, sedate and violent.

a) *Patient room (sedate).* Sedate patients are normally treated in open-type dormitory housing. These rooms are very much like semiprivate dormitory rooms. Four electrical outlets (two duplex receptacles) should be provided per bed (one duplex receptacle on each side of the bed). All receptacles should be safety-type receptacles with tamperproof screws. Medical gases and communication systems are not usually necessary.

b) *Patient care (violent).* Patients in this category range from physically violent to suicidal. These rooms should therefore be designed to provide as little danger as possible to both the staff and the patients. The staff usually continuously monitors these patients.

  1) *Medical gases.* For the treatment of medical or emergency cases, one vacuum outlet and one oxygen outlet should be provided. These should be protected and securely concealed when not required, in a locked cabinet or shallow locked closet.

  2) *Electrical power outlets.* Three duplex outlets should be provided. These also should be protected and securely concealed when not required, for example, in a shallow locked closet. The general configuration should be similar to acute care beds [4.3.1 b) 2)].

  3) *Communications.* Audio monitoring should be provided via a concealed speaker microphone. Provisions should also be made for staff to summon help.

4.3.9 Rehabilitation areas

a) *Drug and alcohol abuse.* Patient rooms are similar to dormitory-type psychiatric patient rooms (sedate). Also, there should be detoxification rooms for medical treatment and observation of newly admitted patients. These should be similar to those for violent psychiatric patients, and equipped for medical treatment. See 4.3.8 a) and b) for the requirements of these rooms.

b) *Occupational therapy or ADL.* This area is occupied mostly by patients with new handicaps. Special care should be taken to make their transition back into society a smooth one.

    1) *Light switches.* Light switches should be located 36–42 in (915–1070 mm) above the floor. For convenience, no more than two switches should be located on a single plate. Switch action should be simple and positive. While large area "decorative" type rocker switches permit easier operation by forearm, elbow, etc., normal high-quality toggle-type switches are not impossible to operate. Normal toggle switches should have full-sized handles for this operation. Care should be taken to locate all controls (switches, outlets, thermostats, etc.) away from corners and to avoid placing controls over counters, since these locations are particularly inconvenient for persons using wheelchairs.

    2) *Electrical power outlets.* In general, electrical outlets are placed at least 24 in (610 mm) above the floor. In areas designed specifically for use by disabled persons, 24–32 in (610–815 mm) high outlets are recommended.

    3) *Telephones.* Telephone dials, handsets, and coin slots should be located within 48 in (1220 mm) of the floor. Wherever possible, push-button type instruments are recommended over conventional rotary dial sets. Handsets should be on 36 in (915 mm) or longer cords.

4.4 References

This chapter shall be used in conjunction with the following publications:

NFPA 70-1996, National Electrical Code® (NEC®).[2]

NFPA 99-1996, Health Care Facilities.

UL 498-1993, Attachment Plugs and Receptacles (DoD).[3]

---

[2]NFPA publications are available from Publications Sales, National Fire Protection Association, 1 Batterymarch Park, P.O. Box 9101, Quincy, MA 02269-9101.
[3]UL publications are available from Underwriters Laboratories, Inc., 333 Pfingsten Road, Northbrook, IL 60062-2096.

Chapter 5
Emergency power systems

5.1 General discussion

Emergency power systems are required for all health care facilities. The basic requirements are defined in various local, state, and federal codes. Organizations such as the Joint Commission on Accreditation of Hospitals also have standards that require adherence.

This chapter describes requirements and equipment that are recommended for health care facility emergency power systems and their operation. Suggested methods for system design, installation, testing, and maintenance are also included. The main components of emergency power systems are the generator sets, the automatic transfer switches, the engine generator controls, the engine cranking batteries, and the battery charger. Additional equipment may include synchronizing and paralleling equipment for multigenerator set installations, utility peak demand reduction controls, elevator emergency power selector systems; and bypass/isolation switches for automatic transfer switches and for uninterruptible power supplies (UPSs).

The following codes and standards offer guidance and mandatory requirements for the design of essential electrical systems in hospitals and other health care facilities:

- ASME A17.1-1993[1]
- EGSA 100B-1992
- EGSA 100C-1992
- IEEE Std 446-1995
- NEMA ICS 10-1993
- NEMA PE5-1985
- NFPA-20 1996
- NFPA 70-1996
- NFPA 70B-1994
- NFPA 70E-1995
- NFPA 72-1996
- NFPA 75-1995
- NFPA 99-1996
- NFPA 101-1994
- NFPA 110-1996
- NFPA 111-1996
- NFPA 418-1995
- SAE J537-94
- UL 1008-1989

---

[1]Information on references can be found in 5.13.

5.2 Generator sets

An engine-driven generator set with on-site fuel supply is the predominant type of emergency power source in hospital and health care facilities. Gas turbine driven sets have not found much usage up to the present time because their starting time normally exceeds the 10 s "on line" requirement specified in NFPA 70-1996, National Electrical Code® (NEC®) and NFPA 99-1996. However, turbine manufacturers have recognized this problem and some sets are becoming available with improved starting times. For a discussion on gas turbines, refer to IEEE Std 446-1987.

Capacities of the engine driven type sets range from approximately 5 kW (6.25 kVA) to 2000 kW (2500 kVA). Gasoline engines are normally used in the lower ranges while diesel engines are used almost exclusively for capacities of 100 kW (125 kVA) or more. Code exceptions sometimes permit the use of off-site fuel supplies for natural gas and low pressure, gas-driven engines when there is a low probability of both the outside electrical utility and off-site gasline failing simultaneously. Gas engine generating sets are generally available in sizes similar to diesel.

5.2.1 Location

The preferred location for a standby generator set is the ground floor of the facility. Careful consideration must be given to the location of the standby generator set in order to minimize interruptions caused by natural forces common to the area (e.g., storms, tornadoes, hurricanes, floods, earthquakes or hazards created by adjoining structures or activities).

Proximity to fuel supply, effects of generator noise and adjacent occupancies, location of exhaust stacks relative to fresh air inputs, and the ability to remove/replace the unit for maintenance or upgrades are also important issues in placing the generator.

Basement locations are to be avoided when they are subject to flooding. It is also more difficult to conduct combustion air, cooling air, and exhaust gases away from engines located in basements.

If engine generator sets are installed above ground level, additional vibration isolation between the generator set and the floor is frequently required to prevent structural damage to the building.

Standby generator sets may be added to existing buildings in a separate enclosure. Controls and transfer switches are usually located inside the main building. The enclosure should include sound attenuation and environmental protection.

5.2.2 Mounting

Two cardinal rules for installing standby generator sets are as follows:

a) Do not attach a generator set directly to a concrete floor. It will crack the structure and transmit unacceptable vibration.

b)   Do not directly attach any rigid system, that is, exhaust, remote radiator cooling, fuel lines, nonflexible conduit, to an engine on vibration isolators. The relative motion will eventually fatigue and crack the attachment.

5.2.3 Vibration isolation

A sheet of fiberglass or waffle neoprene (rubber) mounting pads between the generator set base and the floor may provide adequate vibration isolation where optimum isolation is not required. Spring-type vibration isolators are available. These are also placed between the generator set base and the floor. Spring type vibration isolators have different load ratings. Select the correct number of properly sized isolators to support the total generator set (including water and oil) weight. Locate the isolators so that no isolator is overloaded. Spring-type vibration isolators typically have an efficiency of 95% or better. This means that less than 5% of the vibration of a generator set will be transmitted to the floor. When spring-type vibration isolators are used, the generator set rocks around the crankshaft-generator shaft axis during start-up and shut-down. There is also some rocking during single step load changes of 50% or more of generator capacity. Flexible connections should be used in external lines such as electrical conduit, exhaust pipe, and fuel lines as a minimum, and may also be used in coolant lines to a remote radiator, lube oil makeup and drain lines, and engine air intake. Additional generator set mass gives additional vibration isolation. The generator set mass may be increased by attaching an inertia block weighing one or more times the generator set package weight. With greater mass, the vibration energy has less effect. Spring isolators are then placed between the inertia block and the supporting structure to further reduce transmitted vibration (see figure 5-1). This arrangement is frequently used when generator sets are installed on floors above ground level. If the generator set package is mounted to an inertia block supported by earth, it may be isolated from the floor of the building by pouring a rubber gasket between the two surfaces (see figure 5-2). Table 5-1 lists the load bearing capability of various materials. Lining the inertia block excavation with tamped sand or gravel will minimize the vibration transmitted through the earth to nearby equipment. Installations should be coordinated with and reviewed by the responsible structural engineer on the project.

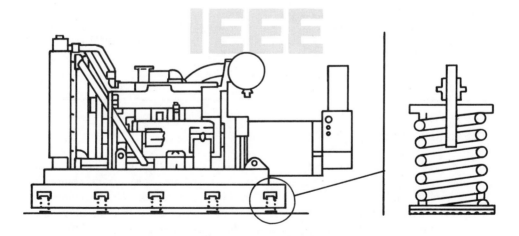

Figure 5-1—Steel-concrete inertia spring mounts

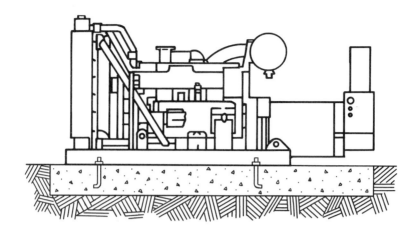

Figure 5-2—Poured rubber gasket between two surfaces

Table 5-1—Load-bearing capabilities of various materials

Nature of bearing material	Safe bearing capacity (lb/ft^2)
Hard rock—granite, etc.	50 000–200 000
Medium rock—shale, etc.	20 000–30 000
Hardpan	16 000–20 000
Soft rock	10 000–20 000
Compacted sand and gravel	10 000–12 000
Hard clay	8000–10 000
Gravel and coarse sand, compacted fine sand	8000–8000
Medium clay	4000–8000
Loose fine sand	2000–4000
Soft clay	2000

5.2.4 Exhaust system

In order to produce rated power, the exhaust system restriction at the engine must not exceed the engine manufacturer's recommendations. In addition, the exhaust system components must not impose undue stress on the engine exhaust outlet connection. Weight, inertia, relative motion of components, and thermal growth from temperature change all contribute to stress on the engine exhaust outlet. The exhaust system should also prevent water from entering the turbocharger or the engine proper. Common sources of water are rain, snow, and condensation of exhaust gas. As a final consideration, the exhaust gas should be directed so that it does not have an adverse effect on the air cleaner, the cooling system, the generator set ambient temperature, or the operator.

If an engine must work against excessive back pressure in the exhaust system, the usable engine power is reduced. Also, the air–fuel ratio is reduced because of incomplete scavenging of the cylinders, the fuel economy is reduced, and the exhaust temperatures increase.

The exhaust back pressure imposed in a given engine installation depends on the size of the exhaust pipe, the number and type of bends and fittings, and the silencer selection. Tight bends usually contribute the most to high-exhaust back pressure. Back pressure is inversely proportional to the fifth power of pipe diameter. Therefore, a small increase in exhaust pipe diameter dramatically reduces system back pressure. The engine manufacturer can normally provide the exhaust gas flow and temperature. The pressure developed in the pipe can be determined from figure 5-3. The exhaust silencer manufacturer can provide the pressure drop through the silencer for a given flow and temperature. The pressure developed in the pipe and elbows plus the pressure drop through the silencer gives the back pressure at the engine.

Provisions should be made for relative movement between the exhaust piping and the engine so that no damaging stresses will be imposed on the exhaust system components because of engine mounting flexibility or thermal growth.

A 50 ft length of pipe expands over 3 in when the temperature is raised from 70–800 °F (21.1–426.7 °C). The most common method of obtaining flexibility is through the use of flexible piping (spiral- or bellows-type). Flexible sections are required in the piping between any components where either relative motion or thermal growth will subject the components to excessive stresses. The optimum location for the flexible section is within 4 ft of the engine exhaust outlet. For proper installation, the flexible pipe should not be used to form pipe bends or compensate for misalignment.

Black iron schedule 40 pipe is most commonly used for permanent installation where the weight is not a factor.

There are many ways to obtain the desired flexibility while still adequately supporting the piping and other components in the system. To reduce the loading imposed on the exhaust manifold or the turbocharger, it is necessary to support long lengths of piping from the surrounding structure. However, flexibility should still be maintained through the design of the support and the use of flexible connections. The weight of all external engine exhaust piping should be supported so as not to impose any dead weight loads on the engine exhaust outlet connection.

Rain and snow should not enter the exhaust outlet opening. Counterbalanced flapper-type rain caps are used in many installations. Conical and other ventilating covers are not widely used since they produce a relatively high exhaust pressure or are not suitable for operation in the prevailing exhaust temperature. Exhaust outlets that point upward are preferred since they do not direct the exhaust noise toward adjacent structures. Where the noise in a specific direction is not a problem, horizontal exhaust outlets may be used. Cutting the end of the pipe at a 45° angle with the top extended is normally adequate to prevent the entrance of rain and snow. If horizontal exhaust pipes are used, care should be taken so that the exhaust gas will

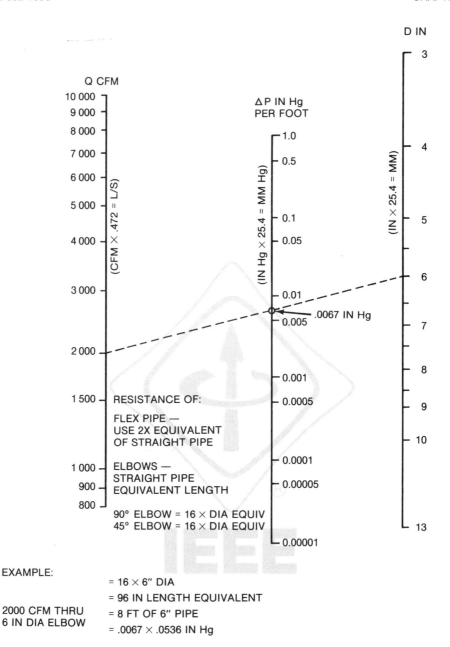

Figure 5-3—Back pressure nomograph

not be drawn back into the engine room with the ventilation air. Care should also be taken in the location of the exhaust outlet point so that exhaust gas will not be drawn into any of the outside air intakes. The exhaust gases are dangerous, and the distinctive odor is very annoying. The cost to correct an improper exhaust installation can greatly exceed the initial cost of a properly designed installation.

From an aesthetic point of view, care should be given to the selection of location of the exhaust outlet point and the tendency, over a period of time, for exhaust gas carbon deposits to accumulate on any nearby structures.

Water is formed in the combustion of gas, gasoline, or diesel fuel. Therefore, a condensate trap and drain valve should be installed in the exhaust system. The condensate trap should be as close to the engine as practical and located at the lowest point in the system.

In multiengine installations, special consideration should be given when manifolding or joining the exhaust runs from two or more engines into one common exhaust run. Engines will have a lower back pressure if each exhaust enters the exhaust flow at an angle toward the flow, rather than opposing the flow (refer to figure 5-4).

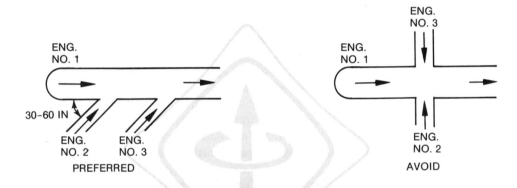

Figure 5-4—Exhaust pipe manifolding plan view

If all engines are not run at the same time, the exhaust gas from the operating engines can condense in the engine that is not running. This may cause a hydraulic lock in the stopped engine. Check valves in the exhaust lines have not solved this problem and, in general, are unsatisfactory in exhaust systems.

5.2.5 Air supply

A generator set requires air for combustion and cooling. Even when remote radiator or heat exchanger cooling systems are used, cooling air flow is required to remove the heat produced by the generator as well as the heat radiated by the engine and exhaust system.

Generators are normally rated for operation in a 104 °F (40 °C) ambient temperature. If the air intake is to be higher than 104 °F (40 °C), some reduction of the output rating is required. The engine manufacturer can give the engine combustion air requirements at rated load and will define the maximum air restriction permissible and the recommended air intake temperature range. The engine air intake system should be able to supply clean combustion air to the engine without excessive restriction and within the manufacturer's temperature range. Dirt is the basic cause of wear in an engine. The effectiveness of the air cleaner and air piping system has a significant impact on engine life and maintenance costs. Dry-type air cleaners filter the air through a replaceable pleated paper element. The efficiency of a dry-type air filter is normally greater than 99.9% at any air flow. Dry-type air cleaners do become plugged and can provide excessive air restriction when dirty. Oil bath air filters have an efficiency greater than 98% at rated air flow. This efficiency decreases to approximately 95% at 15% of rated flow. Oil pullover into the engine is possible at excessive air flows. However, oil bath air filters do not become plugged or offer excessive air restriction at rated air flow. Dry-type air filters are preferred for standby generator sets.

Most standby generator sets for hospitals have an engine mounted air cleaner that meets the engine requirements for adequate clean air.

When a generator set mounted radiator and fan are used, the fan pushes the air in the room through the radiator and out of the building. Under load, the air from the radiator is normally at 150–185 °F (65–85 °C). If the air flow were reversed, the room temperature would approach 150–185 °F, which is much too hot for the engine, the generator, or for any people in the room. When the fan is pushing radiator air out of the room, there must be an adequate area for air to enter the room. If the radiator fan delivery is known, this area can be calculated to give a maximum air intake velocity. An air intake velocity of up to 20 mi/h (30 ft/s or 9 m/s) is frequently acceptable. If the fan delivery is unknown, an air intake area equal to 1 1/2 times the radiator core area is frequently used as a rule of thumb.

The air intake area is preferably located to the rear of the generator set. Fresh air then flows around and through the generator, then past the engine and through the fan and radiator. Frequently the intake air has to enter at the top or the sides of the room. In such cases, air flow outside the room should be checked to make sure that radiator and engine exhaust are not drawn back into the room with the intake air. Regardless of location, the fresh air intake should be provided with a fine mesh screen to minimize the accumulation of dirt, insects, and debris in the generator set room.

Many standby generator sets do not have a fan and radiator in the engine room. A remote mounted radiator or heat exchanger is frequently used. Installations without a radiator fan require auxiliary room ventilators to remove the heat from the room. Installations with a radiator fan in the generator set room normally have adequate room air flow and the following calculations are unnecessary. The heat produced by the generator and radiated by the engine at rated load is approximately 35% of the kW rating of the generator. This percentage can be 5% higher for units under 100 kW and 5% lower for units over 500 kW. Uninsulated exhaust pipes and mufflers within the generator set room add to the heat that must be removed by the auxiliary ventilation system.

The auxiliary air flow required is determined by the heat that is to be removed and by the acceptable temperature rise in the room. Many engines begin to have a significant loss of power when combustion intake air temperature exceeds 120 °F (49 °C). Maximum ambient air temperatures vary widely. A 100 °F (37.8 °C) ambient covers most of the more populous regions of the world. The difference or acceptable temperature rise is 20 °F (11 °C). The specific heat of air at constant pressure (C_p = 0.24 Btu/lb °F) is essentially constant for air over a range of 80–130 °F (27–54 °C). The density of air changes with barometric pressure as well as altitude. At standard conditions, air density is 0.075372 lb/ft^3 at 500 ft. Multiplying the specific heat by the density at 500 ft gives a heat coefficient of 0.018089 Btu/ft^3 °F. For general use, this may be rounded to 0.018 Btu/ft^3 °F. From this, the air flow in cubic feet per minute (cfm) is equal to the rate of heat rejection divided by the heat coefficient and the acceptable temperature rise.

$$C = \frac{Q}{0.018T} \tag{1}$$

where

C	is air flow in ft^3/min
Q	is heat rejection in Btu/min
T	is acceptable temperature rise in °F

One kilowatt is the equivalent of 3412 Btu/h, or 58.87 Btu/min. Substituting this in equation (1) yields

$$C = \frac{kW \, 10^3}{0.305T} \tag{2}$$

where

C	is air flow in ft^3/min
kW	is heat rejection to room in kilowatts
T	is acceptable temperature rise in °F

Example: A 250 kW generator set is to be installed in a hospital basement. The radiator and fan are remotely mounted on the roof of the building. The maximum outdoor design temperature is 105 °F. It is desired to limit the engine room temperature to 120 °F.

The temperature rise in the room (ΔT) is 120 °F – 105 °F = 15 °F.

The heat produced in the room at rated output will be approximately 35% of rated output, or 0.35×250 kW = 87.5 kW. From equation (2), the air flow is

$$C = \frac{87.5 \times 10^3}{0.305 \times 15} \text{ or } 19 \, 126 \text{ ft}^3/\text{min}$$

5.2.6 Cooling

Almost all standby generator sets 50 kW and larger use liquid-cooled engines. The cooling air flow requirements for air-cooled engines should be obtained from the engine manufacturer.

Liquid-cooled engines usually have a generator set mounted radiator and engine drive fan. The selection of radiator core, fan, shroud, guards, fan drive ratio, etc., is made to provide adequate cooling of the engine. However, this selection is based on a free flow of cool [normally 100 °F (37.8 °C) or less] air to the radiator core and a free flow of air away from the core. The quantity of air required is normally listed by the manufacturer or generator set assembler.

The arrangement of the power room and the facilities availability (that is, raw water) normally dictate whether a radiator or heat exchanger is used for a liquid cooled engine. If there is a choice, a generator set mounted radiator is normally preferred. It is independent of an external source of water and there is normally an adequate supply of combustion and generator cooling air. With a set mounted radiator, there is no coolant flex connection, long coolant lines, pumps, or coolant shut-off valves, all of which are potential trouble sources.

Remote radiators do provide a means of removing fan noise to a noncritical location. Heat exchangers are not a noise source and also do not require power from the engine for a fan, but the electric fan motor adds to the emergency system load. A heat exchanger cooled unit can normally deliver 3–5% more power from the generator.

The combination of a heat exchanger feeding a remote radiator should be avoided if at all possible. Such a system has all of the disadvantages of each system at approximately four times the cost of either system. Since the cooling capacity of both the heat exchanger and radiator depend on the temperature difference of the cooling media, both the radiator and the heat exchanger must be approximately doubled in size.

Ducting may be required to take the hot air from the radiator to the outside. The ductwork must be smooth and free from obstructions, seams, fins, leaks, or sudden bends. If louvers or grills are added to the exit, then the frontal area must be increased accordingly in a smooth transition to the larger opening size. If bends in the duct are unavoidable, then turning vanes may be required to reduce pressure loss.

A heat exchanger cooling system is sometimes used where a source of cool water is available. Sources of water may be from a city water supply, or from sea, river, lake, or well water. In a heat exchanger system, the engine cooling water flows in a closed loop from the engine to the heat exchanger and back to the engine. Raw water from the city, sea, etc., flows in a separate circuit within the heat exchanger and removes heat from the engine cooling water. If a city water supply is being evaluated as a source of water from the heat exchanger, the possibility of interruption during a prolonged emergency has to be considered. For health care facilities, this method of cooling is not recommended if one of the other methods is available.

Also, if the water from the heat exchanger is to be dumped into the sewage system, it should not violate local conservation or natural resource ordinances, or overload the sewage system. Some heat exchangers may require a pressure reducing valve to limit the pressure supplied by a city water system to an acceptable valve for the heat exchanger.

Remote radiators fall into two categories:

a)   Radiator located horizontally remote from the engine.

b)   Radiators located vertically remote (above) the engine.

The primary concern when a radiator is horizontally remote is that the water pipe resistance to flow does not exceed the engine driven water pump capability. The engine manufacturer will normally list the total permissible pressure on the pump and the maximum allowable external friction head. External pipe should be free of obstructions, excessive bends, elbows, tees, or couplings. It should be clean and free of rust, scale, weld slag, or corrosive material. It should not collapse while being formed or while in service. The internal diameter should be greater than the water pump inlet diameter. Figures 5-5 and 5-6 may be used for estimating pressure drop in pipe, fittings, reducers, etc. The external circuit should be coupled to the engine via a flexible connection that permits thermal expansion of the line and engine movement without restraint.

Valves and couplings should normally be provided between the engine and the remote cooling system. By closing the valves, the engine may be serviced without draining the entire cooling system. Care should be taken to prevent the valves from being left closed accidentally. If this occurs, the generator set will be rendered useless.

Since many engine coolant systems are not readily compatible with an auxiliary booster pump, the engine manufacturer should be consulted before an auxiliary booster pump is specified. It is a good practice in health care facilities to avoid designs that depend on auxiliary power systems energized by the system that they support or by other external power systems subject to the same disturbance.

Installations where the radiator is below the engine level are rare and can cause problems. The primary problem is usually an air lock that prevents water circulation. A prime requirement in such installations is the proper location of air vents in areas where air pockets are likely to form in the cooling system.

Installations where the radiator is above the engine level are quite common. The maximum height of the radiator above the engine is limited by the static pressure that can be imposed on the cooling system seals and gaskets without leakage. The engine manufacturer should be consulted if a limiting head or pressure is not available. The friction head should still be within the engine manufacturer's limits and may be estimated from figures 5-5 and 5-6.

If a higher radiator position is necessary, the engine should be separated from the radiator circuit. Figure 5-7 illustrates such a system, although many variations are possible. Both circuits circulate from a common reservoir, commonly called a "hot well," "hot tank," or "compound cooling" system. With the basic hot well, the engine merely pumps coolant to and from the tank. The tank acts as a blending tank, an expansion tank, and holds the radiator and line coolant when the radiator auxiliary coolant pump is shut down. When vertical radiators are used, it may be beneficial to put coolant in at the bottom of the radiator. This keeps the radiator filled during operation. The tank should be vented to the atmosphere in order to accommodate the large changes of coolant volume in the tank. A sight glass on the hot tank is recommended, with markings for the "run" and "stopped" levels. High and low marks on both levels are helpful. It is a good practice to oversize cooling systems to allow for a 10% reduction in cooling capability owing to deterioration over the operating life.

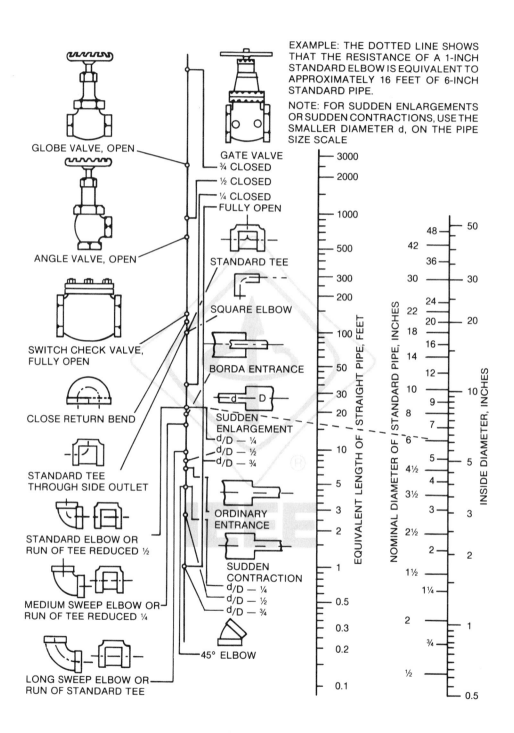

Figure 5-5—Resistance of valves and fittings to flow of fluids

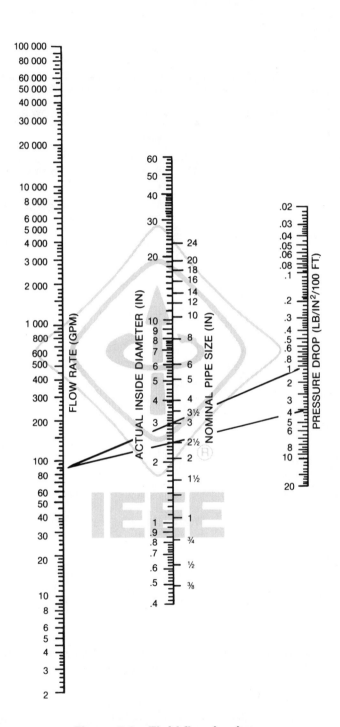

Figure 5-6—Fluid flow in pipe

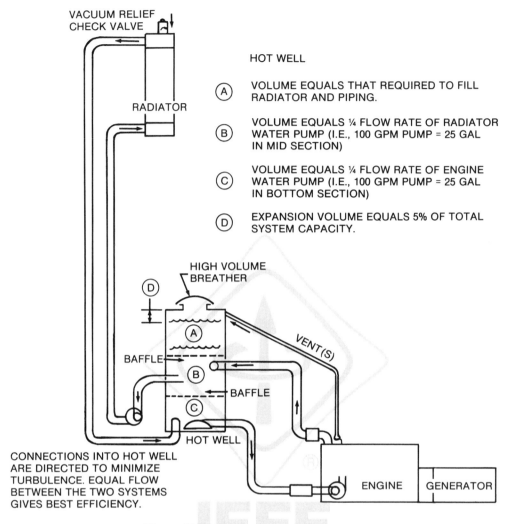

Figure 5-7—Hot well cooling system

5.2.7 Temperature

Provisions should be made to maintain the generator room at not less than 50 °F (10 °C) or the engine water jacket temperature at not less than 90 °F (21.1 °C), to ensure reliable engine starting.

Electric coolant heaters are the most common method of maintaining the engine coolant above 90 °F. In order to assure fast starts and good load acceptance, one engine manufacturer recommends that standby generator set engine coolant be maintained at a minimum of 120 °F (49 °C). Settings may vary depending on the engine design. Thermostatically controlled tank-type jacket water heaters provide coolant circulation that heats the entire engine. These heaters must be turned off when the engine is running.

Electric oil immersion heaters may be used to maintain lubricating oil temperatures. Oil heaters are frequently controlled by the same thermostat as the jacket water temperature.

5.2.8 Cranking

Battery electric systems and compressed air systems are used for cranking standby generator sets. The selection of a cranking system depends upon the type of engine, customer preference, and a readily available energy source, such as compressed air. Each system has certain advantages under specific conditions.

Electric cranking is the most common starting method and offers a compact, convenient, economical, and dependable method of cranking engine-driven standby generator sets. The engine portion of the system consists of a cranking motor, batteries, and some method of connecting and disconnecting the cranking motor to the batteries. In emergency power applications the batteries are normally maintained and recharged by a battery charger powered by the essential electrical system.

Many engine cranking motors are "positive engage" type. In this type of cranking motor, the starter pinion must be fully engaged with the engine ring gear before cranking commences. The system works quite well about 98% of the time. However, approximately 2% of the time a pinion tooth abuts directly with a ring gear tooth and the motor does not crank. To eliminate this problem, "cycle cranking" is preferred. In cycle cranking, a cranking period is followed by a reset period. This is followed by subsequent crank and rest periods. The cranking motor pinion is turned slightly at the start of each rest period and the probability of successive tooth abutments approaches zero. Cycle cranking also reduces heat rise in the starter motor windings. The timing of the crank and rest cycles is usually combined in an automatic cranking panel. The automatic cranking panel should also include some means to terminate cranking when the engine starts and a method of disabling the engine safety shutdown controls (other than overspeed and overcrank) during starting.

NFPA 110-1996 requires the battery capacity to be sufficient for two successive cranking attempts, that is, two 75 s cranking cycles or two 45 s continuous periods. The engine manufacturer will normally define the battery capacity required to meet this requirement. The definition will usually be in terms of cold cranking amperes (CCA) as defined by SAE J537-94. This standard is essentially applicable to lead-acid batteries (and variations thereof) only. Nickel-cadmium batteries are widely used for engine cranking. EGSA 100B-1992 may be used to specify either lead-acid or nickel-cadmium battery performance.

When a plentiful supply of compressed air is available, air can be an economical method of starting a standby generator set. Two types of compressed air starting are used.

a)   *Air motor.* An air motor drives a ring gear from the air starter motor pinion. This is similar to the electric starter. It is usually used on 1200 r/min and 1800 r/min engines.

b)   *Direct air injection.* Compressed air is injected into the individual cylinders by an air distributor system. This system is usually found on only the larger engines that operate at 900 r/min or below. It has the advantage that full engine torque is produced during cranking. This produces rapid acceleration.

To prevent problems, air starting systems require a sufficiently sized air tank and an auxiliary source of compressed air. An air tank with sufficient capacity to provide five 10 s cranking attempts, as required by NFPA 99-1996, will take up considerable space and could be a significant factor in determining which starting method should be used. Electric motor-driven air compressors are the most convenient means of recharging air tanks. However, during a utility power failure, these compressors are unavailable. An auxiliary gasoline engine-driven air compressor is one solution to this common problem and is recommended for air start installations in health care facilities.

When a facility does not have a reliable supply of compressed air readily available, the electric start method is more practical and economical.

5.2.9 Governor

A governor regulates the emergency generator set engine speed, which is directly proportional to frequency. Although gear reduction is used to couple gas turbines to ac generators, it has not been widely accepted on internal combustion engines. When an engine is directly coupled to an ac generator, the engine must run at 3600, 1800, 1200, or other lower synchronous speeds to produce 60 Hz. The governor regulates the amount of fuel delivered to the engine at various loads to keep the speed or frequency relatively constant.

The traditional mechanical and hydraulic governors utilize rotating flyweights to sense speed and a spring (speeder spring) as a reference. More sophisticated flyweight governors use hydraulic pressure to turn a shaft that is connected to the engine throttle or rack. Many hydraulic governors can operate isochronously, that is, at the same speed at no load and full load, and maintain the speed or frequency steady state stability within ± 0.25%.

All electric and electro-hydraulic governors are available that sense speed from pulses generated by a magnetic pickup mounted adjacent to an engine gear, usually the flywheel ring gear. Electric governors provide the same characteristics as hydraulic governors, but have the advantage of a faster response time. Electric governors are also available with numerous accessories that may be useful in specific applications. These include the following:

a)   Electric load sensing for isochronous load sharing among paralleled generator sets

b)   Electric load sensing for "load anticipation" to further reduce response time

c)   "Ramp acceleration" to provide a controlled acceleration rate and reduce frequency overshoot on start-up

d)   Electronic speed adjustment to adjust engine speed for synchronizing generators

e)   Reverse and forward power monitors that provide an output signal if power flows toward the generator, or when a preset output power level has been reached, or both

A reduction in the frequency response time of single unit generator sets with the "load anticipation" option is observable on a frequency strip chart recorder. However, this decrease in response time of a few tenths of a second is not readily discernible in a health care facility. "Load anticipation" on single unit generator sets essentially doubles the governor cost, and is more difficult to connect correctly. Load sensing governors for single unit engine applications are rare.

Lights, motors, heating, and most other power equipment will operate satisfactorily if the frequency remains between 60 Hz and 62 Hz. This is approximately a 3% frequency droop—that is, 61.8 Hz at no load, 60.0 Hz at rated load. For many computers to function properly, the frequency must be 60.0 ± 0.5 Hz. If any of these computers are to be operated directly (not through a UPS) from a standby generator set, an isochronous governor is required. Given the increasing use of computers and microprocessor-based controls, isochronous governors are being applied more frequently in health care facilities.

5.2.10 Fuel supply

In order to operate properly, an engine should have an adequate supply of fuel that meets the engine manufacturer's recommendations. All installations should incorporate a fuel filter to remove flakes, dirt, metallic chips, and water from whatever source, including condensation.

A day tank, sometimes called a "service tank" or "ready tank," is recommended for all standby generator set installations. A day tank provides an ample supply of clean fuel at a relatively constant head, regardless of the fuel level in the bulk storage tank. The day tank does not necessarily hold a day's supply of fuel. More commonly, a day tank is specified to hold at least the amount of fuel that would be burned in 1 h at rated load. A day tank provides a readily available supply of fuel independent of bulk storage and acts as an emergency supply in the event of failure of the auxiliary fuel pump, the connecting fuel lines, or the float-control switch. For diesel engines, it also acts as a relief and bypass tank for diesel fuel that is returned from the injectors. When the bulk storage fuel level is far enough above the day tank to give adequate gravity flow, a float valve or float switch and fuel shut-off solenoid should be used. In other installations, a day tank fuel transfer pump should be used. A primary filter is usually recommended between the bulk storage tank and the day tank. In multiple engine installations, a single common day tank is sometimes used. Such arrangements should be equipped with appropriate fuel isolation valves for the maintenance of individual systems.

The capacity of the bulk storage tank is essentially determined by the expected length of a disaster that might interrupt fuel delivery. Since this is a very subjective criteria, it is noted that bulk storage tanks usually have less than a 30-day fuel supply, and more than a 3-day fuel supply. A common recommendation is that 14 days of fuel storage capacity be installed. However, the user should carefully review his own particular problem and specific needs. Many diesel engines operate satisfactorily on Number 2 fuel oil. When oil-fired boilers are used, a common bulk storage tank is often used for the furnace and the emergency diesel generator set. Water condensation and contamination is the primary problem with long term storage of fuel. There will also be some evaporation, particularly of the more volatile parts of gasoline. Sometimes there are comments that bacterial action may contaminate diesel fuel, but these claims are difficult to substantiate. Storage of diesel fuel for up to one year is satisfactory. After this, samples should be taken at six-month intervals to assure that fuel deterioration has not occurred. A check for water in the fuel storage tank should be made every two weeks. This is particularly important in above ground storage tanks. Chemical additives are available to extend fuel storage time.

5.2.11 Ratings

Internal combustion engines are rated in horsepower or kilowatts, or both, and on output at a given speed, intake air temperature, and barometric pressure or altitude. Although gas turbines use a gear reduction to produce a synchronous generator speed, gear reducers have not been widely accepted on gasoline or diesel engine-driven generator sets. Most internal combustion engines must therefore operate at the synchronous speeds of 3600 r/min, 1800 r/min, 1200 r/min, 900 r/min, etc., to produce 60 Hz. As the speed is decreased, the mass and cost increases in a generally linear relationship. However, 3600 r/min internal combustion engine generator sets are, in general, limited to 50 kW output or below.

Engines are rated in horsepower and kilowatt output. The engine kilowatt rating should not be confused with the generator kilowatt rating. As a rule of thumb, 1 1/2 horsepower is required from an engine to produce one electrical kilowatt from an engine. Some of the engine power is required to drive the radiator cooling fan, while the largest power loss is within the ac generator itself.

Nonturbocharged gasoline and diesel engines have an inherent limit on the power they can produce at a given speed. The limit is essentially established by the amount of air that can be pulled into a cylinder for combustion. If excess fuel is used, combustion is incomplete, and the excess fuel goes out the exhaust as carbon (smoke or soot), carbon monoxide, and unburned hydrocarbons.

This limitation does not apply to turbocharged engines. As engine load increases, the turbocharger forces more air into each cylinder, which can now burn additional fuel to produce additional power. If the fuel or air is not limited by some means, this can become a self-sustaining continuity until stresses exceed the breaking point or something melts. Any turbocharged engine can be fueled to produce 10% additional power, but the useful life of the engine will probably be reduced. The engine manufacturer's published standby ratings of engines are normally the maximum ratings that the manufacturer believes, from experience and test, will give satisfactory service. Standby ratings are frequently published with no overload capability, although additional capability can usually be demonstrated.

5.2.12 Sizing the alternator

The alternator should be sized based on two types of loading. These are the maximum continuous load the alternator will carry and the motor load that the alternator will be required to start.

First, consider the maximum connected load. This load includes the lighting, heating, and running motor loads that the alternator will be required to carry at one time.

As an example, consider a small facility with a 100 kW lighting load, 50 kW of water heaters, a 25 hp blower motor on the heating and air-conditioning system, a 50 hp air conditioning compressor motor and two 25 hp elevator motors.

Therefore, the total connected running load is as follows:

25 hp Code G blower motor

$$kW = \frac{68 \text{ running A} \times 230 \text{ V} \times 0.8 \text{ pf} \times 1.73}{1000} = 21.7 \text{ kW}$$

50 hp Code G air-conditioning compressor motor

$$kW = \frac{130 \text{ running A} \times 230 \text{ V} \times 0.8 \text{ pf} \times 1.73}{1000} = 41.4 \text{ kW}$$

25 hp Code G elevator motor

$$kW = \frac{68 \text{ running A} \times 230 \text{ V} \times 0.8 \text{ pf} \times 1.73}{1000} = 21.7 \text{ kW}$$

25 hp Code G elevator motor

$$kW = \frac{68 \text{ running A} \times 230 \text{ V} \times 0.8 \text{ pf} \times 1.73}{1000} = 21.7 \text{ kW}$$

Total motor running load = 106.5 kW
Lighting load = 100 kW
Water heaters = 50 kW
Total running load = 256.5 kW

Now consider the total motor load the alternator will be required to start. It is virtually impossible to start all four motors at the same time; however, since there is nothing to prevent it from happening, consider this to be the worst-case condition. Since most motor starters will drop out at about 60% voltage, we should limit the voltage dip on motor starting to 35%. Motor starting capability of alternators will vary depending on the alternator, type of exciter, voltage regulator, and voltage regulator accessories used.

Most present-day alternators have a minimum across-the-line motor starting capability of 0.5 hp/kW with a 35% voltage dip. The total connected motor load in the example is 125 hp; therefore, the required alternator motor starting kilowatts would be

$$kW = 125 \text{ hp} \times \frac{kW}{0.5 \text{ hp}} = 250 \text{ kW}$$

A more precise calculation can be made by using a computer program. Many of these programs are PC-based, and may be available at no cost by the generator manufacturers. These programs accurately match specific generators and allow the designer to input data on the electrical systems of the building. Alternately, the manufacturer's representatives may perform this service for the designer.

The continuous running load of 256.5 kW is slightly larger than the 250 kW motor starting requirement and would be the determining load. Since the demand for electric power is continually increasing with new appliances and lighting added from time to time, an allowance for future requirements should be made. A general industry practice is for the load to be not more than 80% of the alternator rating on a new installation. Applying this rule to the example, the kilowatt requirement would then be an alternator of

$$\frac{256.5 \text{ kW}}{0.8} = 320.6 \text{ kW}$$

Since this is not an even rating, the next higher rating of 325 kW would be utilized.

Systems with a significant number of variable speed drives, or other nonlinear loads (static uninterruptible power supply systems, computer power supplies, battery chargers, etc.) often experience high harmonic current loads. This harmonic current distortion is usually more severe when supplied by the generator since a generator is not as "stiff" as the utility. The generator manufacturer must be made aware of these harmonic loads.

Since many motors, such as elevators and air compressors, cycle on and off, the resulting voltage dips can occur at many times other than initial generator starts. Systems must be designed to keep these voltage dips within the 10% (maximum) often required by computers, monitors and other electrically sensitive equipment.

5.2.13 Voltage regulators

There are four basic types of voltage regulation systems available today. They include

a)   The static exciter-regulator, which not only regulates the alternator voltage but also supplies the excitation power to the alternator field.

b)   The brushless self-excited automatic voltage regulator.

c)   The brushless separately excited automatic voltage regulator.

d)   The self-excited, self-regulated system that does not use a separate voltage regulator.

The first three systems provide typical voltage regulation of 0.25–2% and the fourth provides typically 4% regulation. All systems may be adequate for health care facilities, provided the connected loads can withstand the voltage variations. Refer to Chapter 9, which deals with voltage variation susceptibility of hospital medical equipment and instrumentation.

1)   *Static exciter-regulator.* The static exciter-regulator is a solid-state device that takes its supply from the main starter output voltage for both the input reference and the power input. The input power is rectified to direct current and is the controlled input through brushes and slip rings to the main field of the alternator. This system has a fast response to load changes and has the motor starting capability of a half-horsepower per kilowatt with a 35% voltage dip (see figure 5-8).

The static exciter-regulator is not self-exciting and requires an external dc source to flash the field for initial voltage buildup of the alternator. This is usually accomplished by a dc circuit connected to the engine starting batteries that is automatically disconnected when the ac voltage builds up.

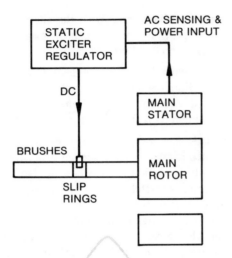

Figure 5-8—Static exciter-regulator system

2) *Brushless self-excited automatic voltage regulator.* The brushless self-excited automatic voltage regulator also takes its supply from the main starter windings for both the reference input and the power input. The input power is controlled by the reference voltage and control portion of the regulator. It is rectified to dc and becomes the output to the exciter starter. This regulator is self-exciting from the residual voltage of the alternator. Typically, the contacts of a normally closed relay or a solid-state relay are used to apply the alternator residual voltage directly to a full wave bridge and to the exciter field. As the ac voltage builds up, the relay picks up, disconnecting the built-up circuit (see figure 5-9).

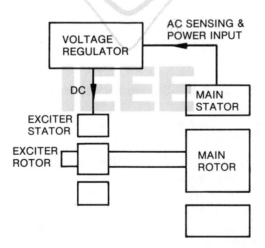

Figure 5-9—Self-excited regulated system

3) *Brushless separately excited automatic voltage regulator.* The separately excited automatic voltage regulator receives input power from a separate source but

135

receives reference voltage input from the alternator windings. Separate input power is usually provided by a permanent magnet generator mounted on the same shaft as the exciter and main rotors.

The permanent magnet generator provides a nearly constant power source under all operating conditions and is not affected by external load. Excitation is greater than the full load requirements of the alternator and is usually high enough to sustain a short circuit current of three times the rated current.

Whereas the static exciter-regulator, the self-excited voltage regulator, and some separately excited regulators sense a lower than normal output voltage and "turn on" to increase the excitation to the exciter field to bring the output voltage back up to normal, some separately excited voltage regulators work in reverse. Since the permanent magnet generator always provides more excitation than is required for normal voltage output, the voltage regulator must act to suppress the excitation. Therefore, when a lower than normal output voltage is sensed, the voltage regulator "turns off" to increase the excitation to the exciter field to bring the output voltage back up to normal (see figure 5-10).

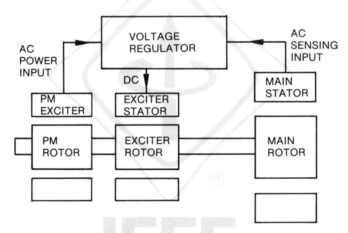

Figure 5-10—Separately excited system

This system has a fast response to load changes and has the motor starting ability of 3/4 horsepower/kilowatt with a 35% voltage dip.

4) *Self-excited, self-regulated system.* The self-excited, self-regulated system does not use a separate voltage regulator. There are various methods to accomplish this, but in almost all systems voltage buildup occurs from residual voltage or residual voltage plus the addition of permanent magnets in the field circuit. The excitation required for no load voltage is supplied by a portion of the main starter winding voltage. The output voltage is maintained under load by using the load current to provide excitation to the exciter. Most exciter fields utilize direct current; however, it is also possible to use alternating current in the exciter field (see figure 5-11).

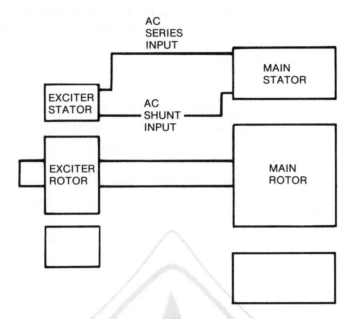

Figure 5-11—Self-excited self-regulated system

Since these systems utilize the load current for exciter power, they are very responsive to load changes and have a motor starting ability of 1 hp/kW with a 35% voltage dip.

5.2.14 Parallel operation

To operate two or more generators in parallel, provisions should be made for the generators to share the reactive load current proportionally and prevent circulating currents. Proportional sharing of the real kilowatt load current is controlled by the engine governor.

The static exciter-regulators, self-excited regulators, and the separately excited regulators are all capable of parallel operation when equipped with parallel provisions.

The two methods of controlling or sharing reactive load current when paralleling generators are the voltage droop method and the cross-current compensation method.

a) *Voltage droop method.* The parallel module for the voltage droop method consists of a low secondary current transformer (CT) installed in generator phase 2 when the regulator sensing is from line 1 to line 3. If three-phase sensing is used, a second CT installed in phase 1 is also required. Figure 5-12 shows a single-phase sensing arrangement. The CT develops a voltage signal across an adjustable resistor connected across the CT secondary that is proportional in amplitude and phase to the generator line current. This voltage is connected in series with the voltage applied to the voltage regulator sensing circuit. The result is that the voltage applied to the voltage regulator sensing circuit is the vector sum of the generator ac voltage and the voltage developed by the paralleling module. The voltage supplied by the paralleling module is small in comparison to the generator voltage.

When a resistive load (unity power factor) is applied to the generator, the voltage across the paralleling resistor leads the sensing voltage by 90°, the vector sum of the two voltages is nearly the same as the original sensing voltage, and no change occurs in the generator output voltage.

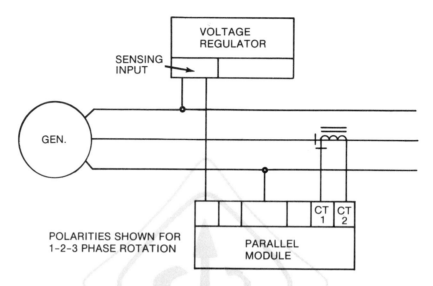

Figure 5-12—Interconnection—single-phase sensing

When a lagging power factor (inductive) load is applied to the generator, the voltage across the paralleling resistor becomes more in phase with the sensing voltage and the vector sum of two voltages results in a larger voltage being applied to the sensor circuit. Since the action of the regulator is to maintain a constant voltage, as in sensing terminals, the regulator reacts by decreasing the generator voltage.

When a leading power factor (capacitive) load is applied to the generator, the vector sums result in a smaller voltage at the regulator sensing terminals and the regulator reacts to increase the generator output voltage.

With two generators operating in parallel, if the field excitation on one generator should become excessive and cause circulating currents to flow between generators, the current appears as a lagging power factor (inductive) load to the generator with excessive field current and a leading power factor (capacitive) load to the other. The parallel compensation circuit will cause the voltage regulator to decrease the field excitation on the generator with the lagging power factor load so as to minimize the circulating currents between the generators.

This action and circuitry is called parallel or voltage droop compensation. It allows two or more paralleled generators to proportionally share inductive loads by causing a decrease or droop in the generator system voltage.

b) *Cross-current compensation method.* The parallel modules described for the voltage droop method of paralleling provide the necessary circuit isolation for the cross-current compensation method of paralleling. Cross-current compensation allows two or more paralleled generators to share inductive reactive loads with no decrease or droop in the generator system output voltage (see figure 5-13). This is accomplished by the action and circuitry described in the voltage droop method and the addition of cross connecting leads between CT secondaries. The output of the first unit CT is connected to the input of the second unit CT, the output of the second unit CT is connected to the input of third unit CT, etc., until all CTs are connected in series.

The final step is to connect the output of the last CT to the input of the first unit CT. This forms a closed series loop that interconnects the CTs of all the generators to be paralleled. The signals from the interconnected CTs cancel each other when the line currents are proportional and in phase (no circulating currents), and no drop in system voltage occurs.

Cross-current compensation can be used only if the regulators are identical and if the regulators on all the generators operating on a common bus are interconnected into a cross-current loop. Generators of different kilowatt ratings may be operated with cross-current compensation if parallel CTs are selected that give approximately the same secondary current at each generator's rated load.

Voltage droop compensation does not require the above interconnection between generator regulators nor matching CT output for different size generators. For this reason, and because of its simplicity, the voltage droop method is the most popular method of paralleling generators.

Some self-excited, self-regulated generators are capable of parallel operation. The previously mentioned self-excited, self-regulated unit using ac voltage in the exciter field can be paralleled with like units and can share reactive load. In addition to the normal requirements for paralleling (same voltage, same frequency, same phase rotation), the units must have drooping voltage with reactive load and their output voltages must be within 2%.

If the voltage on one of the paralleled units is higher than the other, it will try to take the reactive load. The higher reactive load will cause the generator voltage to droop, thus decreasing the voltage and balancing the reactive load between both generators.

5.2.15 Exciters

The two basic exciters in use today are the static exciter and the rotating brushless exciter.

a) *Static exciter.* The static exciter is a solid-state device that derives its input from the output voltage of the main starter. The ac input is rectified to dc, controlled by the voltage regulator and supplied through brushes and slip rings to the main field of the alternator. The static exciter must supply all the power to the main field. Typical power required by the main field on a 200 kW generator is 3 kW.

b) *Rotating brushless exciter.* The rotating brushless exciter is actually a three-phase generator with a rotating armature on the same shaft with the main generator rotor. The voltage regulator supplies excitation current and voltage to the stationary field. The three-phase output from the rotating armature is rectified by a three-phase rotating bridge and the dc voltage is supplied to the main generator field. The power input to the brushless exciter for a 200 kW generator is 0.3 kW.

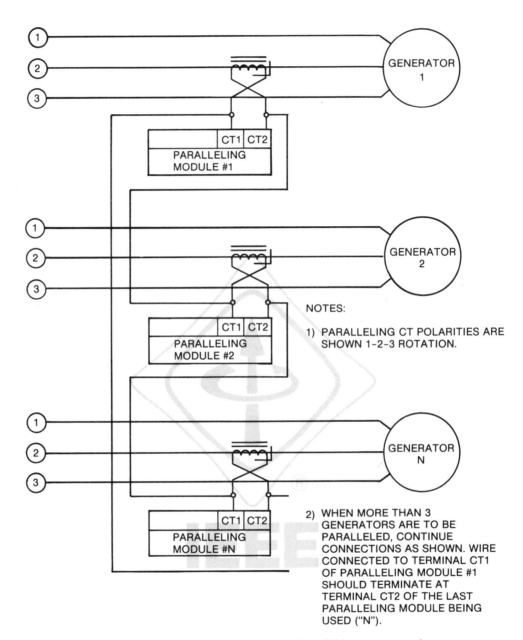

Figure 5-13—Cross-current compensation CT interconnection

5.2.16 Load pickup

Motor starting is the most severe requirement for the generator in terms of voltage dip. As stated earlier, initial starting voltage dip should not exceed 35% in order to prevent motor starters from dropping out. Voltage drops from cycling motors during operation should not exceed 10%. A study should be made to determine that other connected loads will operate satisfactorily when this dip occurs (refer to Chapter 9). The engine power required during motor starting is relatively small since the power factor is low, in the 0–0.4 range.

Full load pickup at rated power and 0.8 power factor will cause a voltage dip in the area of 15–20%. However, this is a more severe requirement for the engine. Since the real kilowatt load will not cause a large voltage dip, the engine must pick up full load. This is usually not a problem for smaller, naturally aspirated engine generator sets, but on larger sets with turbochargers the sudden loading can cause the engine to stall before the turbocharger can return to full speed.

To prevent this from happening, loads can be picked up in sequence. The first loads to be picked up consist of the emergency system transfer switch circuits. These loads must be on the line in 10 s. After a delay, the equipment system transfer switches feeding the motor loads are sequenced to the generator. For more information, refer to 5.3.1.

5.2.17 Exercising

No load operation of diesel engines eventually results in unburned fuel in the exhaust system and in the formation of carbon within the engine. In order to avoid this condition, as well as to check the complete standby power system, the complete generator set should be exercised with the facility load. According to NFPA 99-1996 (8-2.1.2.5):

> Generator sets serving Emergency and Equipment systems shall be inspected weekly, and shall be exercised under significant load and operating temperature conditions for at least 30 min at intervals of not more than 30 days. The 30 min exercise period is an absolute minimum, or the individual engine manufacturer's recommendations shall be followed.

Permanently installed resistive load banks are available to conveniently and automatically exercise the units under the appropriate load.

5.3 Automatic and nonautomatic transfer switches

Automatic transfer switches are used where alternate sources of power are required to automatically ensure power continuity to designated electrical loads in health care facilities. An automatic transfer switch may be defined as an inherently double-throw emergency device that automatically transfers electrical loads from a normal source to an emergency source whenever the normal source voltage fails or is substantially reduced. The switch automatically retransfers the load back to the normal source when it is restored.

Because of its unique position in the electrical system the transfer switch should be a highly reliable device with a long life and minimum maintenance requirements. Transfer switches applied in health care facilities must have electrical characteristics suitable for the operation of all functions and equipment they are to supply. The main characteristics to be considered are as follows:

a)   Types of load to be transferred

b) Voltage rating
c) Continuous current rating
d) Overload and fault current withstand ratings
e) Type of overcurrent protective device ahead of the transfer switch
f) Source monitoring
g) Time delays such as on transfer or transfer-back
h) Input/output control signals
i) Main switching mechanism
j) Ground fault protection considerations
k) System operation
l) Bypass/isolation switches
m) Nonautomatic transfer switches operation
n) Multiple transfer switches versus one large transfer switch per system
o) Need to transfer system neutral

Reliability and economics are the prevailing factors in determining the best selection for the application.

5.3.1 Types of loads

5.3.1.1 Load classification

The types of loads to be served in health care facilities are defined in Chapter 2.

Loads are classified by UL 1008-1989 as follows:

a) Total system loads
b) Motor load
c) Electric discharge lamp loads
d) Resistive loads
e) Incandescent lamp loads

UL requires the marking of transfer switches to indicate the type of load they are capable of handling. The marking "Total System Loads" indicates that the transfer switch can be used for any combination of the loads described above under b) through e). However, the incandescent load may not exceed 30% of the total load unless the transfer switch is specifically marked as suitable to transfer a higher percentage of incandescent lamps. Most transfer switches are rated for the transfer of total system loads, although some may be marked "resistance only," "tungsten only," etc., or a combination of these markings. The burden of the system designer is lessened when the switches chosen are listed and rated for total system loads.

5.3.1.2 Motor load transfer considerations

Two special design considerations are to be weighed by the system designer when motor loads are to be supplied from alternate power systems:

a) The need to avoid nuisance circuit breaker tripping and possible damage to the motor and related equipment when the motor is switched between two energized power sources that are not synchronized.

b) The need to shed motor loads prior to transfer and delay reconnection to prevent overloading the power source to which the load is being transferred.

Depending on the makeup of the load, one or both of the above may require consideration for any given dual power arrangement.

1) *Avoiding damage to motors.* Motors and related equipment can be damaged when switched between two live power sources. During routine testing of the system, or during retransfer from the alternate power source back to the normal power source, both power sources are at full voltage. Experience has shown that motors, especially large three-phase motors of 50 hp or more, when transferred from one energized power source to another energized power source, can be subjected to abnormal inrush currents. This in turn can lead to damage of motor windings, insulation, couplings, and, in some cases, the driven load. The motor overcurrent device may also trip out due to abnormal inrush current, and require resetting. The abnormal currents are caused by the motor's residual voltage being out of phase with the voltage source to which it is being transferred.

The situation is similar to paralleling two unsynchronized power systems. Various control methods that are being used to overcome this problem are:

i)   In-phase transfer
ii)   Motor load disconnect control circuit
iii) Transfer switch with a timed center-off position
iv)   Closed transition transfer to momentarily parallel the power sources

2) *In-phase transfer.* In-phase transfer schemes have been applied to health care facility equipment loads for many years. As shown in figure 5-14, in-phase transfer is often used for transferring low-slip motors driving high-inertia loads on secondary distribution systems.

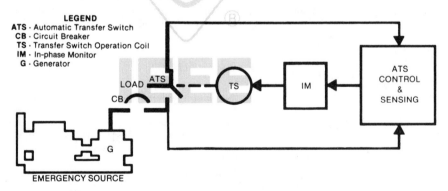

LEGEND
ATS · Automatic Transfer Switch
CB · Circuit Breaker
TS · Transfer Switch Operation Coil
IM · In-phase Monitor
G · Generator

Figure 5-14—In-phase motor load transfer

A primary advantage of in-phase transfer is that it can permit the motor to continue to run with little disturbance to the electrical system and the process that is being controlled by the motor. Some motor loads should not be interrupted and shut down. Concern has been expressed about the slowdown of auxiliary motors that result in pressure surging of boilers or in the cavitation of pumps

[B10].[2] Where it may be desirable to avoid intentionally delayed interruptions so motor controllers will not have to be reset, the in-phase transfer approach is the most practical.

Another advantage of in-phase transfer is that a standard double-throw switch can be used with the simple addition of an in-phase monitor. The monitor samples the relative phase angle that exists between the two sources between which the motor is transferred. When the two voltages are within the required phase angle and are approaching zero phase angle, the in-phase monitor signals the transfer switch to operate and reconnection takes place within acceptable limits. The faster the transfer switch operates, the wider the frequency difference can be between the two power sources without exceeding normal motor starting current at time of transfer [B6].

In-phase monitors should be equipped with filtering and sensing that is impervious to the effects of wave form distortions such as harmonic current.

Under certain conditions, the in-phase monitor should be omitted. Fast transfer has been recognized as a means for the transfer test of power station auxiliaries [B2]. Fast operating transfer switches have been in use on secondary distribution systems for many years. When a motor is being transferred between two synchronized sources, such as two-phase locked utility company lines from the same source, a transfer switch with fast operating time is usually sufficient for successful transfer since the motor does not have time to slow down significantly.

3) *Load disconnect control circuit.* Motor load disconnect control circuits, such as shown in figure 5-15 and similar relay schemes, are also a common means of transferring motor loads [B7]. This arrangement and the following arrangement (timed center-off position) should not be used if the motors cannot be de-energized momentarily during transfer. Momentary de-energization may result in unacceptable disturbances to the electrical system and the process being controlled by the motor.

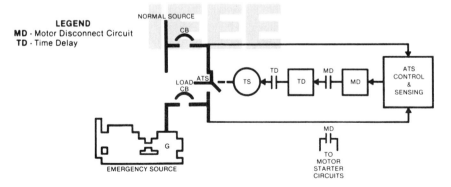

Figure 5-15—Motor load disconnect circuit

[2]The numbers in brackets correspond to those of the bibliography in 5.14.

As figure 5-15 indicates, the motor load disconnect control circuit is a pilot contact on the transfer switch that opens to de-energize the contactor coil circuit of the motor controller. After transfer, the transfer switch pilot contact closes to permit the motor controller to reclose. For these applications, the controller should reset automatically.

The motor load disconnect circuit positively isolates each motor through its own controller, thus preventing possible interaction with other system loads.

A proper motor control disconnect circuit should be arranged to open the pilot contact for approximately 3 s before transfer to the alternate power source is initiated. Depending on the motor's time constant, or whether timed reclosing is provided in the motor controller circuit, it may also be necessary to add a second delay in the motor load disconnect control circuit. If the motor controller circuit does not have timed reclosing and the motor's time constant exceeds 3 s, an additional delay should be included in the motor load disconnect control circuit. A 3 s delay is usually satisfactory. An exception might be large high inertia motors, that may have time constants of 4–5 s. In such cases, it may take six or more seconds for the residual voltage to decay to an acceptable value for reclosing.

When several motors are being transferred, simultaneous reconnection may cause excessive starting inrush currents. In this case the delay can be a sequencer with several timed pilot contacts (one contact for each motor controller circuit).

As these arrangements require interconnection of control wires between the transfer switch and the motor controller, some consideration should be given to the design and layout of the system to minimize control line runs. To overcome this problem, the transfer switch is frequently located adjacent to or within the motor control center.

4) *Timed center-off position.* Transfer switches with a timed center-off (neutral position) have been used as a means of switching motor loads. Figure 5-16 shows a typical arrangement. This arrangement achieves results similar to the motor load disconnect control circuit described earlier.

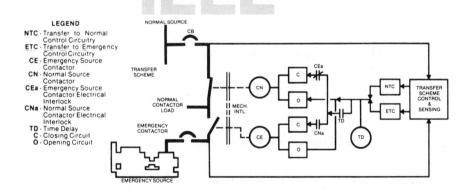

Figure 5-16—Neutral off position

One advantage, provided that timed sequence reclosing is not required, is that interconnections between the transfer switch and motor controller are not required provided the controllers are the auto reset type.

5) *Closed transition transfer.* Closed transition transfer with momentary paralleling of the two power sources is an ideal but more costly solution (see figure 5-17). An uninterrupted load transfer should provide the least amount of system and process disturbances [B8]. Closed transition transfer can only be achieved when both power sources are present and properly synchronized by voltage, frequency, and phase angle. In the case of a failing source, overlap transfer may be extremely difficult, if not impossible, to achieve. Closed transition transfer can only be used during test transfers and retransfer back from the generator to the utility when both sources are at full voltage.

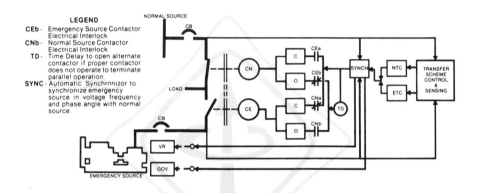

Figure 5-17—Closed transition transfer

With closed transition transfer, the on-site engine generator set is momentarily connected in parallel with the utility source. This necessitates advance approval from the local utility company before specifying and installing the equipment.

Ten to 15 years ago, obtaining such approval was often a problem. However, with the increased acceptance of cogeneration, the picture has changed considerably. In fact, today many electric utilities encourage interconnections with on-site power as an alternate to the uncertainties of building new power plants.

With closed transition transfer, there is even less concern than that of cogeneration. This is because the paralleling of sources is not sustained and lasts only for a maximum of 100 ms. Therefore, the need for protective relaying, as required for cogeneration, is not required for closed transition transfer. The requirement for protective relays, if any, will be determined by the utility company.

5.3.1.3 Sequential loading of the generator

What methods are available to prevent overloading of the alternate source? Such generator sets often have limited capability to supply the total inrush and starting currents of the connected load. For economical purposes, generator sets are often sized to provide full load current plus a limited motor starting capability [B5]. In such cases, it becomes essential to delay reconnection of loads when transferring from the normal power source to the on-site generator.

Article 517 of the NEC requires that the equipment system load (primarily motor load) transfer switches in hospitals be equipped with time delay relays that will delay transfer of the connected load to the generator set. The purpose is to assure that the more important emergency system loads are connected first and established within 10 s of failure. The transfer switches supplying the motors are then sequentially transferred to the generator set.

Another reason for load shedding is the need to "power down" certain loads, such as those utilizing silicon controlled rectifiers (SCRs) to avoid damage to, or failure of, such components during transfer. Various solutions in use today to help solve these problems by adding circuit features to transfer switches are as follows:

a) *Transfer switches with individual time delay circuits on transfer to emergency.* This arrangement is in frequent use today. If there are several transfer switches in an installation, the time delay can be adjusted slightly differently on each transfer switch so that the transfer switches close sequentially onto the generator. Consideration should be given to individual motor inrush requirements, the remaining available starting kVA of the generator, and the importance of the respective loads when determining the sequence of transfer.

b) *Transfer switches with signal circuits for definite disconnection of a single load prior to transfer and reconnection after transfer.* This arrangement was described previously under b) 3) in 5.3.1.2, and illustrated in figure 5-15. With the additional delay described in the text, the control circuit not only assures that the motor is disconnected before transfer, but also prevents the motor load from being reconnected until several seconds after the transfer switch has transferred and reconnected any other loads that are fed by the same transfer switch.

c) *Transfer switches as in* b) *but with multi-signal circuits to sequence several loads onto the generator.* A further refinement of the system described above utilizes several signal circuits when several motors are to be fed by the same transfer switch and it is desired to reconnect them sequentially rather than all at once. Two to nine circuits are commonly provided. The time delay between reconnection steps is adjustable from 2–60 s to allow the starting current to reduce to a safe value before the next motor is signaled to be reconnected. Once the delay is set, it is the same for each step.

5.3.1.4 Transformer load considerations

Dry-type lighting transformers and isolation transformers are generally located on the load side of the transfer switches supplying the life safety and critical branches of the essential electrical system. Isolation transformers are frequently used in anesthetizing locations and in special environments of health care facilities (see Chapter 6).

The electrical and mechanical construction of some of these transformers is such that very high magnetizing inrush currents frequently occur when the transformer is reenergized during a transfer operation. The inrush currents may be as high as 20–25 times rating and may sometimes cause nuisance tripping of the overcurrent protective device. These transformers use grain-oriented square loop steels. The amount of magnetic flux is determined by the conditions that existed when the circuit was last interrupted and is unpredictable. The phenomena exists whether or not the secondary is connected.

There are various solutions to overcome nuisance tripping depending on the manufacturer of the transformers. Sometimes series reactance, impedance starting, and special overcurrent devices are considered as solutions. A solution beyond the transfer switch is necessary because other interruptions, such as momentary outages on the high lines, can cause a similar problem. However, for health care facilities where periodic testing is mandated, a closed transition transfer switch can ameliorate the condition.

5.3.2 Voltage ratings

An automatic transfer switch is unique in the electrical distribution system in that it is located where two unsynchronized power sources are commonly connected to it. This means that the voltages impressed on the insulation may actually be as high as 960 V on a 480 V ac system. A properly designed transfer switch should provide sufficient spacings and insulation to meet these increased voltage stresses.

For this reason, the electrical spacing on a transfer switch should not be less than those shown in UL 1008-1989 (table 15.1), regardless of what type of component may be used as part of the transfer switch.

The voltage ratings for this discussion will be limited to health care facility essential electrical system applications where transfer switches are rated 600 V or less.

NEMA ICS 10-1993 standard voltage ratings of automatic transfer switches are normally 120 V, 208 V, 240 V, 480 V or 600 V, single or polyphase. The standard frequency is 60 Hz. Automatic transfer switches can also be supplied for other voltages and frequencies when required for dc and international applications.

5.3.3 Continuous current rating

A continuous current (load) is defined by the NEC as one that is expected to continue at its maximum value for 3 h or more (NFPA 70-1996).

Transfer switches differ from other emergency equipment in that they must continuously carry the current to critical loads, whereas an engine generator set generally supplies power only during emergency periods. Current flows continuously through the transfer switch whether the switch is in the normal or the emergency position. Automatic transfer switches (ATS) are available in continuous ratings ranging from 30–4000 A.

Most transfer switches are capable of carrying 100% of rated current at an ambient temperature of 40 °C. However, some transfer switches, such as those incorporating integral overcurrent protective devices, may be limited to a continuous load current not to exceed 80% of the switch rating.

When selecting an automatic transfer switch, it is only necessary to determine the maximum continuous load current that the transfer switch must carry. Momentary inrushes, such as occur when lighting or motor loads are energized, can be ignored provided that the switch is UL 1008-1989, "Total Systems Load"-rated. Select an automatic transfer switch that is at least equal to, or greater than, the calculated continuous current.

For new projects, the system designer may specify a transfer switch that will be able to carry future anticipated loads. In such cases, it is advisable to select a transfer switch with a continuous current rating equal to the future total anticipated load.

The transfer switch continuous current rating is found by totaling the amperes required for all loads. Electric heater and tungsten (incandescent) lamp load currents are determined from the total wattage. Fluorescent, mercury vapor, metal halide, and sodium vapor lamp load currents must be based on the current of each ballast or auto-transformer draws, not on the total watts of the lamp. Motor loads are determined by motor full load running currents. Motor inrush and locked rotor currents need not be considered in sizing a transfer switch that is UL-listed for total system loads.

5.3.4 Overload and fault current withstand ratings

Transfer switches are often subjected to currents of short duration that exceed the continuous duty ratings. The ability of the transfer switch to handle higher currents is measured by its overload and fault current withstand ratings. Additional information on overload ratings and fault current withstand ratings can be found in Chapter 3.

5.3.5 Protective device ahead of transfer switch

The type and size of the overcurrent device ahead of the transfer switch plays a significant role in transfer switch application. Refer to Chapter 3 for a discussion on coordinating the protective device and the transfer switch. Protective devices should be coordinated throughout the system so that a fault is cleared by the device nearest to the fault, thereby minimizing load disruption.

5.3.6 Source monitoring

The normal source is most often from an electric utility company whose power is transmitted many miles to the point of utilization. The transfer switch control logic continuously monitors the voltage of and, optionally, the frequency of all phases. Because utility frequency is for all practical purposes constant, only the voltage is usually monitored. For single-phase power systems, the line-to-line voltage is monitored. For three-phase power systems, all three line-to-line voltages should be monitored to provide full phase protection.

In addition to feeder failure, monitoring protects against operation at reduced voltage, such as brownouts, which can damage loads. Since the voltage sensitivity of loads varies, the pickup (acceptable) voltage setting and dropout (unacceptable) voltage setting of the monitors should be adjustable. Typical range of adjustment for the pickup is 85–100% of nominal while the dropout setting is 75–98% of the pickup selected. The usual settings for most loads are 95% of nominal for pickup and 85% of nominal for dropout.

A study should be made to determine the minimum operating voltage of the equipment connected to the load side of the transfer switch.

The brightness of tungsten lamps is generally unacceptable at a 70% voltage level. Fluorescent-type lighting is also voltage sensitive and at 85% of rated voltage, it becomes uncertain as to whether the fluorescent lamp will continue to burn properly. Some manufacturers allow for a voltage range of +5% to –8%. Therefore, a closer voltage differential with dropout set at 90% of nominal is generally required for this type of lighting.

Electronic equipment loads are often more critical. These installations include patient care equipment in health care facilities, x-ray equipment, television stations, microwave communications, telephone communications, data processing centers, and similar applications. Close differential protection is often set for a dropout of 90% of nominal.

Upon loss of voltage in one phase, polyphase motors will single-phase, which may lead to burnout of the motor. While the motor is normally protected by the overload relays in the controller, close differential voltage supervision should be applied to the automatic transfer switch for motor installations so that transfer to the alternate source can be initiated. Differential voltage relays with a close adjustment of 2% for dropout and pickup values will aid in the detection of phase outages and help provide protection when single phasing occurs.

As long as normal voltage is available at or above the preset limit, the transfer switch should remain connected to the normal source. Likewise, if voltage is lost to only one of several transfer switches, then only that transfer switch should transfer to emergency. The remaining switches should stay on normal.

Sensing of the alternate source voltage need only be single-phase since most applications involve an on-site generator with a relatively short line run to the automatic transfer switch. In addition to monitoring voltage, the alternate source's frequency should also be monitored. Unlike the utility power, the engine generator frequency can vary during start-up. Frequency monitoring will avoid overloading the engine generator while it is starting and can thus avoid stalling the engine. Combined frequency and voltage monitoring will protect against transferring loads to an engine generator set with an unacceptable output.

5.3.7 Time delays

Time delays are provided to program the operation of the automatic transfer switch to avoid unnecessary starting and resultant transfer to the alternate supply.

An adjustable momentary outage time delay will override momentary interruptions and reductions in normal source voltage but will allow starting and transfer if the reduction or outage is sustained. The time delay is generally set at 1 s, but may be set higher if line-side automatic throwover arrangements and reclosers on the high lines take longer to operate, or if expected momentary power dips frequently exceed 1 s. If long delay settings are used, care must be taken to ensure that sufficient time remains to meet the 10 s power restoration requirements.

Once the load is transferred to the alternate source, another timer delays retransfer to the normal source until that source has time to stabilize. This timer is controlled by the preferred source voltage monitors and is adjustable from 0–30 min. It is normally set at 30 min.

Another important function of this retransfer timer is to allow the engine generator set to operate under a load for a preselected minimum time to drive out moisture and ensure continued good performance of the set and its cranking system. This delay should be automatically bypassed if the alternate source fails and the normal source is available as determined by the voltage monitors.

Engine generator set manufacturers often recommend a cooldown period for their sets that will allow the set to run unloaded after the load is retransferred to the normal source. A third time delay, usually 5 min, is provided for this purpose. The delay helps to prevent inadvertent high water temperature alarm and lockout when the set is shut down. Running an unloaded engine for more than 5 min is unnecessary, and is not recommended since it can cause deterioration in engine performance.

It is sometimes considered good practice to purposely sequence transfer of the loads to the alternate source where more than one automatic transfer switch is connected to the same engine generator, such as on the equipment branch of the essential electrical system (refer to 5.3.1.3). Utilization of such a sequencing scheme can reduce starting kilovoltampere capacity requirements of the generator. A fourth timer, adjustable from 0–5 min, will delay transfer to the alternate source for this and other similar requirements. NFPA 99-1996 requires the delay on certain equipment system loads.

5.3.8 Input/output control signals

When the transfer switch control panel detects a sustained failure of the normal source, a set of contacts, one normally open and one normally closed, operates to signal starting of the alternate source generator set. These contacts should be rated to handle the dc voltages and currents encountered on engine automatic starting systems.

Additional dry contacts, normally open and normally closed, should be provided on the transfer switch unit for remote annunciation of transfer switch positions and other control functions.

5.3.9 Main switching mechanism

The main switching mechanism of a transfer switch should have the following characteristics:

a) *Electrical operation.* It is usually considered good practice to electrically operate the transfer switch using control power from the source to which the load is to be transferred. This arrangement ensures an adequate source of power for switch operation.

b) *Mechanically held.* Electrically held transfer switches are limited in size, will drop out and disconnect the load if the main coil fails, and have very low fault current withstandability. Conversely, mechanically held mechanisms are not limited in size, will not drop out, and can withstand higher fault currents.

c) *Mechanically interlocked—double-throw.* Normally, the switch mechanism should be of the mechanically interlocked double-throw-type, permitting only two possible positions—closed on normal or closed on emergency. If the interlocking permits both sets of contacts to close at the same time, a system-to-system short circuit can occur. Exceptions are made for center-off and closed transition schemes as previously described under b) 4) and 5) in 5.3.1.2.

5.3.10 Ground-fault protection considerations

Ground-fault protection of electrical systems that have more than one power source (e.g., a load supplied by a utility and engine generator set) requires special consideration when the neutral conductor of the engine generator set is required to be grounded at the generator location, thus creating multiple neutral-to-ground connections. The system must be properly designed to avoid improper sensing of ground-fault currents and nuisance tripping of overcurrent devices. Transfer switches are often furnished with neutral transfer contacts to provide the isolation between neutrals.

Ground-fault protection as applied to emergency power systems is covered in detail in Chapter 3.

5.3.11 System operation

The emergency system and the equipment system should be so arranged that, in the event of failure of the normal power source, an alternate power source is automatically connected within 10 s to the emergency system loads and to the switching devices (time delay or nonautomatic) that are supplying the equipment system loads.

The automatic transfer switch is arranged to achieve this operation. An automatic transfer switch consists of two major components: an electrically operated, double-throw transfer switch, and a control panel (see figure 5-18).

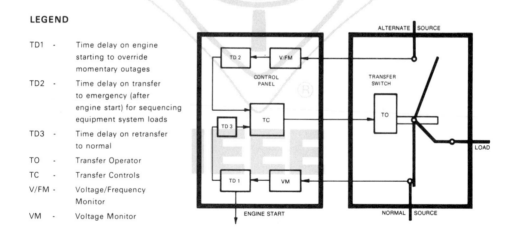

**Figure 5-18—Automatic transfer switch
(consists of the control panel, left, and the switch unit, right)**

The essential electrical system is normally served by the utility power source except when the utility power source is interrupted or drops below a predetermined voltage level as sensed by the voltage monitor (VM). Settings of the sensor should be determined by a careful study of the voltage requirements of the load.

Chapter 3 describes the overall essential electrical system. Failure of the normal source will automatically start the alternate source generator after a short delay (TD1). When the alternate power source has attained a voltage and frequency that satisfies minimum operating requirements of the essential electrical system as sensed by the combination voltage/frequency monitors (V/FM), the load is connected automatically to the alternate power source through the transfer controls (TC) and the main transfer switch operator (TO).

Upon connection of the alternate power source, the loads comprising the emergency system are automatically reenergized. The load comprising the equipment system is connected automatically after a time delay (TD2), and in such a manner as not to overload the generator.

When the normal power source is restored, and after a time delay (TD3), the automatic transfer switch disconnects the alternate source of power and connects the loads to the normal power source.

If the emergency power source should fail and the normal power source has been restored, retransfer to the normal source of power is immediate, bypassing the retransfer delay timer.

5.3.12 Bypass/isolation switches for automatic transfer switches

In many health care facilities, it is difficult to perform regular testing or detailed inspections on the emergency system because some or all of the loads connected to the system are vital to human life. De-energizing these loads for any length of time is difficult. This situation results in a lack of maintenance. In such installations, a means can be provided to bypass the critical loads directly to a reliable source of power without downtime of the loads. The transfer switch can then be isolated for safe inspection and maintenance.

NFPA 99-1996, section 3-3.2.1.1(8), states that health care facilities should consider

> Properly designed and installed bypass arrangements to permit testing and maintenance of system components that could not be otherwise maintained without disruption of important hospital functions.

Two-way bypass/isolation switches are available to meet this need. A typical two-way bypass/isolation switch combined with an automatic transfer switch is shown in figure 5-19.

These switches can perform the following three functions:

a) Shunt the service around the transfer switch without interrupting power to the load. One manufacturer's switch design interrupts the load for a few cycles during operation. In figure 5-20 the bypass (upper) handle is in the bypass-to-normal (BP-NORM) position. The load is fed directly from the normal source through the right-hand BP contact. The isolation (lower) handle is shown in the closed position.

b) Allow the transfer switch to be tested without interruption of power to the load. In figure 5-21 the isolation (lower) handle is in the test position, so the transfer switch can be tested without disrupting the load.

c) Electrically isolate the transfer switch from both sources of power and load conductors to permit the inspection and maintenance of all transfer switch components. In figure 5-22 the isolation handle is moved to the open position, and the load is fed directly from the normal; the automatic transfer switch (ATS) is completely isolated and can be removed without interrupting the load.

The functions outlined above are accomplished by operating two handles in an easy-to-follow sequence. The equipment can be furnished as a complete automatic transfer and bypass/isolation switch for new installations, or as a replacement for existing equipment. Some arrangements can be supplied with a drawout mechanism so that the transfer switch can be easily removed for maintenance.

Figure 5-19—Typical automatic transfer and two-way bypass/isolation switch

In addition to the two-way switches, one-way switches are also available that bypass to only one preselected source. Experience has shown that the somewhat higher price for a two-way switch is fully justified when considering the overwhelming advantages over one-way switches. For example, a two-way bypass/isolation switch allows either power source to be selected to feed the load during bypass. The operator can choose the source that is the more dependable at that time. Furthermore, when the transfer switch is in the test or open position as shown in figures 5-21 and 5-22, a two-way bypass/isolation switch can be used to transfer the load to the alternate source if the source to which it has been bypassed fails. One-way devices cannot provide these features.

Essential loads that warrant bypass switches to permit periodic maintenance of transfer switches should be provided with the capability to transfer in two directions. Such an

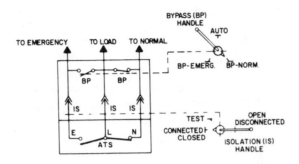

Figure 5-20—Bypass-isolation switch in bypass-to-normal position

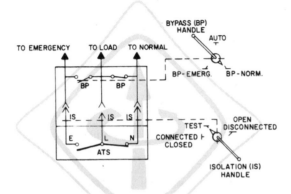

Figure 5-21—Bypass-isolation switch in test position

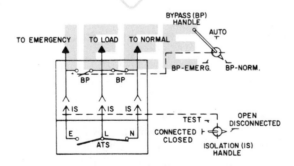

Figure 5-22—Bypass-isolation switch with transfer switch removed

arrangement ensures the backup capability to transfer critical loads to an available normal or emergency power source even if the automatic switch is inoperable.

Only two-way bypass/isolation switches should be furnished with the transfer switches that feed the essential electrical system in a health care facility.

5.3.13 Nonautomatic transfer switches

Nonautomatic transfer switches are sometimes considered for certain code-defined portions of the equipment load and for various nonessential loads, when permitted. For these installations it is necessary that operating personnel make the switchover and that the load not be of an emergency nature requiring immediate automatic restoration of power. For these reasons it is recommended that all loads be transferred automatically whenever possible. When possible overloading of the generator is a concern, it may be more practicable to manually transfer nonessential loads.

Section 700-5(b) of NFPA 70-1996 requires that a portable or temporary alternate source of power be made available whenever the emergency generator is out of service for major maintenance or repair. How this is to be accomplished is left up to the system designer. Whatever approach is used, it should be in accordance with standard practice and equipment for emergency use. One suggestion might be to use a nonautomatic transfer switch.

Devices used as nonautomatic transfer switches should have the same electrical characteristics, rating, and features as an automatic transfer switch except that the control panel is omitted. Operation is achieved either through an externally operable quick make/quick break manual operating handle or by electrical remote push-button control.

Electrically operated nonautomatic transfer switches should derive control power from the source to which the load is being transferred to ensure an adequate power supply to the main electrical operator. Control relays are often used at the transfer switch to avoid voltage drops owing to long control line runs.

5.3.14 Multiple transfer switches vs. one large transfer switch

In small hospitals and nursing homes with a maximum demand of 150 kVA on the essential electrical system, NFPA 70-1996 permits one large transfer switch rather than multiple branch transfer switches.

The system designer should consider the following in determining the best approach:

a)   One single large automatic transfer switch close to the incoming service controlling the entire emergency load, in lieu of individual automatic transfer switches in each branch of the emergency system, may reduce the overall reliability and design flexibility of the system. Maximum protection is better achieved by locating the transfer switches as close to the loads as possible. At this location, the automatic transfer switch will not only monitor the utility and generator power supplies but also the power circuit conductors to the transfer switch.

b)   Maximizing physical isolation of the separate branches and feeders in the essential electrical system may be accomplished by using separate transfer switches in each feeder. Separate transfer switches, in each of the essential load feeders, increase total system reliability because separation of the conductors is maintained all the way back to the utility and generator main distribution switchboards. If one large transfer switch were used, it might require a long main power conductor run. If something happened to this one conductor or the single automatic transfer switch, the complete essential electrical system would be shut down, whereas with the multiple automatic transfer switch approach, only one branch of the system would be affected.

c) There is a need to sequentially transfer the loads in blocks so as not to overload the generator. Multiple automatic transfer switches with adjustable delay on transfer to the generator are generally used for this purpose. If one large transfer switch were used, it might require oversizing the generator or development of a load-shedding, load restoration system.

d) While several small transfer switches that equal the ampacity of one large switch might cost about the same, the additional cost of separate feeders and installation is a factor favoring the use of one large switch.

When branch circuits on the load side of the transfer switch are required to be extra reliable because they are life-sustaining, area protection relays might be a consideration. These relays can sense failures at the load side of the individual panelboard overcurrent devices or directly at the point of utilization. Such relays can signal for remedial action when overcurrent device opening (inadvertent, mechanical failure or overcurrent tripping), circuit wiring failure, equipment failure, or unintentional equipment disconnection occur.

5.4 Engine generator controls

5.4.1 General

The engine generator control panel contains the devices that monitor and control the status and operation of the engine generator system. Interfacing with control components on the engine and the transfer switch is generally required. The control panel should be located near the engine generator set. The assembly and conductors should be protected from the effects of vibration.

NFPA 99-1996 requires that the generator set(s) be equipped with certain visual prealarm and alarm devices, automatic safety shutdown, and an audible alarm device to indicate activation. It further requires a remote annunciator to indicate alarm conditions outside of the generating room at a regular workstation. Where the regular work station periodically is unattended, an audible and visual derangement signal should be provided at a continuously monitored (24 h/day) location. The annunciator is generally located in the boiler plant, fire station, security room, office center, or telephone switchboard.

5.4.2 Safety controls

It is usually preferable to shut down an emergency generator set and correct a problem rather than continue to operate the unit and possibly destroy it in the process. For this reason, safety shutdown controls are required as follows.

a) The controls are arranged to shut the engine down for

1) Overspeed
2) Low lubricating oil pressure

3) Excessive engine coolant temperature

In addition, pre-shutdown anticipatory alarms for low lubricating oil pressure and excessive engine temperature are also provided in health care facilities. When warned of an impending shutdown, an attendant may take corrective action to prevent shutdown for low lube oil pressure and excessive engine temperature. If a governor loses control, engine speed may increase from rated speed to overspeed in less than 1 s and no corrective action is possible. Therefore, a pre-shutdown alarm is not practical for overspeed.

b) Additional indicator lights and/or alarms are specified for

1) Overcrank (failure to start)
2) Battery charger malfunction
3) Low fuel level
4) Low water temperature, e.g., coolant heaters not operating
5) Emergency generator set operating
6) Low coolant level

Indicator lights to show malfunction of many other items may be desirable in specific installations. These may include excessive engine room temperature, remote radiator fan failure, etc.

5.4.3 Automatic starting

The alternate source generator set(s) in health care facilities are normally automatically started and stopped as a function of a control contact on the automatic transfer switch (see 5.3.8 and 5.3.11). The control contact closes to initiate engine start and run, and opens to initiate engine stopping. The contact should be arranged for fail-safe operation.

The engine generator control panel (see figure 5-23) includes an automatic engine start control that operates upon signal of the control contact on the transfer switch to control the various devices on the engine for engine start and run. For example, on a diesel engine, a fuel solenoid valve may be energized to permit fuel to flow into the fuel injectors. At the same time, the cranking motor relay circuit is energized to initiate cranking. The automatic engine starting control includes an overcrank time delay that will sound an alarm and lock out any further cranking if the engine fails to start after a programmed period. A common cranking sequence is 15 s of cranking followed by 15 s rest, repeated for a total of 75 s.

When the engine ignites and attains a minimum speed setting, the cranking circuit is automatically disconnected via any one or more of methods such as speed governor switch, oil pressure switch, ac generator voltage buildup, and battery charging generator voltage buildup. The selection of the proper crank disconnect method is best made at the recommendation of the engine manufacturer.

The automatic engine starting controls also monitor the various engine protective devices described above to sound alarms, to give visual indication, and to shut the engine down when failures occur. The failure lockout circuit requires resetting before the engine can be restarted.

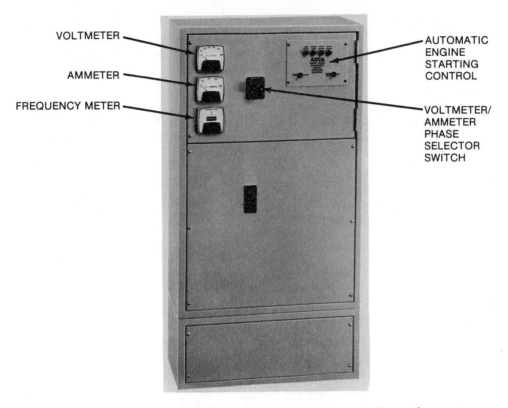

Figure 5-23—Typical engine generator control panel

5.4.4 Typical engine generator set control panel features

In addition to the automatic engine starting control, the engine generator control panel may also include

— Voltmeter
— Ammeter
— Frequency meter
— Voltmeter/ammeter phase selector switch, or separate switches
— Current transformers
— Overcurrent protective device
— Vibration isolators when engine mounted
— Remote annunciator interface

Various other accessories are furnished depending on the application. These might include

— Elapsed time meter
— Panel illumination lamp with ON/OFF switch
— Governor motor raise-lower speed switch
— Voltage adjust rheostat

— Voltage regulator
— Kilowatt meter
— Instrument panel test block to enable connection of power quality instrument

5.4.5 Remote annunciator requirements

Health care facilities require a remote annunciator panel (see figure 5-24) to provide visual and audible indication of

— Low fuel level
— Low water temperature
— Low oil pressure
— High water temperature
— Overspeed
— Overcrank

Visual indication only is required for the following:

— Battery charger malfunction
— Generator is supplying the load

In addition to the above, a derangement contact should be supplied to close for signaling to a continuously attended work station that an alarm condition has occurred.

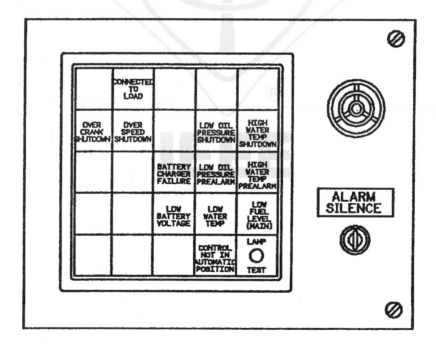

Figure 5-24—Typical remote annunciator panel

5.5 Battery chargers for cranking batteries

5.5.1 General description

A great variety of battery chargers are available. The type selected for a generator set installation will depend upon the electrical equipment used on the engine. Most chargers fall into two categories:

a) *Full battery recovery.* The full recovery-type charger is required on standby generator set installation when a charging generator is not used to restore battery charge. It is usually a high-low rate charger that is automatic in operation. The high rate will recharge the battery, and the low rate will maintain the batteries in prime starting condition.

b) *Maintenance trickle charge.* The trickle-type charger is sometimes used when a charging generator is supplied on the engine. With a trickle charging rate of 2 A, it maintains the battery condition at whatever level was attained when the charging generator stopped. It is not designed to recharge a discharged battery, and for this reason, it may be more reliable to provide a high-low full battery recovery charger even if a charging generator is furnished on the engine.

A battery charger for engine cranking batteries is similar, if not identical, to a dual rate battery charger for standard float application. The primary difference between the chargers is sizing. In engine cranking applications, the battery load is usually several hundred amperes (possibly a few thousand amperes) for only a few seconds. The batteries may need to be relatively large to provide the high breakaway and rolling currents for the cranking motor. On the other hand, the charger is usually small in comparison to the battery ampere hour capacity, because only a small amount of battery capacity is removed with each crank cycle. For example, 1000 A for 15 s equals:

$$(1000 \text{ A}) \frac{(15 \text{ s})}{(3600 \text{ s/h})} = 4.2 \text{ Ah removed}$$

In lead-acid batteries, the individual cell voltages will begin to drift apart and will need to be brought back to the full charge by increasing the charger voltage approximately 10% for 25–30 h every 30 days. This is referred to as "equalizing" the battery. Nickel-cadmium batteries have much less self-discharge over longer periods of time under similar conditions.

Whether lead-acid or nickel-cadmium, both types of batteries need a high rate of charge to achieve a fully charged state.

Many nickel-cadmium battery users have been allowed to believe that because their type of battery does not require periodic "equalizing charges" such as required for lead-acid, that a dual rate battery charger was not needed. They have, as a result, used only a single rate float charger. This type of charger will adequately maintain a fully charged nickel-cadmium battery until it is discharged by an external load. However, once the battery is discharged, it will not recharge to more than 85% at float voltage regardless of the current capacity of the charger. It is also true that with each successive discharge, the nickel-cadmium battery in such a charging circuit will continue to lose capacity. This phenomenon has from time to time been referred to as "memory effect." However, it is simply a result of inadequate recharging of the battery. It can be corrected with a sequence of several high charge and deliberate discharge cycles.

5.5.2 Definitions

ambient temperature: The temperature of the medium, usually air, surrounding the battery charger.

battery charger: As defined in this standard, static equipment that is capable of restoring and maintaining the charge in a storage battery.

charge: The conversion of electrical energy into chemical energy within the battery.

charging rate: The output current expressed in amperes at which the battery is charged.

constant potential charge: A charge in which the voltage at the output terminals of the charger is held to a constant value.

current limit: The maximum output of the battery charger delivered to a discharged battery and load, usually stated as a percentage of output rating and with nominal input voltage supplied to the charger.

float voltage: The voltage maintained across the battery by the charger in order to keep the battery at its best operational condition with minimum water loss. Float voltage is expressed in volts/cell.

equalize voltage: A voltage approximately 10% higher than the float voltage. This higher voltage is used for periodic equalizing of lead-acid and nickel-cadmium batteries. Equalize voltage is expressed in volts/cell.

nominal value: An arbitrary reference value selected to establish equipment ratings.

overcurrent protection: Protection of the battery charger against excessive current, including short circuit current.

short circuit current (of a battery charger): The current magnitude at the output terminals, when the terminals are short circuited and with nominal input voltage supplied to the charger.

5.5.3 Charger ratings

The continuous duty output current rating must be adequate to supply the engine cranking battery charging current plus all auxiliary load requirements.

The charger output voltage rating is dictated by the type of battery and the number of cells being charged.

Float voltage ranges per cell at 77 °F (25 °C) are

— Lead plante at 1.210 *d* electrolyte 2.15–2.19 V
— Lead-antimony at 1.210 *d* electrolyte 2.15–2.19 V
— Lead-antimony at 1.265 *d* electrolyte 2.29–2.33 V
— Nickel-cadmium at 1.35–1.45 V

Equalize voltage ranges per cell at 77 °F (25 °C) are

— Lead plante at 1.210 *d* electrolyte 2.25–2.35 V
— Lead-antimony at 1.210 *d* electrolyte 2.25–2.35 V
— Lead-antimony at 1.265 *d* electrolyte 2.4–2.5 V
— Nickel-cadmium at 1.50–1.60 V

The ac input ranges for 60 Hz are

Nominal voltage	Minimum	Maximum
120	106	127
208	184	220
240	212	254
277	245	293
480	424	508
575	508	608

The rated alternating current supply frequencies are 50 Hz or 60 Hz.

Rated ambient temperature range is 32–122 °F (0–50 °C).

5.5.4 Charger sizing

The worst-case load on the charger is when the battery is discharged and the charger must recharge the battery plus power the load. There are many considerations such as the number of cells, voltage window of the load, input voltage, input frequency, single-phase, three-phase, output regulation, ripple, recharge time, etc., all of which can affect the charger selection.

In general, because engine cranking batteries are seldom discharged very deeply, it is common practice to size the charger by the following equation:

$$I(\text{chg}) = \frac{0.6\,(\text{Ah})}{HR} + I(\text{load}) \tag{3}$$

where

I (chg)	is current capacity of charger
Ah	is ampere hour capacity of charger
HR	is hours to recharge
I (load)	is continuous dc load on the system

It should be understood that battery recharge time actually relates to two different parameters of the charger:

— The current capacity of the charger
— The voltage setting of the charger

Refer to figure 5-25. T_1 is almost completely determined by the current capacity but the charger's current capacity has almost no effect on T_2.

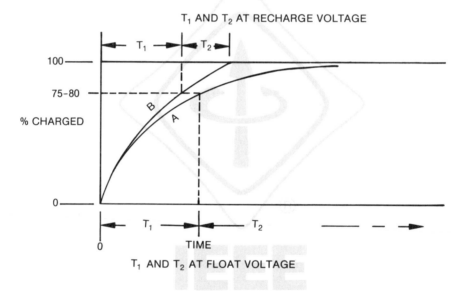

T_1 = The time required to recharge a fully discharged battery to 75–80% charged.
T_2 = The time required to bring the battery from 75–80% charged to 100% charged.

Figure 5-25—Battery recharge time

T_2 is almost completely determined by the output voltage setting of the charger, although this setting has virtually no effect on T_1.

The charger will be in its current limit mode during the first part of T_1 and, as the battery voltage begins to increase, the charger will come out of current limit. A typical curve is illustrated by curve A. T_1 can be cut in half simply by doubling the current capacity of the charger.

The only way to shorten T_2 is to shift up to a higher charging curve, such as shown in curve B, by applying more V/cell to the battery. This is done by adjusting the "recharge" mode ("equalize" for lead-acid systems) of the charger output up to a higher voltage. This may not be as simple as it first appears. There are various potential problems that must be considered:

— Lead-acid batteries are more sensitive to high charging voltages than nickel-cadmium. The extra heat buildup in the plates may cause plate warpage.

— The voltage window of the applied load may not accommodate the increase in charger voltage.

The charger can be adjusted up to 1.65–1.7 V/cell for pocket-plate nickel-cadmium cells without any damage to the battery, but all loads have some maximum voltage above which serious damage will result. One of the following two standard methods is commonly used to effect desired recharge times without damage to the load:

a) *Method 1 (Oversizing).* Since T_1 is a function of current capacity of the charger, but only restores the battery to 75–80% of full charge, the battery can be oversized by 25% and a larger charger used. Even though the battery will not be fully recharged during time period T_1, it will be recharged sufficiently to carry another duty cycle for the specified time period.

NOTE—When specifying the charger, it may be desirable to require "a charger that will restore the battery sufficiently to carry another duty cycle as specified for the battery" instead of "fully recharged" in a given period of time.

b) *Method 2 (Dropping Diode).* Although damage to the battery is possible for lead-acid batteries being rapidly recharged, the nickel-cadmium pocket-plate battery can accept current as quickly as it can release it. There is no danger to the battery as long as the electrolyte level is kept above the surface of the plates (see figure 5-26).

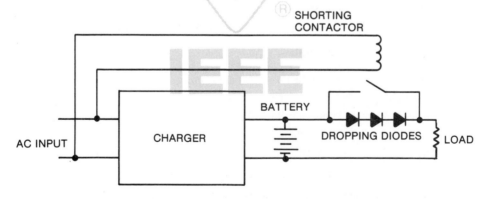

Figure 5-26—Dropping diode circuit (CEMF)

5.5.5 Advantages and disadvantages of lead-acid and nickel-cadmium cells

Although the lead-acid battery and its nickel-cadmium counterpart can be used interchangeably in most applications, there are certain advantages and disadvantages to each type.

The primary advantage to the lead-acid battery is its lower initial cost. The primary advantage to the nickel-cadmium battery is that it is a lower maintenance, long life, more physically rugged battery. For engine cranking applications, a properly sized and maintained nickel-cadmium battery will have an expected useful life of 18–20 years, compared with 2–4 years for the engine cranking lead-acid battery.

Since specifiers may not adequately describe the quality features required in a lead-acid battery, it has been common for lead-acid batteries furnished with generator sets to be of minimal quality, whereas nickel-cadmium batteries are usually made to only one high grade design.

5.5.6 Memory effect on nickel-cadmium batteries

There is a phenomenon in all electrochemical couples that are being inadequately recharged that causes the cell to appear to lose capacity with each recharge cycle.

All batteries have an optimum voltage that is ideal for continuous "float" charging. This voltage results in maximum battery life and minimum water usage. For lead-acid batteries at 1.230 d acid, this voltage is 2.15–2.17 V/cell. For nickel-cadmium batteries, the voltage is 1.4–1.42 V/cell.

In lead-acid cells and nickel-cadmium sinter-plate cells, even if the battery is not discharged the individual cell voltages will begin to drift apart. Approximately every 60–90 days, the lower voltage cells will need to be brought back to full charge by increasing the charger voltage by approximately 10–15% (2.33–2.36 V/cell for lead-acid cells and 1.60–1.65 V/cell for sinter-plate nickel-cadmium cells).

Pocket-plate nickel-cadmium batteries have much less self-discharge, and as a result if a pocket-plate nickel-cadmium battery is not discharged with an external load, it will remain fully charged for many years at 1.4 V/cell. It is therefore a true statement that pocket-plate nickel-cadmium cells do not need to be "equalized." However, to avoid creating real problems in the battery room, it must be understood that the writers of this chapter are not saying the user does not need the dual rate recharging mode of the "float/equalize" battery charger.

5.5.7 Typical performance features

a) The battery charger should be a solid-state, constant potential device whose output potential is regulated by sensing the battery voltage.

b) The charger should deliver full rated capacity to a discharged battery with input voltage variation as shown in 5.5.3.

c) The output float voltage should be maintained within +1% of the nominal setting.

d) The output equalize voltage should be maintained within +2% of the nominal setting.

e) A device should be provided to change the output voltage from float to equalize when conditions warrant.

f) Controls should be provided to adjust the voltage over the range specified in 5.5.3 (float voltage ranges and equalize voltage ranges).

g) The back drain from the battery should not exceed 50 mA with the loss of ac input.

h) The battery charger should be self-protected and the output current should be limited to a safe value under cranking loads.

i)   Surge suppressors should be provided to protect the rectifier from line and load transients. The input and output circuits should be protected with fuses and/or circuit breakers.

j)   An ammeter should be provided to indicate the output current. The meter should have minimum accuracy of 5%.

k)   The charger design and manufacture should satisfy the performance and safety codes of NEMA PE 5-1985 and EGSA 100C-1992.

5.5.8 Optional accessory features

a)   A voltmeter should be considered to indicate the dc output voltage. The meter should have a minimum accuracy of 5%.

b)   An alarm device can be furnished to actuate upon loss of proper charger output.

c)   High dc voltage alarm devices are available to actuate when the charger output voltage exceeds the preset alarm level. This level can be adjustable from equalize voltage to 2.6 V/cell lead-acid or 1.7 V/cell nickel-cadmium. The device should maintain its alarm set-point adjustment within +1%.

d)   A low dc voltage alarm device can be provided to actuate when the charger output voltage falls below the present alarm voltage level. This level should be adjustable from float voltage to 1.75 V/cell lead-acid or 1.0 V/cell nickel-cadmium.

e)   AC power failure alarm devices are available to actuate upon loss of ac input.

f)   An equalize timer can be provided to cover a range of 0–24 h or 0–72 h. When manually activated, this timer will place the battery charger in the equalize mode. At the end of the specified time period, the timer will automatically return the charger to the float mode.

g)   An automatic equalize timer can be furnished to be activated by ac power failure or low dc battery voltage and will place the battery charger in the equalize mode. At the end of the specified time period, the timer will return the charger to the float mode.

5.5.9 Installation and maintenance data

a)   Wire between the battery charger and the battery should be sized to minimize voltage drop.

b)   Adequate clearance should be provided to allow convection cooling of the charger.

c)   All auxiliary loads should be connected to the dc panelboard supplied from the battery bus. Do not connect loads to battery terminals or charger terminals.

d)   The charger should be installed in accordance with the NFPA 70-1996 and NFPA 110-1996.

e)   Periodic inspections, for dust and dirt removal and connection tightening, should be scheduled.

5.6 Synchronizing and paralleling control systems for multigenerator set installations

To supply large loads, two or more engine generator sets are often operated in parallel on a common bus as an emergency power supply. Successful operation of multiple engine generator sets in parallel requires a control system that can provide all the functions needed to operate the generator automatically, plus automatically handle the synchronizing, load sharing, isochronous operation, and load control operations.

The system designer is faced with a number of considerations. Some of the more important are as follows:

- When to parallel
- Engine generator set governor and voltage regulator considerations
- Random access paralleling
- Dividing the load
- Establishing load priorities
- Load shedding
- Load switching means
- Typical system operation
- Sensing
- Control logic
- Instrumentation
- The generator power breaker
- Switchgear short-circuit duty and ratings
- Generator neutral grounding

5.6.1 When to parallel

Emergency power systems having one engine generator are often preferred and are generally more economical. However, there are many situations today that can be handled better by paralleling two or more engine generator sets. Parallel operation is usually justified for one or more of the following reasons:

a) *Economy.* One reason for paralleling two or more sets is for economy. For example, when renovating an existing distribution system, it may not be practical to split an existing large load bus into several sections to be handled by separate generator sets. In this case, two or more generators can be paralleled to match the bus capacity.

Another example of economy is the total installed cost of multiple small sets vs. the cost of one large set, such as five 500 kW sets instead of one 2500 kW set.

A third example is where the load is expected to grow substantially, but because of economics, the initial investment must be minimized. The designer could consider designing the distribution system to accommodate future generating capacity by making initial provisions for paralleling at moderate cost.

Another example occurs when an existing system is to be expanded. (It is more economical to run one large bus instead of several independent feeders.)

b) *Reliability.* An important reason for paralleling two or more engine generator sets is for reliability. For example, part of the emergency load may be so essential that it is desirable to have redundant generator sets to handle the load. Here, when there is a power failure on the normal line, all sets are signaled to start at the same time. The probability that at least one set will start is higher than with an installation with only one set. The first one ready to handle the emergency load does so. Then the other sets pick up the remaining loads as generators become ready.

Another example occurs when all sets are running, but one fails. In this case, some or all of the less important load, such as equipment system load, is dropped so that the remaining sets will handle the emergency load.

c) *Minimizing downtime.* When preventive maintenance or overhaul is being done on an engine, it is required by section 700-5(b) of NFPA 70-1996 to provide backup power. To do so, an additional ready-to-run engine generator set is available when needed.

5.6.2 Engine generator set governor and voltage regulator considerations

The engine generator sets should be furnished with electronic governors and voltage regulators to make them suitable for unattended automatic paralleling and load sharing. The electronic governor provides isochronous operation (constant speed regardless of load), and automatic proportionate load division that enables automatic paralleling of dissimilar size sets. The electronic governor will permit paralleling at any time without necessitating adjustment or requiring droop. Similarly, voltage regulators should be able to achieve automatic reactive load division to provide constant voltage systems.

5.6.3 Random access paralleling

Random access paralleling to the bus employs a synchronizing device for each engine generator set in the system. The reliability of the paralleling control system is high because of a redundancy of parallel logic paths.

Random access paralleling permits simultaneous synchronizing of each set to the bus and therefore achieves parallel operation of sets in the shortest possible time. This is important in health care facilities because the emergency branch must be "on line" in 10 s.

In a random access paralleling system, the first set to achieve nominal voltage and frequency is connected to the bus to make emergency power available within 10 s to the emergency branch transfer switches and their respective loads, and to provide a basis of comparison for synchronizing the remaining sets. As the remaining sets come up to voltage and frequency, they are synchronized and paralleled to the bus, at which time the equipment branch transfer switches transfer in delayed sequence to connect the equipment loads.

5.6.4 Dividing the load

When paralleling two or more engine generator sets, it is necessary to consider the capacity of each set relative to the total load. The system should be arranged to inhibit the connection of additional loads to the alternate source power bus until sufficient generating capacity is on the bus. To do this, the essential electrical system load should be divided into parcels, or blocks, that can be safely connected to the alternate source bus without overloading the engine generator sets. The size of the load blocks is a function of the individual engine generator set capacity.

For example, if the load is 1800 kW and the engine generator sets are to be 500 kW each, then the load may be divided into three blocks of 500 kW each, with a fourth block at 300 kW. Such a system would require four 500 kW engine generator sets. However, if two 900 kW engine generator sets were used, the same load would be divided into two blocks of 900 kW each.

Sometimes it is necessary to examine the load in terms of how it can be suitably divided and still satisfy the needs of the various essential loads. In this case, the size of the load blocks determines the size and number of generator sets needed.

5.6.5 Establishing load priorities

Once the load block size is determined, then the sequence in which these loads are added to the bus should be decided upon. Each load block is assigned a priority rating. This rating specifies how many engine generator sets must be on the bus before a particular load may be transferred. For example, the first priority would be the emergency system loads, the second priority would be the "delayed automatic" equipment loads, and the third priority would be the manually switched (nonautomatic) equipment loads.

5.6.6 Load shedding

As with adding loads to the bus, the ability to shed loads is also determined by the size and number of engine generator sets. Load shedding is necessary when the connected load exceeds the capacity of the on-line engine generator sets. This situation can occur upon malfunction of an engine generator set, or upon a drop in bus frequency. The initiation of load shedding and resulting reduction in connected load will allow the surviving engine generator sets to service the highest priority (emergency system) loads without interruption in, or degradation of, the power delivered.

5.6.7 Load switching means

There are several ways to switch loads on and off the generator bus. Inasmuch as the system is a dual-source power system, there is already a built-in switching means in the system, which is the automatic transfer switch. It is generally a simple modification to cause the automatic transfer switch to be controlled in both directions for load connect and load shed operation.

When more than one class (priority) of load is fed from a given automatic transfer switch, a remote control switch can control the lower priority load on the load side of the automatic transfer switch. Another method would permit the load connect to be controlled by the automatic transfer switch, with the load shedding achieved by shunt tripping circuit breakers. However, care should be taken in the application of the shunt trip approach when molded case circuit breakers are used, because shunt tripped breakers must be manually reset unless equipped with electrical operators. It may be good practice to have automatic resetting means. Also, consideration should be given to the anticipated number of operations to which the circuit breaker will be subjected.

There are as many approaches to load switching as there are applications for emergency power. The preferred approach for any application is determined by the requirements of the application with due consideration to reliability, flexibility, and economics.

5.6.8 Typical system operation

A typical multiengine automatic paralleling system depicting some of the load switching schemes previously mentioned is shown in figure 5-27. The following sequence of operation refers to the line diagram in figure 5-28. The system is comprised of three engine generator sets as the emergency source. Any one engine generator set has sufficient capacity to supply priority one and priority two loads.

Figure 5-27—Typical automatic paralleling system for four engine generator sets, including nine automatic transfer switches

The operation is for a random access paralleling system. The generator sets are connected to the bus in random order as they become available.

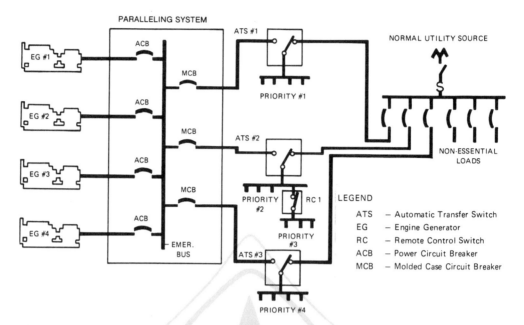

Figure 5-28—Typical multiengine automatic paralleling system

The loads are connected to the emergency bus in ascending order of priority beginning with priority one. For load shedding, the loads are disconnected in descending order of priority beginning with the last priority of load to be connected.

Upon a loss of normal source voltage and expiration of the momentary outage delay as determined by any one or more of the automatic transfer switches (ATS) shown in figure 5-28, a signal initiates the starting of all engine generator sets. The first set to come up to 90% of nominal voltage and frequency is connected to the alternate source bus. Life safety and critical loads are then transferred via ATS #1 and #2 to the bus upon sensing availability of power on the bus. (RC1 opens before ATS #2 transfers.) As the remaining engine generator sets achieve 90% of the nominal voltage and frequency, their respective synchronizing monitors will control the voltage and frequency of these oncoming units to produce synchronism with the bus. Once the oncoming unit is matched in voltage, frequency, and the phase angle with the bus, its synchronizer will initiate paralleling. Upon connection to the bus, the governor will cause the engine generator set to share the connected load with the other on-line sets.

Each time an additional set is added to the emergency bus the next priority load is transferred in a numbered sequence via additional switches, such as RC1 and ATS #3, until all sets and essential loads are connected to the bus. Control circuitry should prevent the automatic transfer or connection of loads to the bus until there is sufficient capacity to carry these loads. Provision is made for manual override of the load addition circuits for supervised operation.

Upon restoration of the normal source of supply as determined by the automatic transfer switches, the engines are run for a period of 5–15 min for cooling down and then shut down. All controls automatically reset in readiness for the next automatic operation.

The system is designed so that reduced operation is automatically initiated upon the failure of any generator set through load dumping. This mode overrides any previous manual controls to prevent overloading the emergency bus. Upon sensing a failure mode on an engine, the controls automatically initiate disconnect, shutdown and lockout of the failed set, and reduce the connected load to within the capacity of the remaining generator sets. Controls should require manual reset under these conditions.

Protection of the engine and generator against motoring is provided. A reverse power relay, upon sensing a motoring condition on any generator set, will initiate load shedding, disconnect the failing generator set, and shut it down.

5.6.9 Sensing

The paralleling system is subject to various transients in voltage and frequency that are the result of changes in loading on the system. The sensing devices must ignore these normal transients while responding to harmful ones. Basically, four types of relays are used in paralleling systems: voltage, frequency, synchronizing, and power.

a) *Voltage relays*. There are various methods of sensing the magnitude of an ac sine wave. For example, there are peak, peak above average, and rms detection. Each method has its own distinct characteristics. The rms method is preferred.

The advantage of rms detection is that the trip settings of the relay are directly related to the ability of the power line to supply the load. Therefore, the trip points of the relay will coincide exactly with the values determined from rms metering regardless of power line distortion. Other relaying techniques may provide erroneous trip points when compared to rms metering on high-distortion power lines.

Because generator power capacity is small in comparison to the utility, load changes may generate large voltage transients. Consequently, the relay must differentiate between transient and long term conditions. Thus, a means of distinguishing this difference should be included in the relay. A preferred method is to include an adjustable time delay within the relay to override momentary system transients. The time delay should start the instant the power line voltage goes below the preset relay limits; it should reset to zero when the voltage is restored within those limits. This, in effect, provides zero differential around the monitor trip settings.

b) *Frequency relays*. As in voltage detection, there are also many techniques for sensing frequency. Therefore, careful consideration should be given to selecting the proper type of frequency relay to meet the needs of the power system and the load. The most important considerations in selecting a frequency relay are the effects of waveform distortion, line voltage regulation, line transients, and ambient temperature on the relay trip settings.

Waveform distortion is more often caused by nonlinear loads connected to the power distribution system. The distortion becomes more pronounced as the load causing the distortion approaches the size of the power source. Distortion often occurs when the load is fed by static power converters utilizing silicon-controlled rectifiers and thyristors. These devices are commonly found in UPS systems, variable frequency ac motor drives, computers, and other electronic equipment. For example, where thyristors are "gated on" well within the voltage cycle, as in phase control, high currents can flow over only a portion of the cycle, resulting in nonlinear loading and wave form distortion. Figure 5-29 is a graphic representation of the effects of distortion on a fundamental sine wave.

Sudden load changes may, in addition to voltage transients, cause momentary frequency shifts. The frequency relay selected to protect the power line should have the capability of discriminating between momentary and sustained frequency variations. The typical methods of protecting against momentary or sustained outages are to provide trip point differentials and time delays. The advantage of a trip differential is to provide acceptance of a power line frequency that may be perfectly adequate under sustained load conditions. Time delay on trip is normally used to prevent false relay response due to large frequency transients.

To obtain the best possible operation, both types of protection should be incorporated into the same relay.

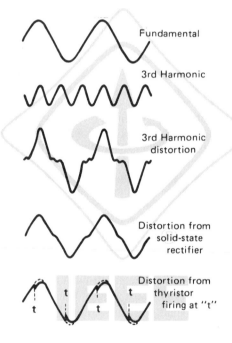

Figure 5-29—Distorted voltage wave shapes

c) *Reverse power relay.* When power sources operate in parallel on a common bus, the voltage and frequency of each source is common. Neither voltage nor frequency relays, nor any combination of them, can distinguish a malfunctioning engine generator set from an acceptable one. The only way to determine proper operation on the bus is to measure the power output of each engine generator set. When a set is delivering power to the bus, it is operating properly. When a set is drawing power from the bus, it is motoring, and there exists the possibility of a malfunction. It is normal to have power flow to the set from the bus for short periods when the bus is lightly loaded. Five to ten percent or less of set capacity is normal. At this load level, all that keeps the sets in synchronism is the exchange of synchronizing (circulating) currents causing this reverse power. Therefore, the relay that measures for this condition should be set at a high enough value to ignore this harmless condition. However, it must be set at a low enough value to detect a malfunction. How much is enough depends on the engine. Some engines will draw only 1–2% of their full load rating when motoring, while others will draw 8–10%. This determines the range of adjustability of the trip setting (that is, between 0–10%). In the absence of manufacturer's data, field tests may have to be run to determine proper settings.

Many kinds of reverse power relays are available. They fall into two general classifications: electro-mechanical and electronic. The electro-mechanical type uses induction disc sensing and is reasonably inexpensive. However, it needs annual or biannual calibration checks due to its sensitivity to temperature, dust, age, moisture, etc.

The electronic type is a solid-state reverse power relay that provides repetitive accuracies without the need for regular recalibration. Whichever type is used, it should have an integral adjustable time delay to ignore transient conditions caused by light loading and switching large blocks of load. Single-phase sensing is adequate since the generator, when acting as a motor, is a balanced load.

d) *Synchronizing.* Sources are considered synchronized when their sine waves are equal, i.e., the sources to be paralleled must be equal in the following ways:

    1) Phase angle
    2) Frequency
    3) Voltage
    4) Rotation

All four of these conditions should be satisfied when paralleling engine generator sets.

Figure 5-30 shows five voltage sources. No two of them are synchronous.

Paralleling such sources can cause substantial damage to the engine, the generator, and/or the system. Synchronizing is, therefore, the most critical operation in the system. Due to tolerances in equipment, there should be some allowance for differences in parameters. However, when these differences become too great, the result is out-of-synchronism paralleling.

To produce minimum disturbances, the differences should be minimized. The Electrical Generating Systems Association (EGSA) states that the maximum allowable differences are as follows:

—Voltage: 5%
—Frequency: 0.5 Hz
—Phase Angle: 5°

The synchronizer should sense the existing difference in voltage, frequency, and phase angle, and then take corrective action, if necessary, to reduce the differences to the acceptable limits stated by EGSA.

Electronic governors are used to control the speed of the engine generator set. These governors are basically analog devices. Thus, the direct input of an analog signal proportional to the frequency difference will produce the necessary speed adjustment. This eliminates the need for a motorized potentiometer assembly, which can be a potential source of malfunction.

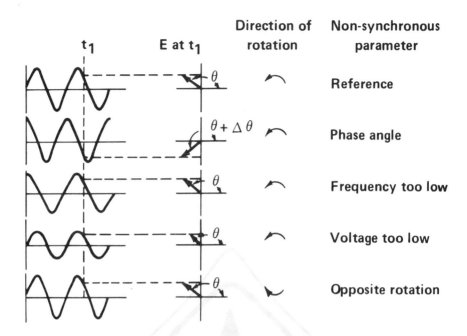

| t₁ | E at t₁ | Direction of rotation | Non-synchronous parameter |

Figure 5-30—AC sine waves representing differences in phase angle, frequency, voltage, and rotation

5.6.10 Control logic power sources

In the design of a control system for paralleling engine generator sets, the choice of power source is limited to the generator output, the engine starting batteries, or switchgear batteries.

a) *DC control power.* In an emergency power application, the generators are normally not running. Consequently, upon an outage of the normal source, the only available power source is from batteries.

  There are good reasons for using the same batteries for control power as are used for engine cranking. For example, utilization of all engine batteries provides redundant power sources for the control logic. The minimal control power drain does not normally require any additional considerations in the sizing of the batteries. The control circuit burden is typically less than 1% of the engine battery ampere hour rating. In addition, this drain is only imposed while the system is in operation. When in the standby mode, the system draws minimal control power for indicating lights. Choosing the engine starting battery as a control power source instead of a separate switchgear battery eliminates the need for maintenance and the charging equipment for an additional set of batteries.

  When engine cranking batteries are used, they provide redundancy in control power availability. An uninterruptible control power source selector device can provide for drawing control power from any combination of batteries with respect to an individual battery's ability to supply power. The device must provide positive isolation as well as prevent a fault in one bank from discharging the other batteries.

b)   *DC control logic*. The dc control logic provides for the starting, stopping, and monitoring of the engines. When malfunctions occur, dc control logic removes the faulty
set from service and initiates appropriate action to protect the remaining sets. In addition, the control logic for multiple generator set systems must be adequate for operation at the voltage levels it is subject to.

The dc control logic should accept the generator-on-line signals in whatever order they
occur to cause loads to be connected in a predetermined order of priority. The logic
should also accept generator availability signals as determined by the respective generator voltage and frequency relays to permit the first unit available to be connected to
the bus.

Each system should be furnished with an audible alarm to annunciate a malfunction,
and with a visual alarm to identify the source of malfunction. When a silencing circuit is used in conjunction with the audible type alarm, it should be reset automatically either upon correction and clearing of the malfunction, or upon the occurrence
of another malfunction.

c)   *AC control power*. AC can be used in the control system only when the functions are
such that they occur while a generator is operational and where load transients will
not affect the operation. For example, it is desirable to use the generator as a power
source for closing the generator main power circuit breaker. Closing this circuit
breaker at ac potentials requires substantially less current than at dc battery potentials. The opening current for this circuit breaker should be drawn from the battery
source so that a generator set can be removed from the line upon the loss of ac generator output. As shunt tripping requires substantially less current than closing, battery
capacity is generally adequate for tripping purposes, but needs to be calculated for
the anticipated sequence of events representing "worst case."

5.6.11 Instrumentation

Instrumentation helps to facilitate periodic inspection, preventive maintenance, and calibration essential to proper system operation and longevity.

Since the relays and controllers in the system are highly accurate (up to ±0.25%), the instruments that measure the performance of these devices should also be accurate. Switchboard-
type 1% accuracy instruments are preferred, as the application is comparable to service
entrance-type applications.

The minimum complement of instruments should include the following:

a)   An ammeter for each generator with a means of switching to measure current in each
line
b)   A voltmeter with switching means to measure each line-to-line and line-to-neutral
voltage
c)   A frequency meter, preferably having a 55–65 Hz scale with division for 1/10 Hz, to
measure engine speed
d)   A wattmeter to indicate engine performance, and, optionally, a varmeter to indicate
reactive load sharing

The ammeter furnishes data on generator loading and voltage regulator performance and adjustment. The voltmeter permits adjustment of the voltage regulator for proper operating voltage. The frequency meter permits adjustment of the governor for proper operating frequency. The wattmeter permits adjustment of the governor for proper load division between engine generator sets operating in parallel. The wattmeter also permits engine adjustments based on loading.

5.6.12 Generator power circuit breaker

The generator power circuit breaker serves two functions. First, it provides protection to separately excited generators against overload and short circuits (self-excited shunt generators are protected by inherent design). Second, it operates as a switch to make on inrush loads and break continuous current as well as stalled motor currents. The breaker must be capable of repetitive operations.

Air circuit breakers and insulated case circuit breakers are commonly used for the generator circuit breaker.

Figure 5-29 illustrates how the generator power circuit breaker fits into a typical system. For more specific information on health care facility essential electrical systems including protection, coordination, and selectivity, refer to Chapter 3. However, it's important here to reiterate the need for selectivity in essential system overcurrent protective devices. The purpose of the generator circuit breaker is not to disconnect faulted circuits from the generator. This function is handled by load-side overcurrent devices that are selectively coordinated with the generator circuit breaker.

The generator power breaker should be of the five-cycle closing type, and include dc shunt trip, alarm contacts, and interlock contacts for interfacing with the system. Sensing and trip units for proper coordination of trip curves within the distribution system are required with the breaker for overcurrent and short circuit protection.

The code requires the overcurrent protective device to be located at the generator, which is the source of supply for the emergency conductors. For installations where the generator switchgear is not located immediately adjacent to the generator, separate switching devices for paralleling should be furnished in the generator switchgear cubicles.

5.7 Utility peak demand reduction controls

The control of utility peak demand within a health care facility is somewhat different from the usual peak demand control systems employed in most other types of facilities. There are generally no loads that may be completely shed at the time that coincides with the peak demand without having a significant effect on operations. Many other types of facilities are able to control peak demand by use of a programmable load demand controller that de-energizes such items as electric space heating, electric water heating, air conditioning chillers and auxiliaries, blowers, fans and other comfort loads. In health care facilities, utility peak demand reduction can be achieved by transferring some of the essential electrical system loads over to the emergency generator set(s).

5.7.1 Special requirements for health care facility loads

For health care facilities, NFPA 99-1996 has provided an exception to its paragraph 8-2.3.2 as follows:

> 3-3.2 *Exclusive Use for Essential Electrical Systems*. The generating equipment used shall be either reserved exclusively for such service or normally used for other purposes. If normally used for other purposes, two or more sets shall be installed, such that the demand and all other performance requirements of the Essential Electrical System shall be met with the largest single generator set out of service.
>
> Exception: A single generator set shall be permitted to operate the Essential Electrical System for (1) peak demand control, (2) internal voltage control, or (3) load relief for the external utility, provided any such use will not decrease the mean period between service overhauls to less than three years.

The purpose of this exception, which first appeared in the 1977 edition, is to allow the use of the engine generator set(s) for the purposes described in the exception.

5.7.2 Type of electrical load billing

Health care facilities are generally served by a utility. Billing by the utility is normally based on the following:

a) Total consumption of the facility in kilowatt hours.

b) Peak demand charge computed on the highest average power demand recorded during the billing period. The utility determines demand charges by measuring the power consumption during a given interval (usually 15 min). This procedure is repeated for each succeeding interval during the billing period (usually 1 month) with the demand charge being based on the highest recorded value during peak time hours. Peak time hours are defined in the utility tariff. The demand indicator indicates the highest interval (e.g., 15 min) and is manually reset to zero each time the meter is read. For larger installations, the information may be stored digitally for analysis. In other cases, it may only store and indicate the highest interval. The consumer is frequently billed for a percentage of the maximum demand charge (often 90%) for the next 12 months, or for a percentage of the contracted capacity (often 75%), whichever amount is larger. In addition, other miscellaneous charges such as fuel adjustment charges, low power factor penalties, etc., may be assessed.

Many utilities may also assess a standby charge. This is intended to compensate the utility for reserving generating capacity to restore power when the on-site generator set(s) is not available.

5.7.3 Advantages of utility peak demand reduction

From the type of utility billing as described above, the control of demand can save money for the customer. If the demand is closely controlled, the user will be able to avoid high demand charges, which will be used for billing not only for the month in question, but also for the subsequent 12 months. In addition, contracted capacity charges can be reduced because smaller demand will be made upon the utility's generating capacity.

5.7.4 Load demand controllers

Power management is usually accomplished by a microprocessor that receives information from a kilowatthour meter with a pulse initiator. This information is stored and accumulated during the demand interval (e.g., 15 min) and the average kilowattage computed. The controller receives these signals continuously, and updates its prediction of peak demand. The controller thus becomes a predictor of when a predetermined peak demand will be reached, and also when the load will fall to acceptable levels. The controller initiates control of the load demand control system, so that loads will be transferred to the on-site generating system when the demand approaches this predetermined level and then restored to the utility as the load is reduced back to the acceptable level. Therefore, the demand can be reduced without compromising the routine of the health care facility by using the in-house generating system.

5.7.5 Types of load demand control systems

Two types of load demand control systems are available: operation in parallel with the utility, and operation independent of the utility. The selection of the system to use is based on the policies of the utility company. If the utility company will permit parallel operation with its service, parallel operation is usually the preferred method. However, many utility companies prohibit this practice, or require protective relaying that may make it impractical for the health care facility. When this is the case, operation independent of the utility is mandatory. Obviously, the first step in system selection is to ascertain the practices of the utility involved.

a) *Type I—Operation in Parallel with the Utility.*

1) *Operation in Parallel with the Utility—Semiautomatic.* When the load demand controller senses that the preset peak demand is being approached, the controls will start the generating set and operate an audible and visual signal to alert the operator of the condition. The operator will then manually synchronize the output of the generator with the utility source and assume its rated portion of the load through the systems controls. When the load has fallen to within acceptable limits, a second set of signals will direct the operator to manually transfer all of the load back to the utility source, and after the prescribed unloaded running time, shut down the generator. If during the operation of the system in the load demand control mode there should be a failure of utility power, the system will revert to an emergency power system, serving the essential electrical system through the system's automatic (and manual) transfer switches.

2) *Operation in Parallel with the Utility—Automatic.* When the load demand controller senses that the preset peak demand is being approached, the controls will start the generating set, automatically synchronize its output with the utility, and cause its rated portion of the load to be assumed by the plant. Engine governors can be controlled to cause engines to assume only that portion of load in excess of the demand limit or a constant preset kilowatts, whichever is desired.

   Generator excitation can be controlled to cause the generators to operate at a fixed power factor. This power factor is set at the job site to the average power factor present during peaking conditions. Multiple engine generators should be started in sequence when the peak demand limit is exceeded. When the load has fallen to within acceptable limits, the load will be automatically retransferred to the utility, and after the prescribed unloaded running cool down time, the controls will shut down the machine. Appropriate audible and visual signals should be provided to indicate the various conditions of the system. If during the operation of the system in the load demand control mode there should be a failure of utility power, the system will revert to an emergency power system, serving the essential electrical system through the system's automatic (and manual) transfer switches. Figure 5-31 shows how a large emergency power system, consisting of two on-site generators operating in parallel, might be utilized to operate in parallel with the utility to reduce utility peak demand charges.

b) *Type II—Operation Independent of the Utility.* Unlike the systems employing operation in parallel with the utility, which requires no interruption of power for its operation, operation independent of the utility requires an interruption of power to the various loads. For this reason it is suggested that loads served from the essential electrical system not be selected as those to be served by the system when it operates in the load demand control mode. Rather, such loads as noncritical electric cooking equipment; air conditioning chillers, fans, pumps, and cooling towers; electric heat and loads of a similar nature should be selected. This can be accomplished by providing a separate panel or panels designated to serve these loads and providing a system of mechanical key interlocks to allow such loads to be served either from the utility or from the generator. The system would operate as follows.

1) When the load demand controller senses that the preset peak demand is being approached, the controls will start the generating set, and operate an audible and visual signal to alert the operator of the condition. The operator should take the following steps to transfer the loads to the output of the generator:

   i) Trip the overcurrent device(s) serving the load demand control panel(s) from the utility source.

   ii) Remove the key from the key interlock device for the overcurrent device above, place it in the key interlock device for the overcurrent device(s) serving the load demand control panel(s) from the generator, and operate the key.

   iii) Close the overcurrent device(s), placing the loads on the output of the generator. When the load demand controller senses that the load has decreased to within predetermined limits, a second set of signals will be initiated, notifying the operator to manually retransfer the loads by reversing the procedure described above.

2) If during the operation of the system in load demand control mode there should be a failure of utility power, the system will revert to an emergency power system, serving the essential electrical system through the system's automatic (and manual) transfer switches.

The above system can also be arranged for complete automatic operation. With increasing use of closed transition transfer, loads can be transferred without power interruption.

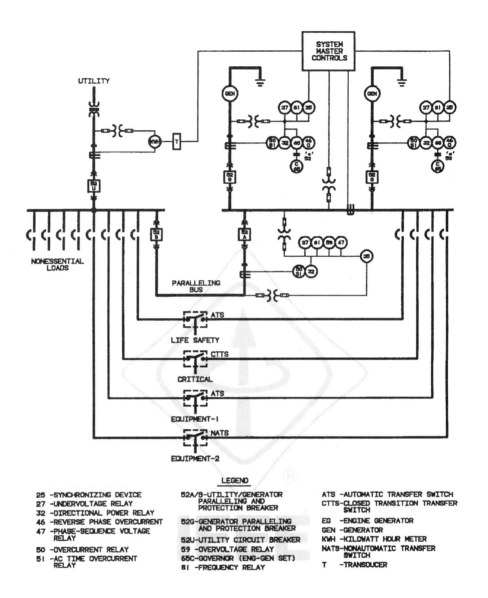

Figure 5-31—Conceptual one-line diagram illustrating the utilization of an on-site paralleled emergency generator system for utility peak load demand reduction or cogeneration in a health care facility

5.8 Cogeneration

Up to the present time, cogeneration has been applied infrequently in health care facilities. However, the combined electrical and heat demand of typical hospitals makes them ideal candidates.

A cogeneration system is defined as any system where a single source of thermal energy (fuel) drives two separate processes. An on-site generating system with heat recovery fits this definition.

In a conventional engine-driven generator set, considerable energy is dissipated in the form of heat lost to exhaust and to jacket water. In a cogeneration system, this heat loss is minimized by systems that convert the otherwise wasted heat energy to usable energy for process systems requiring steam or heat.

The electrical generating portion of the cogeneration system can operate in either of the two following ways:

— Isolated from the utility
— In parallel with the utility

When operating in parallel with the utility, in addition to the standard controls, the design must incorporate protective relaying, as required in guidelines issued by the local utility.

Figure 5-32 shows a typical cogeneration system operating in parallel with the utility. It is identical to a utility peak load demand reduction system except that the engine generator sets would be equipped with a heat recovery system. The recovered heat may be applied to domestic hot water or to absorption chilling.

A basic design objective of all utility paralleled systems is that there be an immediate separation of the two electrical power sources whenever transient phenomena, such as transmission disturbances or reclosing actions, occur on the utility power lines. Immediate separation isolates the small on-site power plant from possible damage.

The same protective relaying that protects the on-site plant from unsatisfactory utility disturbances, also serves to prevent backfeed from the on-site system into a dead utility line.

Device 52A in figure 5-27 is the circuit breaker that ties the on-site cogeneration bus to the utility service.

A typical protective relaying scheme is shown for Device 52A. An automatic synchronizer is connected across Device 52A to ensure proper conditions for paralleling. The synchronizer should control generator voltage, frequency, and phase angle to match the utility source parameters.

Protection against malfunction or abnormality when the utility service and generator(s) are operating in parallel is provided to immediately open Device 52A. Such operation ensures isolation of the two sources. This is essential to personnel safety. It ensures that the generator(s) do not backfeed the utility grid or the rest of the building load.

A typical protective relaying arrangement and circuit breaker (Device 52G) for each generator set is also shown.

An additional accessory to consider for the generator control system is a Var/Power Factor (Var/pf) controller. A Var/pf controller biases the generator voltage regulator so that a constant operating power factor is maintained on the generator. Generator voltage can therefore track the normal excursions of the utility service without kilovoltampere overloading.

The Var/pf controller continuously adjusts generator field excitation to produce a generator current that varies inversely with system voltage. Because the power factor is set at a constant 0.9 pf, the actual load on the generator in kilovoltampere remains constant. At constant kilovoltampere and constant power factor, the real work load on the engine also remains constant, assuring optimal life for the generator set.

In parallel with utility applications, the speed of the engine does not vary; therefore, the governor will not call for changes in fuel setting. A loading control interacts with the governor through the load sharing lines to cause kilowatt output to go to a preset level. The control measures the input from the utility source and causes the output of the generator to vary to maintain constant power import from or export to the utility.

System control layout varies from installation to installation, so that only a general idea of design can be given here. To ensure that the system meets all specialized design requirements, including operating in parallel with the utility, the system designer would work very closely with the equipment manufacturers and the utility company during the preliminary design stages for guidance in selecting appropriate controls and relaying to assure proper coordination.

5.9 Determination of mean period between service overhauls

In order to determine compliance with the exception to 3-3.2.1.5 of NFPA 99-1996, the engineer should establish that the mean period between service overhauls will not be decreased to less than three years. In order to determine the mean period between service overhauls, the expected hours of operation of the engine as an emergency power unit, the expected hours of operation in the peak demand reduction or cogeneration mode, and the manufacturer's anticipated mean operating hours between major service overhauls must be known. A good rule of thumb, based on a high quality of maintenance, is shown in table 5-2.

Table 5-2—Mean period between service overhauls

Engine speed	Minor overhaul[a] operating hours	Major overhaul operating hours
1 800 r/m	6 000 and 12 000	18 000
1 200 r/m	8 000 and 16 000	24 000

[a]A minor overhaul is defined as replacement of valves, inserts, valve guides, injection capsules, rings, and gaskets.

5.10 Elevator emergency power selector systems

The need for limited continuous elevator service in hospitals, nursing homes and related health care facilities is obvious. For this reason every applicable code and standard requires that such limited electrical service be maintained. For hospitals, both NFPA 99-1996 and the

NEC require that elevators be on the equipment system of the essential electrical system, and both require the following:

> Elevator service that will reach every patient floor, ground floor, and floors on which are located surgical suites and obstetrical delivery suites. This shall include connections for cab lighting and control and signal systems.

> In instances where interruption of power would result in elevators stopping between floors, provide throwover facilities to allow the temporary operation of any elevator for the release of patients or other persons who may be confined between floors.

This does not require that all elevators in multi-bank installations be served from the essential electrical system, but does require that each elevator be capable of being connected to the system one at a time on a selective basis.

General practice dictates that one elevator, on a selected basis, be connected to the essential system, with provisions to disconnect this elevator from the system and to connect any other.

The obvious advantage of such a system is to keep the use of the alternate source generator within reasonable limits without unduly compromising passenger safety or the movement of patients during an interruption of normal power.

In the design of such systems, several potential problems should be addressed. Solutions to deal with regenerative power and the problems associated with providing proper controls to establish sequencing of the elevators when they are receiving power from the generators need to be considered. Special consideration must be given to elevators utilizing silicon controlled rectifiers in lieu of motor generator sets. Elevator manufacturers proposing the use of such equipment should be consulted during design in order to avoid complications.

5.10.1 Problems associated with regenerative power

The nature of the electrical load imposed by elevators on either the normal or emergency power supply is very similar to that imposed by any other piece of alternating current motor-driven equipment of equivalent horsepower, except in one very important respect that is of major consideration to the electrical engineer. Under certain load conditions, an elevator actually generates electrical energy that is fed back into the power supply. For example, a fully loaded elevator moving in the down direction is actually producing energy that ultimately takes the form of electric power that is also supplied to the elevator. This same situation also occurs to a lesser degree when an empty elevator is traveling up. This phenomenon produces two problems that must be dealt with in the design of the emergency power system. The first of these problems applies only where a relatively small emergency generating set is utilized, in which case the regenerative power from the elevator can actually cause overspeed of the emergency generating set and possible speed governor tripping. This problem is solved by making certain that the total emergency power load that is connected to the emergency generator is at least twice the size of the elevator load. If the load is distributed in this manner, the regenerated power from the elevator system is easily absorbed by the other devices that comprise the emergency power load. For example, if the total electric load imposed by the elevators that are required to operate on emergency power is 150 kW, then the total emergency power load, including these elevators, should not be less than 300 kW.

The second of these two regenerative problems becomes more evident during the actual transfer from normal to emergency power, or from emergency to normal. If this transfer is permitted to take place at a time when the elevator system is regenerating voltage that is out of phase with the power source to which it is being reconnected, power transients can be introduced into the supply source which may trip the circuit breakers controlling the power supply. The solution to this problem requires that the transfer function take place only when the sources are in phase or the elevators are at rest. Intentional time intervals to permit the elevators to come to rest before transferring to the alternate power source is one solution. Operation is normally initiated via control contacts on the transfer switch.

A transfer switch with an "in-phase monitor" is another solution. These devices are capable of monitoring the phase angles of both power supplies, and signaling for transfer when the normal power and emergency power are in phase (see figure 5-14). The transfer is then made automatically and the timed intervals as described in the preceding paragraph are not required when this device is furnished. It is not necessary to have the elevators at rest prior to restoring the service from emergency to normal power, or when switching to emergency power during a routine test of the emergency generator set while normal power is available.

A second consideration would be the use of a timed center-off position transfer switch. This device would normally function with an offtime of 25 cycles to possibly 60 cycles. It may also be furnished with time delays beyond these values if desired. Utilizing such a device would allow normal starting current surges for motor applications.

5.10.2 Sequence of elevator operation on emergency power

On normal power supply failure, all elevators will be brought to a stop by the automatic application of a brake which brings the car to a rest and holds it in that position. This almost invariably results in "trapping" elevator passengers in the stalled car between floors. After the establishment of emergency power and the expiration of the above interval, one elevator in each group of elevators descends automatically to a lower floor, where it parks with its doors open in an inoperative condition. Each elevator in each group then goes through this same sequence one at a time until all elevators have returned to the lower floor. At this time, one preselected elevator in each group resumes normal automatic operation. The elevator control system prevents any more than one elevator in each group from operating at any given time in order to avoid overloading the emergency power supply source. All elevators will continue to be illuminated.

When the system is ready to return to normal power service, each elevator in emergency condition will stop at the next available floor, where it will park inoperative with its doors open. At this time, the system can be transferred back to normal power operation and all elevators can resume normal service to the building. The above operation requires that a signal be provided to the elevator control equipment indicating that the system is ready to transfer back to normal power. This signal must be given prior to the time at which the transfer back to normal power is to occur. If an elevator has been removed from automatic service for inspection, independent service, fire service, etc., it does not receive an automatic return signal.

If an elevator failure occurs during the sequential lowering operation that takes place on the establishment of emergency power, that car is automatically removed from service, and the next car in order assumes the lowering sequence. If an elevator is in normal service operating on emergency power and it becomes inoperative, that car is automatically removed from service, and another elevator starts operating from the emergency power supply.

Examples of available options. The following are available as emergency features.

— *Automatic car selection, express to lobby.* In the event of normal power failure, the elevators can be arranged to automatically return on emergency power to a pre-programmed floor, one car at a time. Operational features such as independent service should be overridden allowing the elevator return. After all cars have been returned to this floor, a preselected elevator shall remain on emergency power. Emergency power should be supplied through the normal machine room feeders. A pair of wires carrying emergency power is supplied to the controller designated by the elevator contractor in each machine room to supply a signal indicating power failure and activation of emergency operation. All other controls and provisions for operation of each elevator on the emergency power supply are generally provided and installed by the elevator contractor.

— *Manual car selection, express to lobby.* In the event of normal power failure, the elevators should be controlled by a manual selector switch located in the lobby control panel. When actuated, this manual selector switch selects which elevator will receive emergency power. After receiving emergency power, the elevator will automatically express directly to the floor where the selector switch is located. After all elevators have been returned in this manner, a single elevator may be selected to continuously operate. Operational features such as independent service are overridden, allowing the elevator return. Emergency power is supplied through the normal machine room feeders. A pair of control wires carrying emergency power should be supplied to the controller designated by the elevator contractor in each machine room to supply a signal indicating power failure and activation of emergency operation. All other control and provision for operation of each elevator on the emergency power supply is generally provided and installed by the elevator contractor.

— *Automatic car selection, stop at nearest floor.* In the event of a normal power failure, the elevators can be arranged to automatically start on emergency power, travel to the nearest floor and shut down. This is done one car at a time. Operational features such as independent service must be overridden to allow this operation. After all cars have been stopped at a floor, a preselected elevator remains on emergency power. Emergency power is supplied through the normal machine room feeders. A pair of control wires carrying emergency power should be supplied to the controller designated by the elevator contractor in each machine room to supply a signal indicating power failure and activation of emergency operation. All other controls and provision for operation of each elevator on the emergency power supply are generally provided and installed by the elevator contractor.

— *Integral controls.* All controls for the elevators, including all of the equipment required for the automatic power selection, should be provided as an integral part of the elevator system. Elevator specifications should be checked to see that these features are included.

— *Independent controls for emergency power transfer.* In some cases, primarily in existing facilities, it may be impractical to incorporate the controls and devices required for emergency power transfer into the elevator manufacturer's equipment. Systems are available that provide group mounted automatic transfer switches, control logic devices and sensing, and a remote selector panel. The operation of the system is essentially as described for the integral systems. The system should be carefully coordinated with the elevator manufacturer to ensure proper operation. One advantage of the independent system is that it can be designed such that the equipment system automatic transfer switch can be smaller than with integral systems (see figure 5-32).

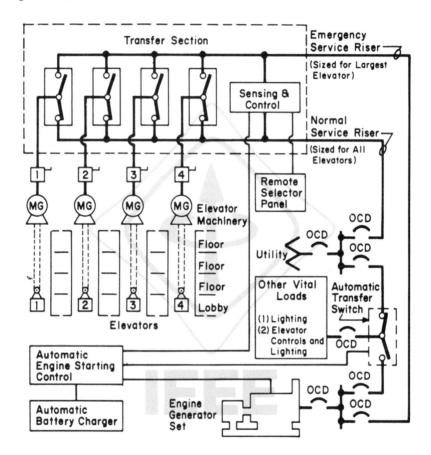

Figure 5-32—Elevator emergency power transfer system

5.10.3 Summary

In the design of emergency power requirements for elevator systems, the following items should be considered:

a) Determination of number and location of elevators that will be required to operate on emergency power.

b)   Determination of whether regenerated power will be a problem, and if so, determination of steps required to absorb it.

c)   Determination of required control connections between the emergency power system and the elevator control system for selected transfer scheme.

5.11 Uninterruptible power supply (UPS) systems

UPS systems are highly efficient (85–92%) power converting devices that provide a regulated ac voltage at their output terminals regardless of the quality of the source at their input terminals.

In the event of a total power loss at the UPS input, output power is generally provided by means of a bank of batteries. An inherent, additional benefit of the UPS is its ability to filter spikes and power aberrations from the ac source between the input and output terminals. These power problems could result from natural causes or buffer line disturbances on the utility power, or they could be caused by disturbances, such as load switching, within the facility itself.

Uninterruptible power is generally not specified by code requirements for hospitals or health care facilities. However, UPS systems are increasingly being incorporated into such electrical designs. Typical applications include backup support for sensitive laboratory and diagnostic equipment, life-support equipment in intensive care units, data processing systems, and for illumination in life-support areas.

UPS systems are generally static (power electronic) devices, although there are hybrid systems available that combine static and mechanical components. It should be noted that static UPS systems are nonlinear loads that cause harmonic distortions on the distribution system. A careful evaluation should be made to prevent the distortion from having adverse effects on other loads and equipment including overheating of the engine generator set(s) [B4]. Acceptable harmonic distortion should be specified to ensure full warranty.

A static UPS consists of a rectifier to convert the input ac power to dc, a bank of batteries, an inverter to reconstitute the ac sine waves, and a static switch. Refer to figure 5-33 for a typical single-line diagram.

The static switch is part of a bypass system that provides a means to bypass the critical load back to utility power without interruption in the event of a system short circuit or overload, an inverter malfunction, or for planned maintenance.

The battery most often used in UPS installations is the lead-calcium cell. It is usually used due to its low cost, its discharge characteristics, its low hydrogen evolution, and consequently its low water usage. It is extremely important to be able to predict the number of discharge cycles and the depth of discharge when specifying batteries for a UPS system. Alternate batteries that can handle more and deeper discharge include lead-antimony and pure lead batteries.

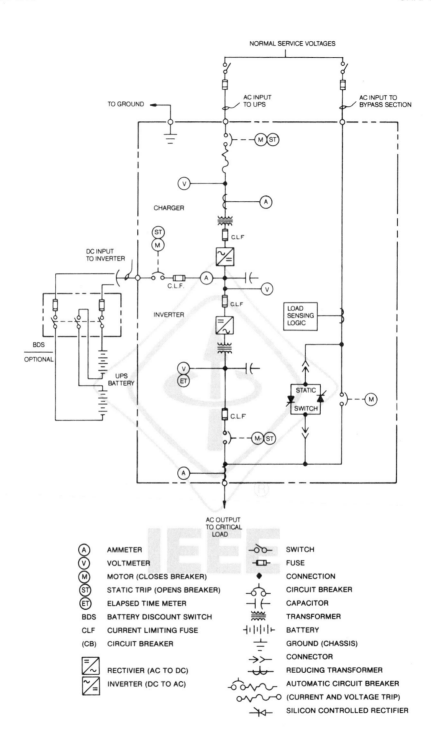

Figure 5-33—Typical UPS one line

The normal UPS configuration is called "reverse transfer." This term is used because the output of the UPS inverter supplies power to the critical load during normal operation. The system transfers to the utility only in one of the alternate modes of operation, as previously noted.

UPS systems are frequently fed from the load side of a transfer switch for sustained operation. Closed transition transfer switches are becoming more frequently recommended as the transfer device by UPS system manufacturers to reduce stresses caused by the momentary interruption experienced with open transition switches [B3].

The rectifier is supplied from the utility and in turn supplies dc power to the input of the inverter. In the event of loss of utility power, the inverter receives its power from the battery. When the input voltage and frequency returns to the predetermined level, the rectifier begins supplying power to the inverter and also begins recharging the discharged battery bank.

Reverse transfer UPSs can supply single-phase or three-phase outputs. Single-phase output units can have either a single-phase or a three-phase input. Typical single-phase units are sized to supply a load ranging from 0.5–50 kW, and three-phase units from 15–600 kW. UPS manufacturers have the capability of paralleling units for additional capacity. They can also offer a forward transfer unit in the 0.5–10 kW range that prepackages the UPS and batteries in a common enclosure.

The design of a UPS system involves both electrical and environmental considerations. The first step is to calculate the UPS module ratings (rectifier, battery, inverter, static switch, and wraparound maintenance bypass switch combination). Determining factors are the present load, power factor, diversity of application, and future load additions and deletions. An alternate approach would be to size the UPS module to handle the anticipated load and the battery bank for the present load. Expansion can be achieved by paralleling an additional battery bank in the future. A common reserve time for the battery bank is 15 min.

The power connections to a UPS involve the battery bank, the input to the rectifier, the bypass circuit, and the output. The output and bypass feeders should be sized to handle the output capability of the UPS module. The rectifier is sized to handle the output of the inverter plus recharging a discharged bank of batteries. The input feeder and the generator set (when applicable) must be sized larger than the load to handle the additional current. The battery feeder is determined by the maximum dc discharge current and to limit voltage drop to specified conditions. As the battery begins discharging, the dc current rises as the voltage falls. Maximum dc current occurs at the point of low dc voltage shutoff. A rule of thumb is to allow a maximum 2 V drop in the conductors (calculated at maximum dc current).

A separate disconnecting/overcurrent device should be provided for both the input and the bypass feeders. Additionally, an overcurrent/disconnection device should be incorporated in the total scheme and located near the battery bank for required protection. In larger UPS modules, care should be taken to limit the dc voltage to 250 V as required by the NEC. A convenient method of achieving this would be to split the battery bank into two equal segments and connect the two across the center pole of a three-pole battery disconnect switch, as shown in the single-line diagram.

Isolation of the UPS module can be incorporated into the design through a maintenance bypass scheme. This is accomplished by first placing the UPS in a bypass mode, then closing a maintenance bypass device, and last, opening a nonautomatic circuit breaker or unfused device at the output of the UPS. The UPS is then completely isolated both from the critical load and from the building electrical system. This transition is accomplished without an interruption in the power supply to the critical load.

UPS system manufacturers can supply a remote annunciator panel, when specified, to monitor the status of the UPS system. This feature is good practice and should be located in the same area as code-required annunciator panels.

A final electrical consideration in the UPS design is the coordination between sizing of the protective devices at the output of the UPS inverter (usually a circuit breaker) and those on the load side. Consideration should also be given to the same coordination for the situation when the UPS is in either its bypass or maintenance bypass modes.

The following are three environmental considerations in the installation of a UPS:

a)   The heat output of the UPS

b)   Maximum ambient operating temperature and relative humidity of both the UPS module and the batteries

c)   The hydrogen emission of the batteries

The heat output of the UPS is a measure of the module efficiency (typically 85–92% at full load). This heat must be removed to prevent exceeding the maximum operating temperature of both the UPS module and the batteries. Generally, the maximum operating temperature of the UPS module is considerably higher than a temperature that would adversely affect the batteries.

Provisions should be made for sufficient diffusion and ventilation of hydrogen emitted from the batteries to prevent the accumulation of an explosive mixture. This means keeping the hydrogen from reaching a level of 1% by volume of the room. If the battery room is air-conditioned, the exhaust air should not be returned to the building's air distribution system. The battery room should have its own exhaust system connected to the outdoors.

Ideally, the batteries should be located in their own room. If the batteries are not the cabinet-mounted, valve-regulated type, a substantial screen should partition them off to limit access only to qualified persons. There are a variety of rack configurations available. Consult the battery manufacturer and the UPS manufacturer to determine proper space and location limitations. Consult the building code to determine the seismic zone and specify seismic-rated battery racks accordingly. An eyewash area should be located in the vicinity of the battery bank in accordance with the Occupational Safety and Health Administration (OSHA).

UPS systems are state-of-the-art designs to which technical improvements are constantly being made. An example of this is the use of microprocessor diagnostics that enable the rapid identification of equipment problems based on critical point monitoring. This feature is of particular benefit to the health care industry where up-time of the UPS is important to its proper operation.

5.12 Maintenance

NFPA 99-1996, generally considered a minimum by authorities having jurisdiction, requires certain testing and maintenance procedures. Appendix C, included in NFPA 99-1996 for information purposes only, provides a maintenance guide to assist in the establishment of a maintenance program.

NEMA, NFPA, and equipment manufacturers have publications prescribing recommended minimum requirements. Rapid diagnosis of trouble or system failure is made easier by performing the acceptance testing and maintenance procedures established by the equipment manufacturers.

Unless space is critical, the designer should lay out the generator based on the manufacturer's largest dimension recommendations. Working space for doors, oil drainer, and minor maintenance should be considered.

For new facilities, where testing and maintenance programs have not been previously established prior to start-up, a manual should be prepared that includes the following:

a) General description of operation
b) Manufacturer's technical manuals
c) Test log
d) Maintenance log
e) Piping diagrams
f) Wiring diagrams
g) Spare parts list
h) Special tools
i) Source of emergency assistance
j) Maintenance schedule

Testing may be automatic or nonautomatic. In either case, personnel are required. Maintenance personnel may grow lax when automatic exercisers are used as they are likely to skip the witnessing of the test. Many hospitals prefer manual testing since there is always the risk of a nonscheduled surgery being performed at the time an automatic timer may call for a load interruption test. For installations with limited personnel capability, a maintenance and testing contract may be desirable.

When transfer switches are installed in remote infrequently accessed locations, it is good practice to provide an annunciator at the building operator's central control room to permit remote monitoring and testing. As building automation becomes more popular, the ability to properly monitor, test, and control the emergency power system should keep in step to improve reliability and performance as well as encourage more frequent testing and maintenance.

When the emergency generator set is out of service for maintenance or repair, the essential loads may be vulnerable in the event a utility power failure should occur. The emergency power distribution system designer should make provision in the design of the system so that a portable generator can be readily connected during these periods. See NEC section 700-5(b). Nonautomatic push-button operated transfer switches, such as described in 5.3.12, may help to readily facilitate the connection of a portable generator into the system.

5.13 References

This chapter shall be used in conjunction with the following publications:

ASME A17.1-1993, Elevators and Escalators.[3]

EGSA 100B-1992, Performance Standard for Engine Cranking Batteries Used with Engine Generator Sets.[4]

EGSA 100C-1992, Performance Standard for Battery Charges for Engine Starting Batteries (Constant Potential Static Type).

IEEE Std 446-1995, IEEE Recommended Practice for Emergency and Standby Power Systems for Industrial and Commercial Applications (IEEE Orange Book) (ANSI).[5]

NEMA ICS 10-1993, Industrial Control and Systems, AC Transfer Switch Equipment.[6]

NEMA PE5-1985 (R 1993), Utility Battery Chargers (ANSI).

NFPA 20-1996, Installation of Centrifugal Fire Pumps.[7]

NFPA 70-1996, National Electrical Code® (NEC®).

NFPA 70B-1994, Electrical Equipment Maintenance.

NFPA 70E-1995, Electrical Safety Requirements for Employee Workplaces.

NFPA 72-1996, National Fire Alarm Code.

NFPA 75-1995, Protection of Electronic Computer/Data Processing Equipment.

---

[3]ASME publications are available from the American Society of Mechanical Engineers, 22 Law Drive, Fairfield, NJ 07007.

[4]EGSA documents can be obtained from the Electrical Generating Systems Association, 1650 South Dixie Hwy, FL 5, Boca Raton, FL 33432.

[5]IEEE publications are available from the Institute of Electrical and Electronics Engineers, 445 Hoes Lane, P.O. Box 1331, Piscataway, NJ 08855-1331.

[6]NEMA publications are available from the National Electrical Manufacturers Association, 1300 N. 17th St., Ste. 1847, Rosslyn, VA 22209.

[7]NFPA publications are available from Publications Sales, National Fire Protection Association, 1 Batterymarch Park, P.O. Box 9101, Quincy, MA 02269-9101.

NFPA 99-1996, Health Care Facilities.

NFPA 101-1994, Life Safety Code®.

NFPA 110-1996, Emergency and Standby Power Systems.

NFPA 111-1996, Stored Energy Emergency and Standby Power Systems.

NFPA 418-1995, Standard for Heliports.

SAE J537-94, Storage Batteries.[8]

UL 1008-1989, Automatic Transfer Switches (DoD).[9]

5.14 Bibiliography

Additional information may be found in the following sources:

[B1] "Area Protection Assures Emergency Power When Failures Occur Down-Stream," *AscoFacts*, vol. 2, no. 6., Automatic Switch Company, Florham Park, NJ.

[B2] Averhiil, E. A., "Fast Transfer Test of Power Station Auxiliaries." *IEEE Transactions on Power Apparatus and Systems*, vol. PAS-95, no. 3, May/June 1977.

[B3] Castenschiold, R., "Closed Transition Switching of Essential Loads." *Transactions on Industry Applications,* vol. 25, no. 3, May/June.

[B4] Davis, W. K. and Stratford, R. P., "Operation of UPS on Emergency Generation, " Petroleum and Chemical Industry Conference, IEEE PCIC 1987 Annual Meeting.

[B5] Fischer, M. J., "Designing Electrical Systems for Hospitals," vol. 5 of *Techniques of Electrical Construction and Design*. New York: McGraw-Hill, 1979.

[B6] Gill, J. D., "Transfer of Motor Load Between Out-of-Phase Sources," *Conference Record, Industry Applications Society,* IEEE-IAS 1978 Annual Meeting.

[B7] Kelly, A. R., "Relay Response to Motor Residual Voltage During Automatic Transfers," *AIEE Transactions*, vol. 74, pt. II, Applications and Industry, Paper 55-427, Sept.1955.

---

[8]SAE publications are available from Customer Service Department, SAE International, 400 Commonwealth Drive, Warrendale, PA 15096-0001.
[9]UL publications are available from Underwriters Laboratories, Inc., 333 Pfingsten Road, Northbrook, IL 60062-2096, USA.

[B8] Lewis, D. G. and Marsh, W. D., "Transfer of Steam-Electric Generating-Station Auxiliary Busses," *AIEE Transactions*, vol. 74, pt. III, Power Apparatus and Systems, Paper 55-96, June 1955.

[B9] *On-Site Power Generation: A Reference Book.* EGSA, Chapter 7, p.138, 1993.

[B10] Squires, R. B., "Analytical Studies of Large Induction Motor Behavior During Bus Transfer." Gibbs & Hill, Inc. A paper presented at the conference for Protective Relay Engineers, Texas A&M University, College Station, Texas, 27 Apr. 1973.

Chapter 6
Electrical safety and grounding

6.1 General discussion

6.1.1 Scope

This chapter discusses the basic engineering involved in obtaining electrical safety in health care facilities through proper design of the electrical distribution system. It also provides a perspective on the electrical hazards in hospitals so the engineer has the background to design an electrical system to mitigate these hazards. Factors involved in making design decisions regarding electrical safety and some of the various options will be discussed.

6.1.2 Introduction

During the period from 1940 to 1970 there were serious problems and accidents in hospitals that required major additions and changes to the codes and standards for health care facilities. Many of these changes involved the facilities' electrical distribution systems and were a result of the increase in the complexity of procedures, equipment, and instrumentation used. The design engineer should know and understand the latest codes and standards so that designs and options regarding electrical safety may be presented to the hospital accurately.

The general level of safety requirements for electrical devices and installations has increased over the past years. Examples of this are the continuing changes to UL standards, the National Electrical Code® (NEC®) (NFPA 70-1996)[1], and NFPA 99-1996. The NEC or any other NFPA code or standard can only be enforced if it is adopted as being applicable by an authority having jurisdiction. Any governmental body or administrative agency may or may not incorporate NFPA codes or standards into its own health building or construction codes. Even if the NFPA codes or standards are not incorporated into local codes, it is good practice to at least review them. Good electrical safety often means going beyond the code as this is only the minimum requirement. Understanding local standards is mandatory for any designer.

This chapter will concentrate on special requirements of a health care facility over and above those normally required for a commercial facility. Principal differences are in layout, care of installation, quality of components, and special devices required.

Since all of the details contained in referenced documents cannot be duplicated in this chapter, it is highly recommended that these be obtained, studied, and their applicability to a particular facility determined.

The patients in a hospital are either ill or incapacitated and rely on others for care, and as such, they are often physically incapable of taking self-protective action. These patients may be brought in contact with electrical equipment routinely, and this may take place in a wet

---

[1]Information on references can be found in 6.9.

environment or in the presence of flammable vapors, such as alcohol or ether, plus supplemental oxygen. The patient may also be subjected to invasive procedures of various types.

The design shall take into consideration the electrical safety of not only the patient, but also of the nurse, doctor, and any other health care provider working in the environment. Hazards can exist not only in the familiar ampere ranges, but also at the milliampere/microampere levels, and short duration short-circuit kiloampere ranges.

Among basic safety features required are insulation, overcurrent protection, adequate dependable power (especially for life support equipment), reliable grounding, and coordinated protection to guard against shock or burns from leakage and fault currents.

6.2 Physiological parameters

An understanding of some of the physiological parameters involved should give the designer of hospital care facilities a better understanding of the factors involved in the development of a safe environment for the patient.

6.2.1 Cell excitability

The individual nerve and muscle cells have a small inside-to-outside potential of the order of 90 mV because of chemical differences. Excitation of the cell for transmission of a nerve impulse or muscle contraction can be produced by chemical or electrical imbalance from the normal resting state. The levels involved are nonlinear in amplitude and time so that creation of perceived shock and contraction is not simple. To a certain extent, this explains the variances in expressing levels of shock in ranges rather than specific values. There are many variables of nonlinearities present.

6.2.2 Nerve reaction to electrical stimuli

Nerve reaction to electrical stimuli involves sending a message to the brain that exposure to an unsafe condition has occurred. A current density at a nerve location will cause stimulation to one or more nerve cells, and in different areas of the body, may create different sensations.

6.2.3 Muscle reaction to electrical stimuli

A current introduced into the heart through the diffused connection provided by a liquid-filled catheter may cause no cardiac reaction, while the same current could produce a cardiac reaction if introduced through a very small metal electrode. At low levels, the nonlinearities become a factor, so that the difference between a constant current source and a constant voltage source becomes important. Current density is an extremely important factor.

Faulty equipment that produces improper stimulation of the cardiac muscle can create disorganized contractions called fibrillation, with little or no pumping of blood. Electrical stimuli will cause a severe contraction of hand muscles that can create grasping of an energized conductive object without the ability to let go. Heavy currents across the chest can cause contraction of muscles, adversely affecting breathing and possibly causing suffocation.

6.2.4 Tissue reaction to heat

The principle of current flowing through resistance, thus generating resistant heat, can cause harmful burning in a tissue. In surgical procedures, this process is beneficially used for cutting tissue and coagulation of bleeding sites.

6.2.5 Body/tissue resistance

Body tissue has, in general, a specific resistance that is useful in calculating expected currents. During defibrillation, where massive currents are produced through large electrodes, good electrical contact with the skin is necessary.

The skin, in general, provides a high-impedance barrier to most sources from which leakage currents could flow. Well-prepared contacts for electrocardiographs (EKGs), etc., provide about 1000 Ω between electrodes. Dry, calloused skin may have an impedance approaching 1 000 000 Ω. Wet or saturated body tissue may have considerably less than 1000 Ω of resistance.

6.3 Shock levels

The susceptibility of humans to electrical current has often been demonstrated in power line accidents. Burns, ventricular fibrillation, respiratory paralysis, hemorrhage, and neural dysfunctions are frequent results of contact by a human body between a power source and ground. These effects can also be caused in daily work hazards through misuse of electrical appliances and wiring.

The following values in 6.3.1 through 6.3.4 relate to alternating current sustained by the human body.

6.3.1 Perception

The lowest levels of current that are perceptible to a person start at about 100 μA through a very sharp point, resulting in a high current density. A large contact area, such as a bed handrail, may require 1 mA for perception.

6.3.2 Contraction

Arm muscle contraction and pain may develop with 1–5 mA, and is assured at 10 mA.

6.3.3 No-let-go

Uncontrolled contraction (no-let-go), can start at levels of 6 mA and higher. Up to 30 mA, these reactions increase in intensity, and although such currents are usually non-fatal, temporary respiratory paralysis can occur. Above 30 mA, the chances of a fatality from a variety of causes, including ventricular fibrillation, increase.

For the general patient, the above levels may be lower. The patient may be weak, helpless to free himself, suffering from a damaged or stressed heart, an infant, in a wet environment, or experiencing an increased electrical sensitivity as a result of drug therapy.

There is another class of patient for whom the level of dangerous current is appreciably lower. For these patients, direct electrical pathways to the patient's heart may exist through pacing wires or fluid-filled catheters. Current in the range of 20–300 μA at 60 Hz is sufficient to cause ventricular fibrillation under such circumstances.

6.3.4 Cardiac fibrillation

Cardiac fibrillation is a phenomena in which the muscles of the heart contract in a disorganized manner so that little blood is pumped. Cardiac fibrillation is a complex phenomenon related to concentration, location, duration of current, and timing in the cardiac cycle. Part of the complication of determining a threshold level is that the mere physical placement of an electrode within the heart may cause fibrillation with no current. Under controlled conditions when fibrillation is intentionally produced by direct stimulation, currents of 80 μA and higher are usually required from constant current sources.

Other clinical parameters that may cause the heart to become susceptible to induced fibrillation in the presence of low levels of 60 Hz are the following:

a) Alternating current and electrolyte imbalance
b) Myocardial ischemia
c) Hypothermia
d) Hypoxia
e) The use of drugs such as digitalis, alcohol, or vasodilators

Good engineering design today sets 10 μA at 60 Hz as the maximum allowable leakage current available from any device having leads that may enter the heart.

6.4 Areas of potentially increasing hazards

Subclauses 6.4.1 through 6.4.15 are arranged in a general order of increasing electrical hazards. No such arrangement is absolute as practices, usage, and maintenance vary. In addition, for most areas the true increase from type-to-type is so slight, this order can easily be changed.

6.4.1 Waiting rooms, offices

Good standard commercial specifications can be followed in these areas.

6.4.2 Corridors

Corridors historically have been high abuse areas as far as electrical receptacles are concerned. Therefore, receptacles should be selected to withstand heavy physical abuse. Oftentimes, corridor receptacles are used for supplying power to cleaning machines, which are taken into a patient room. Requirements would therefore also include insulated equipment grounding conductor and metal conduit. Hospital grade receptacles or equivalent are recommended.

6.4.3 Psychiatric patient room

A psychiatric patient room is to be treated as a general care patient room. For the number of circuits and outlets, see the NEC and NFPA 99-1996. While not common, it is possible to have a psychiatric intensive care unit (ICU) or coronary care unit (CCU) room, in which case it would be treated as a critical patient care area as outlined in the aforementioned references.

Insulated equipment grounding conductor and metal conduit, as well as tamperproof receptacles, are mandatory. Hospital grade receptacles are required.

6.4.4 General medical care

A number of circuits and receptacles should conform to the NEC and NFPA 99-1996 (Chapter 3). Insulated equipment grounding conductor and metal conduit are mandatory. It is required that all receptacles be hospital grade or equivalent.

6.4.5 Critical care patient room

The number of circuits and receptacles should conform to the NEC and NFPA 99-1996. Insulated equipment grounding conductor and metal conduit are mandatory. Emergency power provisions are also mandatory by these standards. It is required that all receptacles be hospital grade. While isolated power is not mandatory, it is often used in these areas where invasive procedures are common. When isolated power is used, the same specifications shall be followed as when it is used in an anesthetizing location. These specifications can be found in the NEC or NFPA 99-1996 (Chapter 3).

6.4.6 Recovery rooms

This is a very difficult area to categorize since areas under this heading can widely vary in use and application. Most often it is an intensive nursing area where the patient is held and observed until he or she recovers from anesthesia. The area should be equipped with insulated equipment grounding conductor, emergency power service, and metal conduit. It is required that all receptacles be hospital grade or equivalent. If the hospital does not plan to use the recovery room for patients requiring life support and invasive monitoring, it should be treated as a critical patient care area. Most hospitals, however, take critical patients directly to the ICU or CCU rather than hold these patients in the recovery room.

The codes do not address the recovery room with regard to the number of receptacles and circuits required for patients.

Consultations with local code authorities and with hospital personnel using this area are recommended before determining these service requirements.

6.4.7 Wet locations

The use of ground-fault circuit interrupters (GFCIs) is appropriate and required for areas such as those used for hydrotherapy. Where power interruption caused by the tripping of GFCIs cannot be tolerated, the use of isolated power is required by the NEC.

A controversy exists as to whether patient dialysis units should be considered wet locations. It depends upon the design of the unit, the type of equipment, and the intended operation. Operating or procedures rooms that often have spilled liquids, lots of metallic grounded objects, and grounded drains need GFCIs or isolated power if interruption of power is not acceptable. Where flammable inhalation anesthesia is used, isolated power is required by the NEC at the time of this writing.

6.4.8 Laboratories

The special precautions for laboratories relate to the type of receptacle to be used. These should be the best grade available. Where these are mounted in a continuous raceway, it is very important to use a good grade of receptacle. Extra care is needed in specifying bonding between receptacle and raceway and various raceway sections in any single location or room. Insulated equipment grounding conductor is highly recommended and may be required by local codes.

6.4.9 Outpatient care units with invasive procedures

Follow the same specifications as those for an equivalent area for inpatient units.

6.4.10 Heart catheterization rooms

Follow grounding procedures as outlined in the NEC and NFPA 99-1996. Determine whether this is a multifunction room with hospital administration, and if it is used as a general anesthesia area, follow anesthetizing location specifications as given in the NEC and NFPA 99-1996. Careful and precise grounding, and hospital grade receptacles are mandatory in this area. It is recommended that at least one grounding jack be provided since some devices used for dye injection require a redundant ground.

6.4.11 Operating rooms (ORs) in which only local anesthetic agents are used

There are times when this area would not have to receive complete treatment as an inhalation anesthetizing location. However, documentation of the intent of use should be obtained from the hospital administration and careful review with local code authorities should be made. In many cases the facts will indicate a full treatment as an anesthetizing location.

6.4.12 Inhalation anesthetizing locations

Follow specifications as they appear in the NEC and NFPA 99-1996 (Chapter 3). Insulated equipment grounding conductor and hospital grade receptacles are mandatory in these locations.

6.4.13 Inhalation anesthetizing locations that become wet locations

This covers almost all ORs, with the exception of some highly specialized areas (such as those exclusively used for ophthalmology). Follow the specifications for "Wet Locations" such as shown in the NEC in addition to the specifications for "Anesthetizing Locations" in the NEC and NFPA 99-1996 (Chapter 3). Insulated equipment grounding conductor, hospital grade receptacles, and metallic conduit are all mandatory. Isolated power may be required in these areas. Emergency power requirements should be provided as specified in NFPA 99-1996 (Chapter 8).

6.4.14 Inhalation anesthetizing locations in which invasive thoracle procedures are performed

These specifications are the same as 6.4.12 or 6.4.13 as appropriate.

6.4.15 Inhalation anesthetizing locations in which flammable anesthetizing agents are used

These specifications are the same as 6.4.12, except follow additional requirements as outlined for "Hazardous Location" in the NEC and NFPA 99-1996 (Annex 2).

6.5 Fire and explosion hazards

6.5.1 Flammable anesthetizing agents

Many of the requirements for electrical safety were developed to minimize the fire and explosion hazards when ether and other flammable agents were used. The use of flammable anesthetics in the OR and the potential problem of explosion required that special electrical safeguards be developed. Since flammable gases can be ignited by static electric discharge, comprehensive methods minimizing the buildup of static charge were developed and used. These included high-impedance conductive floors, conductive footware, clothing for minimum generation of static charge, high-impedance conductivity of elastomeric tubing used within the anesthesia airway path, and grounding of patient electrical devices and exposed metal. Isolation transformers were installed and monitored to indicate when the first line-to-ground fault current would exceed a microampere level or where the arc from the current could ignite the gas.

Unfortunately, the concentrations of ether used for anesthetizing purposes are those that are the most explosive. Most explosions have either occurred within the anesthetizing machine or within the patient. Static discharge, as well as sparks from electrically powered devices, introduced in the explosive atmosphere can cause fires and explosions. Since most flammable anesthetizing agents are heavier than air, the area in an anesthetizing area up to the 5 ft (1.52 m) level shall be treated as a Class I, Group D location as covered by the NEC.

The use of flammable anesthetizing agents is continually decreasing, and as a result, the designer must establish the client's intentions in this regard.

Many new ORs are being designed for exclusive use of nonflammable inhalation anesthetizing agents. The current NEC and NFPA 99-1996 (Annex 2) both require the use of isolated power in all ORs that use flammable inhalation anesthetizing agents. The use of isolated power measurably reduces the risk of electrical shock and completely eliminates the risk of explosion due to flammable inhalation anesthetizing agents.

6.5.2 Flammable cleaning and preparation agents

Several agents, such as alcohol, which is used as a cleaning and antiseptic agent, are volatile and may be ignited, if not properly used, by the spark from electrosurgery devices.

The current, resulting from the high-impedance leakage path produced by splashing or spilling liquids on the equipment or into the electrical receptacles, may cause an alarm of the isolated power system. Carefully followed grounding procedures help to reduce the hazard from this type of situation. It should be noted that these same spills in the absence of an isolated system would probably cause a power interruption or, at a minimum, cause higher current to flow.

6.5.3 Oxygen-enriched atmosphere

The same fire hazards from electrical short circuits that cause fires in electrical devices in other environments can cause fires in health care facilities. These may be aggravated by the fact that the air may be more often enriched with oxygen in a hospital than in other types of environments.

6.5.4 Conductive flooring

Conductive flooring is used to control static electricity in anesthetizing locations where flammable anesthetic agents are administered. In older ORs, the floors are often constructed of special terrazzo that incorporates carbon to form conductive pathways throughout the floor. The floor usually includes a metallic grid so that no point on the floor is more than a few inches from a grounded conductive element.

Some conductive floors are made of conductive ceramic tiles. This method results in a floor that is very stable with regard to the resistance but is apt to have tiles break loose when heavy equipment is rolled over it. The reason for this seems to be that when adhesives are made conductive, they lose those characteristics that contribute to their durability as an adhesive.

Another type of conductive floor is sheet vinyl, which is manufactured with a cushioned backing. It maintains the proper conductivity very well but is prone to be damaged by wheeled OR tables and portable x-ray equipment, and it is easily cut when sharp surgical instruments are dropped on it.

A very common conductive floor is made of squares of hard conductive vinyl. These are placed over a grid of copper tape used to ensure that there is an uninterrupted path of conductivity between any two points on the floor.

The NFPA standard test method calls for a minimum and a maximum resistance between 5 lb (2.27 kg) circular electrodes, 2-1/2 in (6.35 cm) in diameter and covered with metal foil.

Under current NFPA rules, it is not necessary to have conductive floors in nonflammable anesthetizing locations. Where conductive floors exist, it is required that they be tested at least once per year. There is no upper limit of resistance for conductive floors in these nonflammable anesthetizing locations and the lower limit is 10 000 Ω to ensure that the conductive floor does not increase the hazards of electrical shock by offering too low an impedance to ground.

6.6 Environmental conditions relating to electrical safety

6.6.1 Source of leakage currents

Leakage current comes primarily from capacitive coupling between energized conductors and grounded objects, and secondarily from high-resistance paths through or along the surface of insulating materials.

When two conductors in close proximity are energized from the secondary of a distribution transformer, a small current flows between them due to the dielectric properties of the conductor insulation. When these conductors are run in grounded metallic conduit, there will also be leakage between the ungrounded phase conductor of a grounded system and the conduit. In an isolated system, neither power conductor is grounded, so there will be leakage from both power conductors to ground (i.e., to the conduit or grounding conductor). The path is from one conductor to the conduit and on to the other conductor. Current does not flow in the conduit since there is no direct return path to the current source from ground. See tables 6-1 and 6-2.

Table 6-1—Table of leakages contributed by wiring

Materials used	Result
TW wire Metal conduit Wire pulling compound with ground conductor	3 μA per ft (9.84 μA per meter) of wire
XLP wire Metal conduit *No* wire pulling compound with ground conductor	1 μA per ft (3.28 μA per meter) of wire

Table 6-2—Table of leakages contributed by equipment

Device	Leakage [a] range in μa
OR table light (single light without track)	75–175
OR table light (track-mounted)	300–400
Portable OR light	10–100
X-ray viewer (single)	50–150
Electro-surgery machine	100–300
Vacuum pump	50–125
Physiological monitor (single-channel)	30–200
Physiological monitor (eight-channel)	275–350
Heart-lung machine	350–450
Defibrillator	50–125
Portable x-ray (120 V capacitor charge)	30–50
Cardiac fibrillator	15–50
Respirator	100–150
Cardiac synchronizer	75–125
Hyperthermia unit (single patient unit)	125–175

[a]Ranges given are from tests of equipment found in the field and in good working condition. Older equipment exhibited higher leakage currents.

NOTE—Excessive power cord lengths will add measurably to the total leakage of the equipment [i.e., a 60 ft (18.29 m) power cord can add from 60 μA to 130 μA of leakage to an electro-surgery machine].

6.6.2 Limits set by standards

Table 6-3 shows the portable equipment leakage current limits set by NFPA 99-1996 (Chapters 7 and 9). The values are based upon physiological parameters and only after extensive debate by the technical committees responsible for these particular chapters of NFPA 99-1996. The present limits for voltage and impedance of the grounding system in patient care areas are 20 mV and 0.1 Ω, respectively. These voltage and impedance limits can be found in

Chapter 3 of NFPA 99-1996. In general, particularly for the voltage, the actual values measured at the time of acceptance should be much lower than these. Values approaching these indicate that something is wrong with the design or the installation.

Table 6-3—Maximum safe current leakage limits

Type of device	NFPA 99-1996
Portable equipment (patient use)	300 µA
Portable equipment with non-isolated input patient leads	100 µA
Portable equipment with isolated input leads	50 µA
Portable equipment (hospital use, i.e., housekeeping, maintenance, etc.)	500 µA

6.6.3 Protective measures for leakage current

The grounding system is the primary safeguard for bypassing the leakage and fault currents to prevent shock from these sources. The green grounding wire is the required ground and by itself may provide an effective grounding impedance of the order of 0.1–0.3 Ω at the end of a branch circuit. Metal conduit lowers the effective grounding impedance by providing another parallel path.

It should be emphasized that when an ungrounded electrical system is used, it does not diminish the need for an effective, low-resistance grounding system. While the ungrounded distribution system limits the amount of fault current that flows in the fault, it does not eliminate the fault current completely. The grounding conductor is an effective shunt for this current in parallel with the patient and personnel.

Although the magnitude of short-circuit currents is drastically reduced by an ungrounded system, due to the extra impedance inherent with an isolating transformer, the ungrounded system response to line-to-line fault is similar to that of a conventionally grounded system, in that it will activate the overcurrent protective devices and interrupt power to the area. Most faults that occur within appliances are, however, line-to-ground faults as opposed to line-to-line faults and it should be noted that a line-to-ground fault on a grounded system will cause equipment or system power loss compared with an ungrounded system that will continue to operate safely during a line-to-ground fault.

An ungrounded electrical system may be more expensive than a grounded system to install, since an isolation transformer and line isolation monitor (LIM) must be provided. The package convenience of an isolated system in a single enclosure allows its installation in less time than installing individual components. Periodic tests should be performed on this equipment as well as the isolated power system, and records should be kept of the results of these tests. Ten minutes per month should be allowed for each ungrounded system within the hospital. For a conventionally grounded system, maintenance to ensure the integrity of the ground, and to ensure that the ground-fault protection equipment is satisfactory, is at least as demanding. The cost of an isolated power system and the LIM must be evaluated against the benefits, the code requirements, and the insurance premium, if it is not present. The isolated system is still recognized as the safest possible system by the NEC (Article 517) and NFPA 99-1996 even though it is an optional requirement in the ICU/CCU areas.

Usually modern construction adds one or more parallel, redundant grounding paths to the green grounding wire in terms of metal conduit, metal piping, and metal structural members. These paths provide an effective ground impedance at the receptacle in the order of 2 mΩ to 20 mΩ. In addition to providing a low impedance, these elements provide a multipath grid for fault currents so that voltages that do develop within the patient vicinity, even during a severe fault, seldom cause hazardous conditions. Hazardous conditions generally develop when device grounding wires or the connection to the distribution grounding system, or both, fail.

GFCIs and isolated distribution systems minimize these hazards. GFCIs should only be applied where interruption of power is tolerable.

6.6.4 Design factors affecting leakage current

Specific inductive capacity (SIC) is a term that is used by wire manufacturers to evaluate the dielectric properties of the insulation characteristics of a particular wire. Dielectric constant is a term used to define the properties of insulating materials. The two terms, although closely related, are not exactly the same.

The NEC recommends that the secondary conductors of an isolated power system have an insulation with a dielectric constant of 3.5 or less. It should be recognized also that most manufacturers will state the SIC number, which is usually higher than the dielectric constant of the insulation material. Care should be taken to define a particular wire for these low-leakage applications.

It is important to recognize that for the consideration of leakage currents, the insulation quality and thickness limit the capacitive coupling between the conductors and ground. Capacitive coupling is determined by the dielectric constant of the insulation, the conductor length, and the spacing between the conductor and ground. Wire insulation with the lowest dielectric constant may have other properties that are unacceptable. Polyethylene has a lower dielectric constant than cross-link polyethylene, but it also has a lower temperature rating.

6.6.5 Neutral-to-ground short circuits

This is a phenomenon that does not cause problems directly with equipment operation. Such a fault is a common source of ground currents that can produce a serious secondary interference with measurements such as electrocardiogram (ECG) and electroencephalogram (EEG). Most simple circuit testers do not test for this fault.

Another source that needs review is the grounding method used by x-ray and other heavy-duty equipment with regard to the neutral. Sometimes these units use the ground as a neutral return.

6.6.6 Line-to-line faults

Line-to-line faults should be protected by appropriate overcurrent devices coordinated in such a manner that a minimum portion of the system is affected. This requires careful coordination of the various devices in series. Careful design, installation, and maintenance practices are required to minimize nuisance tripping.

Branch circuits need to be planned with regard to occupant usage. The probabilities of a line-to-line fault in one room unintentionally interrupting the power supply to life support systems in another room (perhaps not even adjacent to the room with the fault) need to be minimized.

6.6.7 Line-to-ground faults

Line-to-ground faults can cause service interruption problems, the same as line-to-line faults. In addition, they introduce a current on the grounding system, which can create further problems. Good electrical plugs, receptacles, device construction, and adequate maintenance procedures will minimize these faults. Isolated power systems safely provide continuity of power during a first line-to-ground fault. GFCI short-circuit tripping times must be coordinated with line-side protective device short-circuit interrupting times.

6.6.8 Transformer vault location and electrical disturbances

Since stray magnetic fields can cause problems with EEG or ECG laboratory measurements, precautions should be taken to assure that electrical installations that might create stray magnetic fields are not located adjacent to these measurement areas.

Switching devices may create electrical disturbances affecting electronic diagnostic devices such as cardiac monitors. A diagnostic device that is rendered incapable of providing the medical team with timely information or correct data is as great a hazard to the patient as a fire or an electrical shock. Radiation from the radio transmission on an adjacent building or transients from any large motor, switching capacitor, or capacitors combined with motors can also create problems that must be considered by the design engineer.

6.6.9 Wet locations

On a conventionally grounded system, an electrical shock is always possible when a line power device is operated in the presence of grounded conductive material and a person can bridge the gap between the two.

Large metal decks and floors covered with water present such a possible hazardous condition. A water-covered floor is potentially more hazardous than a dry metal deck because water can penetrate shoes and make better electrical connection to the body. In addition, there is always the possibility of having water splashed into electrical devices, creating contact with electrical sources.

The location of electrical devices near tubs or pools of water where a patient may be treated or where patients swim presents the possibility of shock.

Most ORs are considered wet locations since conductive liquids are frequently spilled.

A bed with an incontinent patient could possibly be considered a wet location. There have been reports of serious shocks when electrical beds had cord controls operated at line voltage. Using sealed, low-voltage, or pneumatic controls reduces the possibilities of these shocks.

Several precautionary steps need to be taken or considered whenever it is routine to have concentrations of conductive liquids on the floor while patients are present.

The first and most important step is to have equipment made for this type of environment properly installed, used, and maintained with care. Steps should be taken to provide splash guards. Metal enclosures containing line-powered equipment should be permanently grounded with an insulated equipment grounding conductor. Line-powered equipment should be located as far from the wetted area as is practical. Particular care should be given to the placing of cord-connected equipment where the cord might fall into a tub, basin, or pool in which individuals will be working or treated. Electrocutions in home bathrooms have most often occurred when electrical appliances were placed near the tub and then were touched or fell into the tub.

Where portable cord-connected, line-operated equipment will be used such as in a hydrotherapy room, GFCIs can be used to provide protection when accidents do occur. In the OR, the isolated power system shall be used, because power interruption cannot be tolerated.

At this writing, the NEC requires GFCIs to be installed in any room or area that has a basin with one or more of the following—a toilet, a tub, or a shower. Accidents could occur with line-powered toothbrushes, shavers, or hair dryers. An alternate to GFCIs would be to eliminate line-powered receptacles.

6.7 Basic safety measures

6.7.1 Insulation

Energized conductors shall be insulated from each other, from ground, from patients, and from hospital personnel. This insulation is created both by the insulating material used and by space separation. Primary insulation protection of cardiac catheters can be provided by properly insulating the exposed end or by making the environment surrounding the catheter as safe as possible.

6.7.2 Grounding

Grounding provides a nonhazardous return path for leakage currents that exist and minimizes the hazard produced when a fault condition develops.

6.7.2.1 System grounding

Grounding in a critical patient care area and in an anesthetizing location is an important ingredient in safeguarding against shock and electrocution. Proper grounding provides a means for dissipating static charges and shunting fault currents and/or normal leakage currents away from patients and attendants.

A good grounding system requires a reference grounding point, usually the grounding bus in the distribution panel, previously referred to in some documents as an equipotential ground. All conductive surfaces in the patient vicinity that are likely to be energized are bonded to the reference grounding point with an effective conductance at least equal to #10 AWG copper wire. Two typical surfaces are the oxygen outlet and the plumbing fixture. All receptacle grounding terminals are grounded to the reference grounding point by means of an insulated copper conductor. The conductor is insulated for corrosion protection and to prevent arcing points between the conduit and the conductor in case of a fault.

Equipment grounding provides a low-impedance path to safely conduct fault currents or leakage currents back to the source. It also is a means of bonding all conductive surfaces together such that the potential differences between such surfaces are minimal. Good grounding is more essential in health care facilities than other occupancies because of the vulnerability of the patients. Patients, especially those that are under an anesthesia, medication, or who are very ill, cannot react to, or otherwise protect themselves from electrical shock as can a normal healthy individual, and these patients are frequently connected to electrical equipment. In addition, potentials that are normally not hazardous to a clothed, healthy person might be dangerous in a health care facility. The nature of a patient's illness may lower his or her natural body resistance due to incontinence, perspiration, or open wounds. The process of diagnosing a patient can make that patient more vulnerable to electrical shock. The grounding system in a health care facility is designed to minimize the voltage potentials that can be created on ground conductor surfaces due to circulating ground currents.

Article 517 of the NEC for the 1971, 1975, and 1978 editions specified and required the use of equipment grounding with maximum resistances for each branch of such a system. While these requirements in Article 517 have been considerably reduced in subsequent NEC editions, equipment grounding in patient care areas still remains more demanding than the general requirements for grounding found in Article 250 of the NEC. Also, the term *equipotential grounding* is no longer used in the NEC and NFPA 99. However, the electrical engineer designing a hospital facility should be cautioned not to assume that the elimination of this term also eliminates all of the special grounding requirements for patient care areas. Careful study of Article 517 of the current NEC and of NFPA 99 should be made to determine exactly what special grounding provisions are required in all patient care areas.

6.7.2.2 Power cord grounding

The green equipment grounding conductor provided in an equipment power cord prevents static potentials from building up to dangerous values on non-current-carrying parts such as housings, cases, and boxes of electrical appliances. If these parts are not properly grounded, a static charge could accumulate to some degree and may reach such a value that it will automatically discharge in the form of an electrostatic spark. Such a static discharge could be a hazard to the patient and the attendant if it ignited some flammable gas or material or provided a shock.

The equipment grounding conductor also provides a path for leakage current and fault current, which could be conducted to an electrical appliance case. The magnitude of this leakage current is dependent on the characteristics of the appliance and the insulation associated with it. The leakage current could result in potential differences between pieces of equipment and could flow through vital organs of a patient if a patient current path was established. One of these conditions is encountered in cardiac catheterization procedures where small amounts of current can cause ventricular fibrillation. An example would be a patient in an electrically operated bed with the patient having monitoring leads that are not isolated. The grounding path could be through the patient via the attendant and the cardiac leads. Since the resistance of the power cord ground conductor is significantly less than the path through the patient, almost all of the current will flow to the grounding conductor.

The resistance of the grounding conductor is of utmost importance. A #10 AWG only represents $0.0001 \ \Omega/\text{ft}$ ($0.000 \ 328 \ \Omega/\text{m}$). In anesthetizing areas, design practice limits the potential differences between conductor surfaces that could come in contact with the patient to 40 mV.

6.7.2.3 Grounding jacks

In previous editions of the NEC, provisions for the connection of conductive non-electrical devices were dictated. These provisions had to be met by supplying each critical patient care area with a specified type of ground jack. Each OR was required to have a minimum of six ground jacks. While this is no longer an NEC requirement, many engineers recommend that at least a single ground jack be provided in each critical care patient area. This ground jack will provide easy connection to the grounding system for the purpose of redundant grounding of any particular piece of exceptionally hazardous equipment and will further allow connecting to the ground system for testing purposes. While the cost of a single ground jack, or even several ground jacks in a room is very low and almost negligible, the benefits provided by having the connection to the ground system conveniently accessible are innumerable. If ground jacks are specified in the project, it is desirable to specify several ground cords that can be used with these ground jacks.

6.7.3 Overcurrent protection

Little difference exists between the overcurrent protection, which shall be provided within hospital environments, and that which shall be provided for other commercial buildings. Where isolated power is used, the secondary circuits fed from the isolation transformer should be provided with two-pole circuit breakers. Care should be taken to obtain the highest quality and most reliable equipment available.

6.7.4 Adequacy of power

With electrical devices supporting life there is a strong need to supply a continuous, adequate amount of power, where and when needed. There is a very reasonable expectation that the power requirements will increase with time, and this should be a design consideration.

6.7.5 Continuity of power

See Chapter 5.

6.7.6 Isolated power

The ungrounded electrical distribution system has been used in certain areas of the hospital for many years. It has been used in anesthetizing locations since 1948.

The term *isolated system* is normally used for an ungrounded electrical distribution system including (or comprised of) all of the necessary equipment as specified in NFPA 99-1996 and in the NEC (Article 517). This system includes the shielded isolation transformer, LIM (see 6.7.9), circuit breakers, and the necessary power receptacles and associated grounding equipment. It is the responsibility of the electrical design engineer to specify each of the components required to establish the total system.

There was always a possibility of selecting incompatible components, and the labor for installing individual components was always quite high. Additionally, the integrity of the total system was difficult to ascertain.

In the early 1960s, the isolated system package or panel, as it was then called, began to appear. Initial units contained the isolation transformer, circuit breakers, and the ground detector. Later, the LIM replaced the ground detector. In 1971, packages appeared that also contained power receptacles, ground buses, and grounding jacks. Most present installations make use of these packaged components. UL standards have been established for these packaged units (UL 1047-1995) and they are available as labeled devices. The use of these packages assures the design engineer of compatible components and of the lowest possible installation cost.

Recent code changes as covered in NFPA 99-1996 (Paragraph 12-4.1.2.6) may not require some inhalation anesthetizing locations to have isolated power.

Prior to 1981, 2 mA of potential current flow was permitted before the LIM alarm sounded. The permissible level today is 5 mA.

The isolated power system is also useful where wet conditions exist, and life support equipment must continue to operate in the presence of one fault-to-ground, such as in an open heart surgery OR. There are other locations in the hospital such as ICU/CCU areas where isolated

213

systems are considered optional but should be given consideration. There are some states that mandate the use of isolated systems in the ICU/CCU areas. It is the responsibility of the electrical design engineer to point out to the hospital where isolated systems must be used and how the use of these systems might benefit the hospital and the patient.

The benefits derived from the ungrounded electrical distribution system are as follows:

a) *It limits the amount of current that can flow to ground through any single line-to-ground fault, which may occur in the system.* For all practical purposes, this eliminates the danger of massive electrical shocks (macroshock) to patients or personnel as a result of this type of fault. It also practically eliminates the possibility of high energy arcing as a result of this type of fault and thus provides protection against the accidental ignition of explosive or combustible materials being used in the area. This feature of the ungrounded electrical distribution system permits typical and practically sized grounding conductors to effectively protect even those patients who might be affected by very small amounts of electrical current. Internally isolated patient monitoring equipment also adds a large factor of safety.

b) *In a grounded distribution system, a line-to-ground fault on the system will operate the overcurrent protective device and interrupt power to the device or the area.* In most cases, this is a highly desirable feature. However, in any hospital area where life support devices are used, this loss of power may create a life support hazard. The ungrounded electrical distribution system responds quite differently to a line-to-ground fault. With this system, the fault does not pose an immediate danger to the patient or to personnel, and power is not interrupted. Only a visual and audible warning is issued. In any case, the device in which the fault has occurred will continue to operate and can be safely used until replacement equipment is available.

Without interrupting power, the LIM of the isolated power system warns of potential failure of equipment connected to the system, as long as the equipment has ground continuity. When the alarm sounds, the system is still safer than if a conventional grounded system were used in the first place. Any current that would flow would be less than if one of the conductors were solidly grounded, as is the case with the conventional grounded 120 V electrical system. The LIM used with the isolated system is the only device connected to the system that continuously monitors (and alarms when necessary) the integrity of the wiring of the room and the equipment connected to the system.

The alternative is frequent laboratory testing of the equipment but there is no assurance that the equipment has not become degraded or defective between test periods. The integrity of the equipment and the integrity of the grounding conductor are especially important for life support systems.

Periodic LIM readings can provide a continuous record of the system and its operation. The LIM is a one-time only cost addition as compared to the continuing cost of periodically checking the system and equipment. With continuous monitoring, the hospital engineering staff is kept on the alert to keep the equipment in excellent operating condition so that the LIM does not go into an alarm condition. The isolated power system gives the surgeon, or other users of the electrical equipment, macroshock protection, the same as if they were using double-insulated or battery-operated tools.

It should be emphasized that an ungrounded electrical distribution system usually provides an early warning that an appliance has a line-to-ground fault. The faults occurring within the appliances can be the result of slowly degrading insulation or components. When the potential leakage caused by these conditions increases beyond the limits set for the ungrounded system, an alarm will sound to trigger preventive maintenance action. This feature is of great value even to institutions that have sophisticated preventive maintenance programs for their appliances and equipment. Even though an appliance is checked on a monthly basis, there is no guarantee that degradation of the unit will not become excessive the day after it has received its monthly check.

Radiologists and pathologists sometimes used isolated power for computer aided tomography (C.A.T., or simply, CT) scanners and multichannel analyzers to protect devices from transients. As patient care areas become populated with computer chips, this may be the trend. The attenuation of the shielded isolation transformer typically produces as much as 50 dB reduction (300 to 1 voltage ratio) in the common-mode noise transient.

6.7.7 Three-phase isolated system

In recent years there have been increasing demands for three-phase power within an anesthetizing location. Special three-phase ungrounded isolation systems are available with UL 1047-1995 listing for these locations. It is generally neither advisable nor practical to try to derive both the three-phase power requirements and the single-phase power requirements from a single isolation system. It is best to provide a separate isolation system for three-phase equipment. Typical devices requiring three-phase power in the OR are laminar air flow devices, photo coagulating equipment (laser), special positioning, and electrical surgical tables.

While much of this equipment is also available in single-phase design, some of the devices are available only in three-phase design, with features not available in the single-phase machine, which the medical team requires. Once a situation of this type is established, it is the responsibility of the design engineer to properly specify and design a three-phase isolation circuit that will give the hospital trouble-free service.

The general rules and conditions for the effective three-phase isolation installation are identical to those for the single-phase isolation system previously described.

6.7.8 Limitations

The isolated distribution system has some limitations as follows:

a) If the ground continuity of the LIM is lost, the total hazard current is not monitored on the LIM and this could give a false sense of security.

b) While chances of microshock are reduced with an isolated distribution system, the line isolation monitor's hazard current alarm level of 5 mA (as well as the previous level of 2 mA) is still too high to completely prevent microshock current levels. Under some circumstances, a catheterized patient could be subjected to microshock.

c) High hazard current conditions can result in alarms that may be disturbing during normal operating procedures.

While the LIM will not uncover all of the possible defects of instrumentation connected to the LIM (such as broken equipment ground wires), it will sound an alarm when hazard currents above the NEC permitted values are encountered. While some hospital personnel may consider this alarm a nuisance, the LIM is a means of predicting the amount of hazard current that could be harmful.

To eliminate some of the so-called "nuisance alarms," the NEC and NFPA 99-1996 were changed to permit a 5 mA LIM alarm level rather than the previous 2 mA alarm level. The 5 mA alarm level permits more equipment to be connected to the isolated distribution system without causing a "nuisance alarm." However, the 5 mA LIM alarm level does not provide the same level of protection against shock as does the 2 mA LIM alarm level.

6.7.9 Line isolation monitor (LIM)

The LIM is an impedance measuring device used with isolated power systems that will sound an audible alarm, and give a visual warning when the line-to-ground impedance of the system has degraded to the point where current flow from any of the power conductors to ground during a ground fault that is in excess of the limits established by the standards.

All LIMs shall provide a meter that will continuously predict how much current will flow through a ground fault if it should occur. It should be carefully pointed out to the hospital staff that the meter does not indicate current that is flowing, but rather predicts the current that will flow if a fault-to-ground occurs.

All LIMs shall provide a means of silencing the audible alarm in the area of use so it does not distract the attention of the medical staff from the procedure being performed at that particular time. The standards do allow that any medical procedure being performed at the time the alarm sounds can be brought to its completion before services must be performed to remove the fault on the ungrounded system as indicated by the LIM. New procedures should not be started until the engineering or maintenance department of the hospital facility has located and corrected the problem and properly documented such action.

The monitor hazard current is the measure of degradation of the isolated system caused by connecting the LIM to the system. When a 2 mA trip level LIM is connected to a perfectly ungrounded system, and if the amount of current that will flow after connection from either line-to-ground is 25 µA, then it is said that the monitor hazard current is 25 µA. A 5 mA trip level LIM would have a monitor hazard current of approximately 50 µA.

LIMs are provided with a means for testing their function. This is accomplished by a test switch that, when energized, will place a simulated fault or other test on the LIM sufficient to cause it to alarm when operated at −15% or +10% of nominal rated voltage. This test verifies the proper function of the LIM and its associated alarms but does not verify the functioning of the total ungrounded electrical system. After installation, the system can be thoroughly tested by applying test faults at the outlets. A minimum of one similar annual test should be performed thereafter. The LIM function should be tested monthly as covered by NFPA 99-1996. When in the test mode, the ground connection to the LIM is disconnected automatically so as not to cause "second fault" on the system and possibly endanger patients or personnel in the area where the test is being performed. All tests should be performed only when the system is not otherwise in use.

The LIM function test is not a means of checking the calibration of the LIM. Since most LIMs are basically complex network analyzers involving solutions of very complex network equations, it is desirable to have all calibrations performed at the factory where adequate and proper test equipment is available.

6.7.10 LIM isolation monitor interpretation

In an OR, a LIM reading of 2 mA means that the impedance of one line-to-ground has deteriorated to 60 000 Ω on a 120 V system and the decision probably will be made to continue the surgical procedure. After the surgical procedure has been completed, the plugged-in equipment should then be examined and the fault should be corrected at the earliest opportunity.

If the indicator on the meter shows full-scale deflection, indicating a severe hazard condition, it indicates that one of the lines has shorted to ground or it could be caused by a combination of high-leakage currents of several instruments. The isolated system is approaching a grounded system. This could create a serious hazard of electric shock to both the patient and to personnel in the event that a second fault occurs. The first fault should be located and corrected at least before starting another surgical operation. The full, let-through current of the circuit breaker could flow if any contact is made with a live (unshorted) conductor.

Because of the mentioned reasons, the LIM meter should be in a plainly visible place—in the operating theater. Means shall be provided for conveniently silencing the audible alarm.

A similar analogy applies to the 5 mA LIM, with the exception that when the meter reads 5 mA, the impedance of one line-to-ground has deteriorated to 24 000 Ω on the 120 V system.

6.8 Design and testing of systems for safety

6.8.1 Identifying particular user needs

It is very important to have a very clear understanding of the expected use of various areas in a health care facility. Electrical codes, standards, and regulations have different requirements for the various areas in a health care facility as compared to other types of occupancies. Many hospitals frequently have continuing changes in requirements because of staff changes and because of advances in technology. Since cost is a very important consideration and since available funds are usually in short supply, it is very difficult to provide maximum flexibility in every area.

The first step is to review with the administrator, or the owner of the facility, the expected initial use, and any anticipated modification in the future. Consideration should be given to changes in safety requirements as well as to possible changes in applicable codes and standards.

6.8.2 Adjusting special design features for each area

The second step is to apply the necessary special design features to those areas identified in 6.8.1 as needing such treatment.

6.8.3 Distribution systems

The choice of voltage of the distribution system can affect its safety in terms of continuity of service. Code changes for requiring ground fault protection on the main service, and reports of nuisance tripping of ground fault protection, indicate that extra careful selection, design, installation, testing, and training for maintenance are essential. Voltages and feeder loads should be carefully selected and analyzed to minimize the possibility of nuisance outages.

6.8.4 Distribution raceway systems

There are a number of options available that have several economic and safety implications. One consideration is the use of either plastic or rigid metal raceways. The raceways provide two major functions: physical protection of the power conductors and redundant grounding. The physical protection becomes of greatest importance in facilities where renovation and changes are frequent.

The redundancy in grounding provided by metal conduit is twofold. The conduit provides a redundant path to the ground. In addition, the physical mounting of the conduit to other conduit, metal studs, other piping, and structural steel members provides a network of redundant grounding paths. These design and inadvertent connections contribute to an effective low-grounding impedance for current flow during fault conditions. Using electrical metallic tubing frequently produces effective grounding impedances in the order of 1–10 mΩ. These values are low relative to that provided by a #10 AWG wire having 1 mΩ/ft (3.28 mΩ/m) resistance.

This natural redundant grounding gains part of its safety advantage by causing fault currents to follow several paths and reducing possible hazardous conditions.

6.8.5 Distribution system-grounded and isolated power

The grounded distribution system is the one usually found in most commercial installations throughout the U.S. The grounded feature aids in tripping overcurrent protection devices during line-to-ground fault conditions. When line-to-ground faults include an individual as part of the circuit, serious shock hazards are possible. Line-to-ground faults also can cause arcing, which is a hazard where any flammable gases are present.

The isolated distribution system is covered in 6.7.6.

6.8.6 Field inspection procedure

Isolated power and a hospital's equipment ground system are unique. It is recommended to have these systems tested and certified before use. This is one way to ensure proper installation and operation. Manufacturers of isolated power systems are generally equipped to test the installed equipment. The testing should preferably be done with the electrical contractor present.

All tests on the isolated system, ground network, and LIM should be in accordance with the NEC (Article 517) and NFPA 99-1996.

The test and certification procedure covers the following:

a) Operational check on all equipment

b) Inspection of the complete installation for applicable code conformance

c) In-depth testing of isolated power system

    1) Line voltage measurements
    2) Line-to-ground impedance measurements
    3) LIM calibration

d) Recording of initial system hazard current readings from the LIM for hospital records (initial hazard current readings represent predicted current leakage with no devices connected to the isolated system)

e) Testing of the ground network

    1) All power receptacle grounds
    2) All ground receptacles
    3) All permanently exposed building material
    4) All permanently installed equipment

f) Complete dissertation on the isolated power system to the hospital personnel including

    1) Basic theoretical concept of benefits of isolated power
    2) Proper use
    3) Proper maintenance procedure

g) Periodic testing and record keeping (a log book with initial hazard current readings is supplied to the hospital with a letter of certification, including all recorded test data)

6.9 References

This chapter shall be used in conjunction with the following publications:

NFPA 70-1996, National Electrical Code® (NEC®).[2]

NFPA 99-1996, Health Care Facilities.

UL 544-1993, Medical and Dental Equipment.[3]

UL 1047-1995, Isolated Power Systems Equipment.

6.10 Bibliography

Additional information may be found in the following sources:

[B1] "Accreditation Manual for Hospitals," by Joint Commission for Accreditation of Hospitals, 1984.

[B2] ANSI/AAMI ES1-1993, Safe Current Limits for Electromedical Apparatus.[4]

[B3] "Guidelines for Construction and Equipment of Hospitals and Medical Facilities," U.S. Department of Health and Human Services, Oct. 1981.

[2]NFPA publications are available from Publications Sales, National Fire Protection Association, 1 Batterymarch Park, P.O. Box 9101, Quincy, MA 02269-9101.

[3]UL publications are available from Underwriters Laboratories, Inc., 333 Pfingsten Road, Northbrook, IL 60062-2096.

[4]ANSI publications are available from the Sales Department, American National Standards Institute, 11 West 42nd Street, 13th Floor, New York, NY 10036.

Chapter 7
Lighting

7.1 General discussion

Lighting technologies and design methods, as well as our understanding of visual needs, have advanced at a pace rivalling that of health care techniques, methods, and understandings. Good design now recognizes the psychological and physiological impact of lighting upon humans, and health care lighting schemes must incorporate these demands to be successful. Such considerations supplement the obvious requirements of the medical and nursing staff for the fulfillment of their responsibilities. Moreover, the technologies used in the health care field have changed, and the addition of such devices as computer screens and patient monitoring systems create visual demands often akin to those in modern offices. Indeed, the very diversity of tasks that occur in any given space of a health care facility greatly increases the complexity of the design process, as the engineer must accurately understand both the proposed uses of the spaces and the visual requirements for those uses. Users and architects continue to demand more aesthetic solutions to the challenges presented to the lighting designer. The electrical engineer designing a hospital therefore seeks to achieve a visual environment dramatically different from the one of the past.

Modern concepts of lighting are "task oriented," that is, lighting should provide precisely the light that is required to efficiently perform specific tasks. In other words, the engineer must provide a lighting system that permits the task to be performed and in which the lighting quantity and quality are not detrimental factors in the task's successful completion. Most health care tasks are inherently difficult, requiring great accuracy and speed, and are performed by a variety of people possessing great variations in visual acuity. The task itself must be evaluated for its requirements of size, shape, color, degree of difficulty, and the haste in which the work must be performed.

The fundamental principles of good lighting design described briefly in the first part of this chapter should serve to provide guidelines and references sufficient for the intelligent and studied application of lighting to the health care environment. Many health care support tasks such as routine clerical, accounting, and other office-related tasks, food service, maintenance, parking, and housekeeping may be treated in the same manner as similar tasks in commercial and industrial buildings. This chapter will treat only those tasks and situations that are unique to health care facilities. The unique application of the basic principles to the health care environment, then, is described in the second part of this chapter. Finally, the lighting system as a whole must be integrated into the essence of the building, so that the needs for maintenance, control, and energy efficiency are met. The entire environment should be evaluated and planned in concert with the interior designer, the architect, the mechanical engineer, and the appropriate staff (both medical and building maintenance). The success of the lighting design cannot be measured in footcandles, but must be measured in the intangibles of comfort, task efficiency, and overall satisfaction.

7.2 Lighting design for hospitals

7.2.1 General discussion

Fundamentals of lighting design have been the subject of a number of excellent books. A complete recap is not the intent here; some knowledge on the part of the user is assumed and only those aspects of lighting design of special relevance in the health care facility shall be covered. The engineer is directed to other literature for more comprehensive treatments of all of the principles of good lighting design. Most notable is the literature published by the Illuminating Engineering Society of North America (IESNA), and in other IEEE materials. Publications that deserve particular attention are

— IEEE Std 241-1990 [B4][1]
— *IESNA Lighting Handbook,* 1987 Applications Volume [B5]
— *IESNA Lighting Handbook,* 1987 Reference Volume [B6]
— *Lighting for Health Care Facilities* [B8]

In particular, the uniformity of illumination, and the luminous ratios set forth in the IESNA guidelines should be adhered to in the design.

7.2.2 Quality factors in lighting

7.2.2.1 Glare—Direct and reflected

The engineer should provide illumination without annoyance or discomfort from luminaires or windows that are sources of glare. Reference to visual comfort probability (VCP) data, available from luminaire manufacturers, is helpful in the selection of luminaires that will not cause uncomfortable glare. The VCP data is calculated by the manufacturer using empirically derived data regarding the brightness characteristics of individual fixtures, room characteristics, and room finishes. Note that this data is calculated under "normal" office-type viewing conditions; in health care facilities it may not be applicable. For instance, the patient is often on his back looking directly up at a ceiling fixture.

Windows often present a source of discomfort. The harsh brightness from the outside, when compared to the indoor levels, can cause eye fatigue. When this ratio of lighting levels exceeds 8 to 10, fatigue is caused by the iris's need to constantly adjust as the person sees within the room. Also, glare will result from the direct view of the sun, clouds, sky, or bright buildings. For this reason, windows should have shades, blinds, draperies, low-transmission glass, or other suitable shielding to control and/or reduce the brightness in the field of view. Hospital staff should not normally face windows in performing their work. Patient rooms should be able to be darkened totally for sleep or comfort.

The reflectance of room surfaces is an important factor in the efficient utilization of light, and, therefore, of lighting energy. It is also important to visual comfort because brightness should be within certain well established limits (ratios) in areas where demanding visual

---

[1]The numbers in brackets correspond to those of the bibliography in 7.5.

tasks are performed. For best utilization of light, the ceiling should be painted white. The walls, floor, and equipment finishes should be within the recommended reflectance ranges of table 7-1.

Table 7-1—Recommended surface reflectances

Surface	Reflectance equivalent
Ceiling finishes[a]	80–90
Walls	50–70
Furniture and equipment	25–45
Floors	15–30
Surgical gowns, surgical drapes	< 30

[a]Reflectance for finish only. Overall average reflectance of textured acoustic materials may be somewhat lower.

To get even higher utilization of light, proposals are sometimes made to employ finishes on walls, floors, and furniture with reflectances even higher than those in table 7-1. Finishes significantly higher or lower in reflectance may cause legitimate complaints about glare, and may upset the brightness relationships necessary for visual comfort. The lighting engineer should be sure to consult with those having the responsibility for finish specifications. Note that certain portions of walls or trim surfaces or room appointments may have higher or lower reflectance than the limits of the ranges of table 7-1 if these areas are thought of as accents and restricted to no more than 10% of the total visual field.

7.2.2.2 Color quality

Color is a complex subject involving both physical parameters that can be expressed in mathematical terms and psychological factors that relate to individual interpretations of color. Certain colors are warmer (redder) in character while others are considered cooler (or bluer). Light sources have such characteristics, and their color should be a factor in source selection in order to compliment a warm, cool, or neutral color scheme. Source colors also help to create a desired atmosphere (or mood) and to delineate different functions within a given area. Warmth or coolness in a color scheme and light source may also be a factor in perceived temperature by occupants of a space, and, therefore, in energy usage.

Certain light sources may have high efficacy of light production with fair or poor color rendition. Others may have excellent color rendition with only moderate efficacy. These factors must be weighed, along with many others, in light source selections for particular applications. High-pressure sodium sources, even with their high lumen-to-watt ratios, for instance, would be unacceptable in an exam room where the need to accurately distinguish color is important.

7.2.2.3 Veiling reflections, distribution, reflections, and shadows

Veiling reflections in tasks reduce visibility by lowering the contrast between details of the task and its background. They occur when a light fixture, bright ceiling, or window and the eye of a viewer are at the mirror-angle of reflection with a specular portion of the visual field. They are often difficult to "dodge" by shifting the viewing angle when luminaires (or windows) that produce the effects are of substantial area, large number, and/or wide distribution.

The most important single tactic for minimizing the veiling reflection effects is geometry. If the sources that light the task can be positioned out of the mirror-angle of reflection with respect to the task and the viewer's eyes, visibility and comfort will be heightened. This approach is frequently practical in single-occupancy rooms where the work location is known. This approach is also possible with built-in workstation lighting, if lights are located to illuminate the task from both sides. Unfortunately, on many such workstations, the sources are positioned under a shelf or cabinet directly in front of the task, often the worst possible location.

In some spaces it is best to position workstations in between rows of ceiling luminaires, with occupants facing parallel to the rows so that most of the light on the tasks comes from the sides and not from luminaires on the ceiling immediately in front of the workstation. Certain lighting distributions may also reduce the effect of veiling reflections such as polarizing light-ing panels, bat-wing lenses, parabolic louvers, and indirect lighting. Indirect lighting works best in large rooms with relatively high ceilings. The objectionable veiling effects are least when the ceiling is uniformly lighted.

Progress has been made in predicting, measuring, and evaluating the effects of veiling reflec-tions. The term "equivalent sphere illumination" (ESI) has been coined as an expression of the relative effectiveness of a particular system to a reference system. At this time there is no scientific basis for translating specific IESNA illuminance recommendations into ESI. How-ever, the ESI concept is useful in comparing practical lighting systems for their effectiveness in reducing veiling reflections.

7.2.2.4 Further considerations

Individual reaction to a space is largely subjective. In recent years, studies of the psychology of lighting have provided statistically significant data as to how groups of people would react to various kinds of lighting. Criteria have been developed that would allow the use of lighting to create impressions of a "public" or "private" space, for example. These criteria could be helpful in applying lighting in such areas as entrance lobbies, patient rooms, dining areas, conference rooms, corridors, and offices. The *IESNA Lighting Handbook,* 1987 Applications Volume [B5], discusses this subject in greater detail.

7.3 Hospital lighting applications

7.3.1 General

Given the general guidelines for lighting design previously discussed, it is now in order to discuss the application of those principles to health care facilities. A space-by-space discus-sion of lighting application will not be attempted here; rather, the reader is urged to refer to the *IESNA Lighting Handbook,* 1987 Applications Volume [B5] or Chapter 10 of IEEE Std 241-1990 [B4] for this information. This chapter will focus instead on some of the unique lighting needs of health care facilities.

7.3.2 Examination and patient observation

Patient examination is a critical portion of the health care practice, and facilitating that task is therefore a primary task of the lighting system in the patient care portions of the facility. The engineer should make every effort to determine these needs in the various spaces, and to provide for them in designing a lighting system that is at the same time free from glare, properly distributed, of adequate illumination levels, with good color rendition, quiet, and controllable.

In determining lighting levels, care should be taken to remember that examination tasks are performed by wide varieties of persons with wide varieties of visual ability. The lighting can be provided by fixed luminaires, luminaires with adjustable parts, or portable luminaires. The specific types should be coordinated with the users and the building maintenance department. Patient and treatment rooms typically require relatively shadowless high-intensity light at the center of a 2-ft diameter exam area where the peripheral intensity is at least 50% of maximum intensity. In other words, spaces such as operating rooms, which use surgical lights to focus a tremendous amount of light onto the patient, should be lit to an ambient level high enough to produce sufficient visual comfort without producing eye fatigue or glare in the eye of the examiner. Controls should be designed so as to allow varying levels of lighting, if possible. The placement of fixed light sources for both examination and general illumination is critical. Disability glare from specular surfaces may obscure the patient. Indirect fixtures; large, low-brightness luminaries; or luminous ceilings are the preferable choices where possible.

Another element important to proper examination is consistency. The fluorescent luminaires selected, for instance, should utilize the same lamp throughout the patient care area so that patient skin tones appear consistent throughout. The lamps should typically be chosen to achieve a high color rendition in order to make skin-tone perceptions more accurate. Similarly, in areas using high-intensity exam lights, the color and color rendering of the lamps for ambient illumination should approximate as closely as possible that of the exam light. In addition to consistency of colors and color renditions, the engineer should pay attention to consistency in lighting levels. As already mentioned, too great a discrepancy between the intensity of an exam light and the room's ambient light can cause problems with fatigue and glare. Similarly, the balance of the operating suite should also have a moderately high lighting level that approximates the ambient lighting level in the operating room in order to allow the surgical team's eyes to become accustomed to these levels. Lighting in patient corridors should be able to be reduced at night to help the eye of the nurse who views a patient in his relatively darkened room. Similarly, the lights at the nurses' station should be controllable so that the levels can be reduced at night to reduce the contrast with the corridor. Finally, any such lighting should provide excellent cutoff features so as not to intrude light into other darkened areas.

7.3.3 Psychological factors and patient comfort

7.3.3.1 General

The patient in the health care facility, as well as the patient's family and friends, is emotionally vulnerable. Patients are understandably frightened or apprehensive. The engineer should design a lighting system that helps put patients at ease. Patients are frequently unable to adjust their position or surroundings to avoid discomfort, and, since the visible world is the primary outside influence on the patient, discomfort in lighting is particularly objectionable. Strange, uncomfortable, or embarrassing treatments add to the patient's trauma and to the challenge of producing a lighting environment that supports the patient's comfort, well-being, and emotional stability. Indeed, the indications are that the lighting system can not only minimize the patient's discomfort, but also may in some cases help to speed his or her recovery. The lighting system should intrude as little as possible into the patient's consciousness, and ideally, it should help to create an atmosphere (such as that of home in the patient room) that enables the patient to relax, feel good, and heal.

Human beings require, for most robust health, lighting that is similar to that of the sun (i.e., having a continuous spectrum and including a small amount of ultraviolet light). The ultraviolet light helps the body generate vitamin D. Vitamin D helps the body process calcium into bones and teeth and thus fights the degeneration of the skeletal system that inevitably occurs from non-use. Full-spectrum light also stimulates the hypothalamus and the adrenal and pineal glands, dilates the blood vessels, helps rid the body of toxins, increases protein metabolism, and lessens fatigue. Recent medical studies have shown that full-spectrum lamps can be used successfully to treat seasonal depression and to help soothe hyperactive children. The engineer should therefore strive to incorporate as much daylight as possible into the patient's life, as well as simulate as much as possible the light of the sun in the artificial sources that must inevitably be used. Fluorescent lamps specified as having a color render index (CRI) of at least 80 and a color temperature of 3500 °K or 4100 °K are preferable in most patient care areas.

7.3.3.2 "Stress relief" in procedure and treatment rooms

Procedure and treatment areas are the greatest anxiety-producing locations in a health care facility and their lighting systems must therefore be designed to minimize the patient's stress. Exam lights, for instance, should be out of the patient's direct line of sight, and as unobtrusive as possible, while still performing their intended functions. Many spaces such as diagnostic imaging rooms do not require direct illumination of the patient at high levels and so may be lit with indirect cove luminaires and incandescent fixtures on dimmers to create a more subdued, relaxed environment.

7.3.3.3 Room lighting

The lighting in a patient room is particularly important to the mental well-being of the patient. This room also is the area where the patient spends most of the time, where visitations occur, and where the patient needs light for self-grooming. For achieving the most optimistic, and therefore, healthful attitude, the patient's self-view must be as pleasing and healthy as possible. The lighting in a patient room must, of course, answer several needs, but among them is boosting the morale of the patient. So, lighting that makes the skin appear gray or sallow should not be used. Again, fluorescent lamps with a high CRI and temperature should be used for these rooms. The addition of incandescent luminaires further warms the appearance of the space, as well as helps to achieve the home-like atmosphere so important in making the patient feel comfortable. Similarly, patients typically feel a lack of control as they are being treated. Patient control in the variety and level of room lighting can thus be extremely beneficial to their sense of well-being.

7.3.3.4 Corridor lighting

The corridor lighting schemes so much in favor in older hospitals—that is, 2×4 fluorescent fixtures spaced periodically throughout the corridors—can no longer be recommended as the method of choice in health care facilities. The regular spacing of overhead fixtures causes an unpleasant strobe effect for the patient being wheeled underneath them. Indirect systems or linear systems along the sides of the corridor are therefore the preferred method, again using fluorescent lamps with a CRI of at least 80 and a color temperature of 3500 °K or 4100 °K. Such a system also helps to create a less institutional look for the facility. See figures 7-1 through 7-3.

7.3.3.5 Daylighting

Many codes now require windows in patient rooms. The benefits of daylighting to the patient have been briefly touched upon earlier. Another benefit of a window, besides the view it provides, is a sense of the passing of night and day. This sensation helps the patient maintain circadian rhythms. Various studies recently have found that sunlight deprivation may disturb mineral metabolism, as well as blood formation, renal and hepatic function, and sexual cycles. Sunlight or full-spectrum light may help increase endurance and resistance to disease, as well as lower blood pressure and improve muscle tone. Adequate sunlight also may help to alleviate depression in patients. Adequate daylighting has similar effects upon the health care staff, with the consequent benefit to the patient of maintaining a higher standard of care. In short, the engineer should be careful to work with the architect and owners to ensure an adequate amount of daylight for the patient.

7.3.4 Housekeeping services

The final "typical" need for lighting in health care facilities that cannot be ignored is the housekeeping services function. The mandated requirements for housekeeping services in a health care facility are vastly different from such functions in other facilities; moreover, the sometimes specialized designs for lighting systems in various treatment rooms must not fail to also provide sufficient lighting for this crucial function.

**Figure 7-1—Two patient corridors, striving for hotel or home "feel,"
in lieu of institutional look**

Figure 7-2—Corridor lighting before remodeling

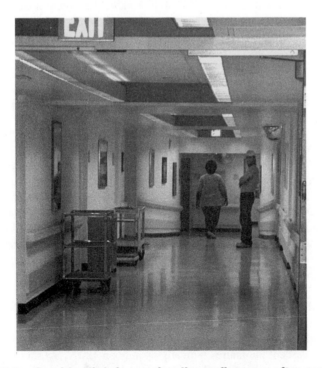

Figure 7-3—Corridor lighting, using linear fixtures, after remodeling

The dropping of small objects, the spilling of liquid, and patient-related accidents require additional light in order to clean hidden floor areas around beds and other furniture. Often, it requires no more than proper switching of groups of lights to provide the proper ambient light. Such lighting should be controllable by the nurse or other staff personnel as they enter the room. In patient rooms, direct fluorescent illumination from the ceiling area outside of the patient's curtain tracks is a possible solution since the angle of the light cast into the bed areas will improve the seeing of objects beneath furniture and between beds. Finally, the lighting equipment selected should lend itself to the need for the high level of cleanliness required in hospitals.

7.4 Considerations in lighting system design

7.4.1 Lighting system design

In designing the lighting system for a health care facility, the engineer must be careful to avoid working in the proverbial vacuum. The lighting for a health care facility, as crucial as it is, must be integrated properly into the building as a whole. In particular, the engineer must consider the impact of light design upon the other trades; for example, the heat generated by the luminaires must be removed from the space by the air conditioning system. The lighting design dramatically affects the overall aesthetic appeal of a space and must be coordinated with the architect and interior designer. The lights and light system voltage must be chosen with due deliberation in order to achieve both the lighting system objectives and a good, efficient, cost-effective electrical distribution system. Finally, the system must be designed with an eye toward the overall energy usage of the facility and the ease of maintaining it in order to facilitate the continued proper operation of the system.

7.4.2 Integration with other building systems

As a dynamic, functioning system, lighting must be integrated carefully with the other systems in the building. The luminaires chosen can substantially increase the cooling load of a particular space, for instance, and certain luminaires can act as diffusers for mechanical systems. The physical placement and dimensions of the luminaires can also impact the routing of ductwork, sprinkler piping, public address speakers, and fire detection systems, especially above crowded ceilings. These problems become particularly acute in areas such as operating rooms, which require very high levels of light (and, therefore, of cooling) as well as strict environmental requirements mandating more than the usual amount of ductwork and diffusers. The lighting, too, significantly affects the aesthetic appeal of a room environment, and the designs must be coordinated with the architect. All of these considerations must be negotiated in order that the lighting system be able to perform its proper functions while at the same time harmoniously interact with the other building systems.

7.4.3 System voltage

Typical interior lighting fixtures manufactured today require either 120 V or 277 V single-phase power. Incandescent luminaires typically operate on 120 V, but more and more of the newer technologies such as compact fluorescent and low-voltage sources that approximate the effects of incandescent luminaires can operate at 277 V. Fluorescent fixtures can operate at either 120 V or 277 V. The choice of lighting system voltage, then, hinges partially on the numbers and types of luminaires required. In a smaller health care facility, especially a hospital, a 120 V system may be the better choice. Since hospitals require several branches of power, three of which (normal, critical, and life safety) will contain some amount of lighting, and power loads that are almost exclusively 120 V, the choice of 277 V to serve the lighting fixtures will require a duplication of panels for these systems (see figure 7-4). Systems that operate on 120 V also allow for complete flexibility in the choice of luminaires. Finally, ground faults rarely occur on systems of 120 V, but do occur with somewhat more frequency on 480 V systems. Accordingly, both the building cost and the reliability of the system will be somewhat enhanced by choosing 120 V as the lighting system voltage.

For medium to large hospitals, 277 V systems may be the preferred choice for system voltage. The higher system voltage permits the use of smaller conductors, raceways, transformers, transfer switches, and possibly a reduced number of panelboards, thereby reducing the electrical room sizes. All of this may offset the costs of providing the extra switchgear mentioned above. The higher voltage, with the correspondingly lower currents, similarly results in lower line losses and operating costs. Finally, 480Y/277 V systems can often be more flexible in allowing future expansion than can a corresponding 208Y/120 V system. All of these variables must therefore be taken into account when selecting the particular system voltage.

7.4.4 Energy

Hospital engineers should be concerned with conservation of energy in the facility. Certain measures can be taken to reduce the lighting energy consumed without simultaneously reducing the efficacy of the system for its more important visual performance. Of fundamental importance in the wise use of energy for lighting is careful attention to the design for each space. The engineer should take care to choose and locate the luminaires as required for proper performance of the tasks for the space, and not merely to achieve some "correct" footcandle level. The engineer should be sure, however, that task and ambient lighting levels are provided as recommended, and are not over or under lighting a space. The engineer should also work with the architect and users to ensure the proper location of portable task lighting in order to supplement the fixed luminaires.

Another potential for energy savings can be realized through the specification of light sources. Newer, more efficient sources can be chosen where appropriate in order to maximize the light produced for the power consumed. These newer sources produce light of various temperature colors and must be applied judiciously in order that the overall lighting quality is not needlessly sacrificed in critical areas. Other limitations of the luminaires may be lack of dimming capability (compact fluorescent, except with specialized dimmers), short life (low-voltage, though their lamp lives are still longer than those of incandescent lamps), long restart times (metal halide), low power factors (compact fluorescent), and higher first cost. The compromises demanded by such limitations are very often worthwhile in terms both of reduced energy usage and aesthetic appeal when the luminaires are properly applied. In particular, the compact fluorescent fixtures can be used in place of incandescent fixtures where dimming is not required, such as in patient night-lights, bathroom luminaires, plenum

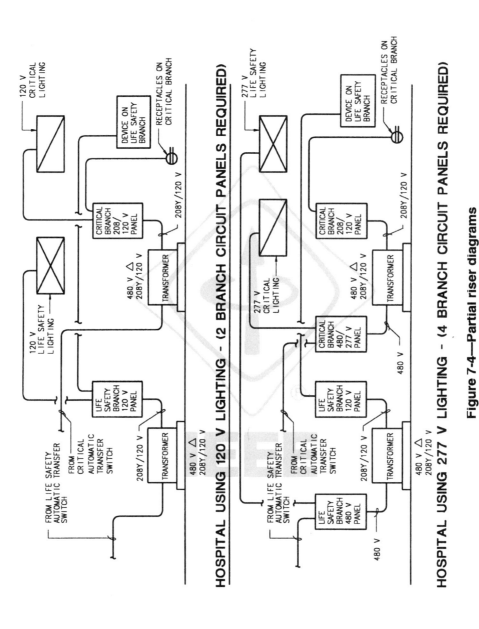

Figure 7-4—Partial riser diagrams

lights, and room vestibules. Low-voltage and color-corrected, lower-wattage metal halide and "white" high-pressure sodium luminaires can add pleasing effects to lobbies, corridors, cafeterias, and other public spaces. Proper use of such luminaires will also lower the amount of energy lost as waste heat that must then be removed by the air conditioning system, and so, use of these fixtures has a two-fold impact on the lowering of energy usage.

Lighting control systems can likewise be specified so as to help reduce use of energy. Switching of lights, such as the use of proximity switches in equipment rooms, bathrooms, conference rooms, and offices can help to hold down the wasteful usage of lighting energy. Infrared or ultrasonic occupancy sensors may be used in selected spaces to respond to movement or body heat and to ensure that lights turn off when those spaces are unoccupied. Dimmer switches can also be used, as can separate switching of both ballasts of two-ballast fluorescent fixtures in offices and exam rooms. Effective use of daylighting in conjunction with switching can also lower energy usage.

Three other methods for energy savings are often proposed; namely, using energy-saving or electronic ballasts, using daylight to obviate the need for luminaires, and using reflectors in fluorescent luminaires. Electronic ballasts, though they cost somewhat more to purchase initially, can help reduce energy usage, without decreasing lighting quality. They also allow the use of daylight compensation, dimming, and lamp lumen depreciation compensation techniques.

Daylighting can be a practical way of saving energy when appropriate, especially in consideration of the psychological and physiological benefits discussed previously. However, the engineer should take care to evaluate windows on their overall energy implications for both the lighting and the heating and cooling requirements. That is, energy saved in electric lighting should be balanced against heat gains and losses through the windows to determine their overall impact on energy use.

Polished metal or foil "specular" reflectors for fluorescent luminaires are frequently touted as a way to get the light of a four-lamp luminaire out of a two-lamp luminaire, thus reducing by half the energy required. Reflectors actually do little to increase the light output of a comparable new and/or properly maintained fixture, but rather, help to focus the light. The reflectors may be used in two ways—to retrofit into existing four-lamp luminaires, or purchased new in lieu of four-lamp luminaires.

Very often, retrofit luminaires with reflectors are compared to existing luminaires that are old and dirty. Lighting levels are also often measured at only one location—directly under the fixture—so that the "test" results may be deceiving. That is, the light distribution of luminaires equipped with reflectors differs from those without reflectors, and, so, the overall lighting uniformity of a retrofitted system using reflectors may be compromised. Further, no standards for the manufacture of reflectors exist, nor have reflectors been in service long enough to accurately determine their life or their ability to withstand cleaning. Finally, the cost to purchase the reflectors and then to install the reflectors in existing luminaires may be hard to offset by future energy savings. The reflectors, of course, will be subjected to the same dirt and lack of cleaning over time as their predecessors, with a corresponding degrading of their light output (i.e., the smaller amount of energy used may not produce the promised equivalent lighting levels).

Several manufacturers produce luminaires with polished metal reflectors. And, some evidence does suggest that an installation using new "reflectorized" luminaires may reduce lighting energy use by 25% over systems of similar luminaires with more lamps. So, the additional first cost of the reflectorized luminaires may be offset by future energy savings, provided their lifetimes are equivalent, and that they are kept properly cleaned and maintained. Judicious use of reflectors may therefore be appropriate, but the engineer is urged to carefully specify reflectors to be engineered specifically for the luminaires to be used, and to carefully examine their photometrics to ensure that the ultimate lighting performance of the room lighting system is not compromised.

7.4.5 Maintenance

Finally, the engineer designing the health care lighting system must remember that the system will remain in service for a long time, and that the system design should facilitate its maintenance. The engineer must take care both to ensure easy access to luminaires, and to specify ones that will facilitate maintenance. Luminaires with "doors" must be installed so that the doors can operate properly. Luminaires that are to be installed in drywall ceilings must be specified to be easily removed. Often, the location of the luminaires in the space is critical, as for instance in atriums where impossibly long ladders would be required for access.

The luminaires themselves must be carefully specified to provide optimum reliability, serviceability, and sanitation. Luminaires are frequently subjected to wash-downs using corrosive cleaning compounds and agents. Sanitation and the resultant frequent cleaning require luminaires with no crevices or cracks that may harbor dirt or other unsanitary miscellany. Lenses, particularly those frequently subject to cleaning or to patient contact, should be gasketed to prevent entry of cleaning agents or patient care fluids. Gasketing should be cleanable; that is, bare, or, if foam type, closed cell foam with a smooth exterior surface. The fixtures must be likewise rugged enough to withstand this cleaning, and must be easily removed and disassembled through plug-in devices to allow for quick and easy relamping, cleaning, and repair. Ideally, the engineer should examine a sample of each luminaire specified in order to ensure its meeting the above needs.

The overall lighting system must also be designed with consideration given to future maintenance. Minimizing the number of different lamps for a facility reduces spare parts inventory and makes spare lamp storage easier. Similarly, minimizing the number of different lamps makes relamping both easier and more accurately performed in the real world. Consistency in choice of lamps in a facility offers the additional benefit that skin tones appear consistent in all areas, rather than appearing different in different areas as a result of different specified lamps. Easily cleanable luminaires are more likely to be cleaned, and easily reparable fixtures are more likely to be repaired.

All of this attention to design for maintenance is crucial since lighting systems degrade over time, and maintenance of the systems is crucial to their continued performance. Facility maintenance engineers must make sure that luminaires remain clean and are relamped on a regular basis in order to ensure the efficient, cost-effective performance both of the system and of the tasks to be performed in the visual environment.

7.4.6 Need for flexibility

Medical procedures change rapidly, and these changes require not only modifications in power requirements for a space, but also in illumination of the space. The system should thus also be chosen to allow for easy future renovation. Adjustable, dimmable, and relocatable luminaires should be used where possible to help solve this problem. Flexible wiring systems with easily relocatable luminaires can help make the task of transforming areas from one function to another much more easily accomplished.

7.5 Bibliography

Additional information may be found in the following sources:

[B1] Beck, William C., "Operating Room Illumination: The Current State of the Art," *American College of Surgeons Bulletin,* May, 1981.

[B2] Cowley, Geoffrey, and Wingert, Pat, "Trouble in the Nursery," *Newsweek,* Aug. 28, 1989.

[B3] Henkenius, Merle, "The Right Light, More than Meets the Eye," *Practical Homeowner,* Dec./Jan. 1990.

[B4] IEEE Std 241-1990, IEEE Recommended Practice for Electric Power Systems in Commercial Buildings (IEEE Gray Book) (ANSI).

[B5] *IESNA Lighting Handbook,* 1987 Applications Volume. New York: Illuminating Engineering Society of North America, 1987.

[B6] *IESNA Lighting Handbook,* 1987 Reference Volume. New York: Illuminating Engineering Society of North America, 1987, Sections 4 and 5.

[B7] Inderd, Russell, and Pankin, Sidney, "Fixtures with Specular Reflective Materials Save Energy," *Electrical Construction and Maintenance,* Nov. 1989.

[B8] *Lighting for Health Care Facilities.* New York: Illuminating Engineering Society of North America, CP-29-1985, ISBN 0-87995-023-4.

[B9] Linn, Charles, "A Place Like Home," *Architectural Lighting,* June, 1990.

[B10] Loper, Dawn M., "Lighting and Health—An Annotated Bibliography," *Technical Document Series,* American Society for Hospital Engineering, May 1988.

[B11] Muma, Scott, "Powerful Magnetic Field a Challenge to Lighting MRI Exam Room," *Architectural Lighting,* May, 1988.

[B12] NFPA 70-1996, National Electrical Code® (NEC®).

[B13] Okula, Marcia, *Lighting in Hospitals.*

[B14] Salfino, Catherine Schetting, "Softening the Blow—Sensitive lighting warms up the spaces of Hartford Hospital's Cancer Unit," *Architectural Lighting,* June, 1990.

[B15] Viola, Diane Berrian, "Designing Lighting Systems for Health Care Facilities," *Electrical Consultant,* Mar./Apr. 1985.

Chapter 8
Communication and signal systems

8.1 System design considerations

8.1.1 Introduction

Communication and signal systems make possible the efficient and timely operations of health care facilities. The ever-increasing cost of health care, together with the accelerating levels of technological sophistication of health care equipment, mandates that communication and signal systems be planned with a thorough understanding of their operational and engineering requirements, as well as the economics of their implementation.

When designing a health care facility for new construction or remodeling, it is necessary to consider all systems and to plan accordingly. Each of the major categories of communication and signal systems, together with their nominal physical plant space and installation requirements, are included in this chapter. Although some systems function as integrated systems, they are often designed as separate entities. Therefore, this chapter treats each system as separate and distinctive.

8.1.2 Planning

Advanced technologies, a large number of combined system possibilities, and a wide range of different available functions, make evaluating various systems difficult. The efficiency of a system is not determined by the number of functions it is capable of; rather, it is determined by its ability to improve the user's daily communication. Functions must be logical and simple to operate, or they will have only theoretical interest. Before deciding upon a system it is imperative to address the following points:

a) *Analysis.* Properly integrated communications in a facility should be one of the key factors in analyzing and designing spaces, equipment, and personnel requirements for each health care function. Properly designed total communication systems can help reduce operating expenses and can increase the effectiveness of staff, both of which may be translated into improved patient care.

   In the earliest planning stages of a project, an analysis of current and future communication needs is required. In preparing such a plan, the design team should take into account the current operating techniques of the facility as well as new techniques that can be applied in the future. They should also consider possible changes in the organization during the next five to ten years. These might include university affiliation, mergers, feeder hospitals, extended care facilities, psychiatric facilities, day-care centers, and other factors and developments that may affect the total plan.

   A study of this type involves both the in-house planning team—the administrator, the medical staff, the nursing staff—and the design team.

Factors that should be considered include the movement of supplies; the communication and traffic flow; the number of inpatients and outpatients handled each day, the number of patients needing emergency treatment, surgical procedures, and coronary care, etc.

b) *Communication and signal systems program.* After the preliminary communication analysis has been made, a communications program may be developed. This program will outline the specific communication requirements in the various departments of the facility and will suggest possible ways of satisfying these communication needs.

To prepare this program, an in-depth study of the internal communication system should be made by the design team. These people may be staff members of the facility's architectural or engineering organization or may be outside communications specialists. The results of this study are then translated into a narrative program matrix, including grid sheets showing total communications.

The planning team should prepare a detailed evaluation of the internal and external communications network, including traffic and feasibility studies for each and every department. These studies should show how each department communicates, with whom it communicates, why it communicates, where it communicates, and what is accomplished by the communication.

c) *Economic analysis.* Comparative analysis should be made of alternatives, including cash flow and life cycle cost analysis.

d) *System supplier qualifications.* It is recommended that communication and signal system suppliers be established companies that maintain a staff of competent technicians qualified to assume proper installation of the systems specified, and capable of providing maintenance and repair for these systems on a contract or job order basis. The supplier should have the capability of dispatching a maintenance or repair truck with a qualified repairman to the job site within 4 h of a request for service on the equipment.

8.1.3 Communication and signal command centers

Critical to the electrical engineer's planning and design efforts are command centers within the health care facility. Command centers may occur at the central operator's (telephone general operations or combined) location, at every nurse's station, in the emergency room, and in the operating suite. It is imperative that these critical areas be planned in detail to facilitate effective staff utilization. Accomplishing this requires a thorough knowledge of the procedures to be carried out at each location—gained through discussions with hospital staff—and a thorough knowledge of the equipment available for each system—gained through contact with vendors and through experience. The following checklist includes equipment that might be found at the key control centers:

a) *Central operations center*
   1) Telephone
   2) Physician and staff register annunciator
   3) Voice paging system microphone
   4) Radio paging system encoder

        5)   Fire alarm fan control for smoke control

        6)   Emergency generator annunciator

        7)   Fire alarm control and annunciator

        8)   Medical gas alarm annunciator

        9)   Emergency elevator control and annunciator

       10) Code blue annunciator

       11) Patient management computer terminal

       12) Blood bank alarm

       13) Clock (connected to clock correction system)

       14) Radio communication systems

       15) Security and administrative communication and alarm systems

b)   *Telephone operator's position.* The telephone operator's position may be located coincident with the central operations center or adjacent to the hospital main entrance and lobby.

        1)   Main attendant console (telephone)

        2)   Code blue annunciator

        3)   Clock (connected to clock correction system)

c)   *Nurse station*

        1)   Telephone

        2)   Intercom

        3)   Nurse-call, nurse-assist, and code blue annunciators

        4)   Medical gas alarm annunciator

        5)   Patient-management computer terminal

        6)   Clock (connected to clock correction system)

        7)   Patient physiological monitors

        8)   Dictation station nearby

        9)   Fire alarm annunciator

d)   *Emergency room control center*

        1)   Telephone

        2)   Intercom

        3)   Nurse-call, nurse-assist, and code blue annunciators

        4)   Emergency medical service communication radio control

        5)   Patient-management computer terminal

        6)   Clock (connected to clock correction system)

        7)   Patient physiological monitors

        8)   Dictation station nearby

e)   *Operating suite control center*

        1)   Telephone

        2)   Intercom

        3)   Nurse-call, nurse-assist, and code blue annunciators

        4)   Medical gas alarm annunciator

        5)   Patient-management computer terminal

        6)   Clock (connected to clock correction system)

        7)   Patient physiological monitors

        8)   Dictation station nearby

8.1.4 The communication and signal system strata

Communication and signal systems are built of three distinct strata, each of which displays its own characteristics. Both the longevity and flexibility of each stratum are key to the proper design of communication systems.

The first stratum, the simplest to understand, is the support structure for communication systems. This includes the spaces for equipment and the support (or enclosure) for cable plant and utilities (power, ventilation, access, etc.) required for a complete, operational system. The support structure is the longest lived stratum and must accommodate changes to the cable plant but will be changed itself only at considerable expense. The backbone support structure (vertical riser) should be expected to last the life of the building.

The middle stratum, much less complex than the communication equipment, is the cable plant that interconnects the equipment. The cable plant includes cable terminals and wall jacks. Its components are often divided into two types: backbone (vertical) and station (horizontal) distribution components. The wire plant can be longer lived than the communications equipment, a characteristic often overlooked during design. Cable plant must accommodate change and may be extended on a weekly basis, but it should not need changing in the sense of replacement except near the end of its functional life or when major changes in use occur in the area it serves.

The last stratum, and the most complex, is the communication equipment itself. This includes both the apparatus that staff use moment to moment and the control electronics defining system functionality. The equipment stratum is the shortest lived and must possess the most flexibility, being required to change its response to input hundreds of times daily, and being subject to changes and additions many times monthly. The communication equipment listed in the previous subclause typifies that found in a typical health care facility.

8.1.4.1 Support structure

8.1.4.1.1 Communication and signal closets

In a broad sense, closets are part of the support structure for communication systems. Closets may contain wire, wire terminations, and equipment. They may be arranged in a hierarchy with satellite closets, main closets, and central or building closets (rooms). Various equipment may be located in cabinets without dedicated closet space.

A single closet may contain equipment and wiring of several communication systems (e.g., telephone terminals, nurse-call controller, patient physiological monitor controller, television system distribution cable, public address system equipment, or data transmission equipment).

A closet or cabinet containing equipment of any kind must be treated differently from those containing wire and terminals only. Considerations for equipment spaces are noted in 8.1.4.1.2.

The relative arrangement and particular location of each cabinet, closet, and room containing communications wire, terminals, or equipment should be treated as if it were a resource for the building being serviced. These are the backbone of a support structure which, if designed carefully, will serve several generations of communication equipment over the life of the building. The criteria below need to be weighted appropriately for each project. Once located and sized, these spaces should be treated as solid and permanent parts of the "structure" of the building.

a) Location criteria

1) Locate cabinets, closets, and rooms in the area they serve to reduce the total length of distribution cables and to satisfy maximum distance requirements of the most restrictive system accommodated.

2) Locate closets such that they do not inhibit future renovations. Suitable locations are adjacent to major corridors, core areas, shafts, and stairs.

3) Locate closets so that mechanical ducts or pipes are not above or below.

4) Locate riser closets in a "stacked" arrangement.

5) Locate closets such that each floor has separate communications closets and electrical power closets.

b) Space requirements

1) Allow sufficient space to accommodate all communication equipment, wire, and terminals, keeping in mind any plans for future expansion associated with each system.

2) Allow sufficient space to conform with all codes governing minimum clearances.

3) Allow sufficient space to install a new system without removing the existing one, for each system that may require a high continuity during remodels and expansions in the future.

c) Interconnections

1) Size the raceway, cable tray, or sleeves serving each closet to accommodate all systems including expected future systems.

2) Add sufficient riser support to replace existing systems without taking them out of service.

8.1.4.1.2 Equipment spaces

Main (central) equipment spaces should be located where space is less valuable to the operation of the facility but as close as possible to the center of the facility to minimize cable plant costs. All communications spaces with equipment must be designed to accommodate each piece of equipment as suggested in 8.1.4.1.1. Other criteria for equipment space design are as follows.

a) *Lighting.* Provide 50 fc task illumination at maintenance locations. Provide controls to decrease light levels at maintenance terminal locations. Closets with terminals should be illuminated also.

b) *Water.* Avoid pipes that enter this space except as required for fire-extinguishing systems and water-cooled air-conditioning units serving that space.

c) *Raised floor.* May be considered in large facilities if required; a height of 12–18 in (30–49 cm) is recommended.

d) *Floor finish.* Provide a dust-free finish to maintain a clean environment. If the floor is concrete, specify a sealed finish to minimize dust.

e) *Ventilation.* Provide adequate ventilation. Most equipment generates heat and will malfunction above certain temperature limits.

f) *Room finish.* Avoid spray-on fireproofing of any exposed structure to maintain a clean environment. If fireproofing is required specify a dropped ceiling.

8.1.4.2 Cable plant

Cable plant provides a signal path between user apparatus and central control equipment for most communication and signal systems. The term covers not only the insulated conductors themselves, but also wall outlets, wire terminals, and cross-connect frames. Support structures include the methods and materials used to support and protect the cable plant.

The choice of conductors used for the signal path is usually dictated by the signal characteristics of the communication system under design. Conductor size and number, insulation type and color, shielding and jacketing are all essentially system-dependent (as is discussed elsewhere in this chapter). The choice of methods for support and protection of these conductors is dependent on system characteristics and local codes. The choice is dependent on the classification of the physical spaces where cable plant will be installed. Three basic methods for support and protection of communications conductors in health care facilities are addressed in 8.1.4.2.1–8.1.4.2.3.

8.1.4.2.1 Area classification for cables

Communication cable is classified by the type of space it is installed in. Typical classifications are listed below:

a) Interior spaces
   1) Exposed to physical damage
   2) In ducts or plenums
   3) In noncombustible ceiling blind spaces
   4) In concealed spaces
   5) In shafts
   6) In hoistways

b) Exterior of building
   1) Aerially
   2) Aerially, over roofs
   3) Underground

    4)   On buildings, exposed to physical damage

  c)   Both interior and exterior in locations that are hazardous due to the presence of flammable or explosive materials

Raceways will almost always be required in the following areas:

— Ducts or plenums used for environmental air
— Concealed spaces
— Hoistways
— Shafts
— Hazardous locations
— Underground

Refer to Articles 725, 760, 800, and 820 of the National Electrical Code® (NEC®) (NFPA 70-1996)[1] for exceptions to the requirement for raceways. Raceways will be required for communications systems that are not power-limited and for life safety systems. For communication circuits that are power-limited, raceways may not be required depending on the system's use. Refer to the NEC, Article 760.

The communications system should be further classified under one or more of the following articles of the NEC by system type:

— Article 640: Sound Recording and Similar Equipment
— Article 725: Class 1, Class 2, and Class 3 Remote-Control, Signaling, and Power-Limited Circuits
— Article 760: Fire Alarm Systems
— Article 800: Communication Circuits
— Article 810: Radio and Television Equipment
— Article 820: Community Antenna Television and Radio Distribution Systems

Wiring methods for each classification of communications system are discussed in the appropriate article. The engineer must be familiar with these articles and with local interpretation by code authorities.

Where communications conductors are installed without raceway, they are considered to be open cabling, and they shall be installed as described in 8.1.4.2.2.

8.1.4.2.2 Open cabling

Open cabling is a wiring method for communications conductors that allows insulated conductors to be installed without the use of an enclosing raceway. Open cabling may be installed within a building, aerially between buildings, or underground.

The installation of open cabling shall comply with state and local codes governing these wiring methods. The decision to use cable-in-raceway versus open cabling shall be made by

---

[1]Information on references can be found in 8.21.

the engineer, and the criteria used in making this decision will usually include installed cost, system operating requirements, local codes, and the level of system flexibility desired.

Any communications system under consideration for open wiring should be analyzed from the following standpoints:

a)   Is raceway required to ensure protection of conductors from impact or other physical damage? These requirements are established by the articles of the NEC listed in 8.1.4.2.1.

b)   Is raceway required to provide shielding from electromagnetic interference?

c)   Is it more economical to expand or extend the system if raceway is employed?

If the answer to these questions is no, then open cabling should be considered for the system. This method of cable support will often be less expensive to install and, in the case of accessible interior spaces, easier to maintain and modify.

Open cabling should be installed so as to minimize physical stress on the cables, and maintenance will be much easier if the cables are neatly trained and supported.

Indoors, these goals may be met by supporting the cable from the building structure at regular intervals. The most common methods for cable support are nylon ties, bridle rings, and cable tray. Nylon ties are the least expensive method initially, but they become less economical if frequent cable rerouting is required. Cable tray provides the most accessible and continuous support but is initially expensive. Outdoors, open cabling will be either direct buried cable, messenger supported aerially, or supported from the building structure in the same manner as indoor runs.

Whenever open cabling is used the engineer should be familiar with the specific article of the NEC covering the communications system. The open cable installation methods allowed by these articles contain restrictions on adjacencies to power and lighting conductors, vertical cable runs, penetration of fire barriers, aerial conductors exposed to lightning, etc.

8.1.4.2.3 Open cabling in plenums

Where open cable wiring methods are selected for installation in air-handling ducts or plenums, the methods for supporting the cables will be the same as previously discussed, but the cable insulation materials must be specified to meet special code requirements. Such cable is frequently referred to as plenum cable.

The installation of open cabling in air-handling plenums must comply with state and local codes governing this wiring method. The choice between cable-in-raceway and open cabling should be made by the engineer, and the criteria used in making this choice will most likely be installed cost and required system reliability.

Limiting the spread of fire and products of combustion is of great concern in health care design and requires special attention. Communications cabling is frequently insulated with combustible materials, and the cabling usually extends throughout the building, concealed in hollow spaces, above ceilings, and in return-air plenums.

The NEC addresses this potentially hazardous situation in Article 300, Sections 300-21 and 300-22. Section 300-21 requires the engineer to design electrical installations within "hollow spaces, vertical shafts, and ventilation or air-handling ducts" so that the possible spread of fire or products of combustion will not be substantially increased. This section also requires approved firestops at openings in fire barriers. Section 300-22 specifically discusses four different hollow spaces where electrical installations are restricted. The following sentences paraphrase these code restrictions:

a) *Ducts for dust, loose stock, or vapor removal.* No wiring of any kind is allowed in these ducts.

b) *Ducts or plenums used for environmental air.* Spaces in this category are "ducts or plenums specifically fabricated to transport environmental air." The code allows certain types of wiring in raceway to be installed in such ducts, but open wiring is not permitted.

c) *Other space used for environmental air.* The NEC clarifies "other space" as "other spaces such as spaces over hung ceilings which are used for environmental air handling purposes." Again, the code allows wiring in certain types of raceway, and in addition, "other factory assembled multiconductor control or power cable which is specifically listed for the use."

d) *Air-handling areas beneath raised floors, data processing areas.* Open wiring is allowed in such spaces under certain conditions. These conditions are listed in Article 645.

It is important to be familiar with Article 300-22, because it defines potentially hazardous "hollow spaces" in a clear way, and broadly states what wiring methods, if any, are allowed in each type of space. However, the engineer should also be familiar with the articles pertaining to the specific communication system that is to be installed, before reaching a full understanding of the NEC wiring requirements for such spaces (see 8.1.4.2.1).

Cable manufacturers can supply single and multiconductor cables that are listed to be applied under one or more of the articles in the NEC.

8.1.5 Power supply

8.1.5.1 General

All electrical communications and signal systems with local control equipment require at least one connection to the building power distribution system to obtain operating power. The manner in which this connection is made in health care facilities is governed by code requirements and good design practices. The goal of these requirements and practices is to ensure a high reliability of communication and signal systems essential to patient safety. The codes directly applicable to this area are the following:

— The NEC

— NFPA 99-1996
— NFPA 101-1994

8.1.5.2 Design considerations—clinics, outpatient facilities, and medical and dental offices

The only code requirements established for communication and signal systems in these occupancies govern the fire alarm system. Where the system is a local energy type, the ac power source should comply with NFPA 72-1996, which requires two sources of supply and a dedicated circuit for the fire alarm system. Wiring methods must comply with Article 517 of the NEC, which in the case of a fire alarm system are no different than Chapters 1 through 4 of the NEC.

If a building in these occupancies contains elevator controls, security, radio paging, voice paging, or visual paging systems, it is good design practice to provide a second source of supply (battery) for each system.

8.1.5.3 Nursing homes and residential custodial care facilities

Occupancies in these categories must first be examined for code applicability:

— Are patients at any time sustained by electrical life support systems?
— Are patients at any time subjected to surgical procedures requiring general anesthesia?

If the answer to both of these questions is no, and if the occupancy is provided with a 1-1/2 h alternate power source complying with Section 517-40 of the NEC, then the engineer must ensure that lighting in communications areas and all alarm systems within the building are connected to the alternate power source.

Where the answer to either of these questions is yes, the occupancy must be provided with an essential electrical system, as described by Article 517 of the NEC.

In these occupancies, the life safety branch of the essential electrical system shall provide power to the following communication and signal systems (and only these systems):

— Fire alarm
— Medical gas alarm
— Communications systems used for issuing instructions during emergency conditions

In addition, the following systems shall be connected to the critical branch

— Elevator communications (sometimes via the telephone system)
— Control systems and alarms required for operation of major apparatus

Wiring methods for connection to the essential electrical system shall comply with Chapters 1–4 of the NEC, except that life safety branch wiring must be kept entirely independent of all other wiring (see Article 517 of the NEC).

Remaining communications and signaling systems not already mentioned and associated with patient care should also be connected to the critical branch.

8.1.5.4 Hospitals

The code requirements for connection of ac power to hospital communications and signaling systems are as follows:

a) Life safety branch (no other systems may be connected)
  1) Fire alarm
  2) Medical gas alarm
  3) Communications systems used for issuing instructions during emergency conditions
  4) Elevator communications (sometimes via the telephone system)
b) Critical branch
  1) Telephone
  2) Nurse-call system
  3) Nurse-assist system
  4) Code blue system
c) Equipment branch
  1) Control systems and alarms required for safe operation of major apparatus
  2) Controls for compressed air systems serving medical and surgical functions

Under both the critical branch and equipment branch headings, the code will allow connection of equipment necessary for effective hospital operation. All communication and signal systems not already mentioned and associated with patient care should be connected to the critical branch.

8.1.6 Computer and combination systems

Microcomputer prices are dropping steadily. This fact, coupled with increasing knowledge and sensitivity in the development and utilization of the required software, promises cost-effective, "user-friendly" solutions to communications problems.

The primary difference between the microcomputer systems and all other systems centers around the functional flexibility and adaptability of the system as controlled by the stored program data processor. Functions; instructions; user terminology, nomenclature, and vocabulary; display formats; message content; and many other variables can be customized for each installation. State-of-the-art systems allow most of this flexibility to be placed in the hands of the user. Capable system suppliers can provide extensive in-service training in system operation, set-up, modification, and testing.

Microcomputers allow many systems to be combined with such functions as bed status, dietary programs, automatic paging terminals, patient and staff directories, etc. Although this combination will work, the overall complexity of the resulting system may render it unusable. It may be prudent to purchase separate stand-alone systems so that the user may depend upon several systems (and operators) in a critical emergency.

8.1.7 Future outlook

There is no question that many individual communication functions of present-day systems will soon be accomplished by integrated systems. The technology of digital computers and data communication links provides the opportunity for this integration, and the pressure of health care costs and advanced medical technology provides the incentive. The engineer should be aware of the direction and intensity of this trend in order to incorporate the greatest possible support for future system changes.

The cable plant will no longer consist of many different types of cables and outlets, but rather one or two cable types with common outlets located in almost every room of the facility. The central control center will no longer contain many different system displays and inputs, but rather an integrated display of various hospital systems. Every user terminal will contain some level of processing power, and the quality of the electrical power supplied to these terminals will be critical. Allowing space for fiber optics, television cable (coax), and data lines at a central building location is wise since buildings built today will still be standing when the next generation of communication systems appears. In any case, space must be allowed for system growth in all riser and distribution networks, since most health care facilities will experience growth, and an on-line system may be switched over to a parallel system. New systems may be added to existing communication network space. The space allocated to communications will always pay for itself in future capability in the communication-dependent health care world.

The trend toward centralization and integration of the communications functions will place increasing importance on the reliability of basic system components, and therefore on the design, installation, and maintenance of those components.

8.2 Telephone systems

8.2.1 Introduction

A health care facility's telephone system, at its most basic level, is an extension of the global public switched network. It provides two-way access between the facility and the rest of the world. But the telephone system can furnish and connect to a wide array of services that augment the usefulness of the basic telephone.

Telephone services are implemented in several forms. Switching devices range from the electronic key telephone system (EKTS), through the private branch exchange (PBX) system, to the central office. A relatively new category, the hybrid system, is a crossbreed between the EKTS and the PBX systems. The EKTS, hybrid, and PBX systems usually reside in the facility (or on the campus) that they serve. The central office consists of utility equipment and usually resides some distance from the facility. The feature list of each system type is long. Each system type best serves a specific set of criteria.

8.2.2 Design criteria for telephone systems

Many health care institutions use a portion of their resources to market themselves to the public. A prospective client's first contact with the institution is often by phone. Therefore, the telephone system must furnish, among other things, an effective channel of communication from the public to the appropriate hospital staff. Though the general goals of each system vary for the particular institution, it is important that each of the following goals be examined for applicability:

a)   Efficient and gracious handling of incoming calls, especially for first time callers, information requests, and people in need of medical assistance.

b)   Providing easy-to-use patient telephone service. This may involve collecting billing information for long-distance calls.

c)   Providing access for visitors to the public network. This is typically accomplished through pay telephone stations, but consideration should be given to furnishing free access for local calls especially near family waiting rooms, etc.

d)   Providing an efficient communication base for administrative and operations staff.

e)   Providing access to the public network for personal use by staff.

8.2.3 System types

8.2.3.1 EKTS

The electronic key telephone system (EKTS) is a direct logical replacement for the outmoded mechanical key system that was common in many health care facilities. The EKTS serves from 2 to 80 telephones.

The modern EKTS, unlike its grandfather key system, is a compact, feature-laden telephone system. It lacks only those services required by larger systems. The EKTS is easy to use and therefore often serves departments within a larger facility, itself being connected to PBX or central office switching equipment. (The former is an off-campus PBX or OPX connection.)

8.2.3.2 Hybrid systems

The hybrid system, between the EKTS and the PBX both in features and size, serves from 20 to 400 telephones.

The hybrid system attempts to maintain the ease of use associated with the EKTS via push-button access while adding the support required for small PBX systems. Some of these systems actually have a PBX mode and an EKTS mode, but do not allow both types of services at an individual instrument. This combination can be advantageous in regard to a couple of features listed in 8.2.4.

8.2.3.3 PBX

The private branch exchange (PBX) system includes a broad range of sizes. Depending on the manufacturer, they may economically serve from 80 to 5000 telephones. This range is extended to from 20 to 30 000 telephones for exceptional cases. Technically, when a system approaches 10 000 telephones it is usually a central office class switch, but when privately owned it is called a PBX.

PBX systems provide support for inexpensive single-line telephones (instruments with a basic 12-button keypad) via feature access codes. The disadvantage of feature codes is that a user without the code cannot access the feature. All state-of-the-art PBX systems support a proprietary multibutton (sometimes called electronic set) telephone with direct access to features via the buttons. Electronic sets are typically several times more expensive than single-line telephones. A PBX system with an appropriate selection of electronic sets and single-line telephones balances economic and operational requirements.

8.2.3.4 Central office

Central office switching serves systems from 1 to 10 000 telephones. Greater numbers are possible when additional exchange prefixes (the first three digits of a seven-digit telephone number) are assigned. In systems this large, utility switching equipment is likely to be on site.

Central office packages provided by local telephone utilities can be tailored to look like local PBX systems. The use of modified single-line instruments, which furnish several useful features internally, fleshes out the central office packages. This arrangement leaves the utility responsible for system maintenance. Central office switching is a viable option for many institutions.

8.2.3.5 Instrumentation

Telephones come in many flavors. The simplest single-line telephone, with its keypad, will run on most systems, but may not be able to access all of a system's available features. Buttons, lights, speakers, digital readouts, headphones, computer terminal displays, and slow scan video are available in varying combinations on the ascending ladder of instrument cost. Many of the features of a particular instrument are dependent on the equipment it is connected to. Most instrumentation is proprietary and will operate only with the equipment for which it was developed. The instrumentation available with a particular system will often determine its applicability in an installation.

8.2.4 System features

The list of available telephone system features may be 300 items long. The features listed below are but a small selection, chosen to highlight a few design issues and to help differentiate the system types outlined in 8.2.3.1–8.2.3.4.

8.2.4.1 Speed dialing

Simply dial a code or press a button, then dial a shorthand number to place a commonly made call. Many instruments will dial five or ten common numbers at the touch of a single button. Most systems offer speed dialing. It saves time, and falls under the general category of efficiency (in the utilization of staff time). A host of other features are intended to improve staff efficiency. Each must be weighed against the added complexity for the user.

8.2.4.2 Intercom

Telephonic intercom describes the ability to dial a number and ring another person on the same switching system. Usually the number is short (2, 3, or 4 digits).

Intercom instruments have an item not found on a standard single-line telephone: a speaker separate from the handset. (In fact, some intercom instruments have no handset.) But a telephone can be equipped with a speaker and made to serve as an intercom station, allowing the called party to answer without touching his handset (i.e., hands are free).

Most EKTS and PBX systems support speakerphones, which allow intercom conversations, but with one difference. PBX systems generally do not allow off-hook voice announcements (enabling an intercom call while the telephone is being used for a telephone conversation). Many EKTSs and a couple of hybrid systems do allow them. Therefore, the design issue to be addressed is that of finding the telephone system that will meet the requirements for the intercom system. See 8.3.

8.2.4.3 System interconnection

From a telephone instrument staff might be able to leave dictation, perform a public address voice page, or send a code to a pocket pager. Most systems have these capabilities. These connections add to the telephone switch load, tie up telephones and, if not specifically controlled, allow universal access to special services. Most telephone systems respond to these concerns, including the ability to control access to special services.

8.2.4.4 Multiple-attendant answering

In larger facilities multiple-attendant positions might be required to handle incoming calls. Most systems support multiple-attendant consoles and alternate answering locations, but some are limited to small numbers, such as 2 or 4. A facility's communication needs should be reviewed so that specific switches considered for purchase will accommodate these needs and not present limitations that could make the switches obsolete.

The basic capacity of a PBX system is described in terms of several parameters. The number of station lines corresponds to the stations required to serve the facility. Attendant consoles are counted separately from other stations. The number of trunks must support the volume of calls to and from the public switched network whether local or long-distance calls. Services like public address paging, radio paging, and dictation have specialized interfaces to the system.

8.2.4.5 DID

Direct inward dialing (DID) is a mechanism for calling an individual telephone (or department attendant) instead of the main operator. DID is available on PBX systems, on most hybrid systems, and via central office switching. This feature can provide the public direct access to several locations in the facility without having to burden the main operator with every call.

8.2.4.6 Voice mail

Voice mail resembles a large answering machine, except that it can be accessed remotely (by both sending and receiving parties). This tool is excellently matched to simple message-passing between people on different time schedules. Some people love it; however, it should not be applied in situations in which an urgent message might be slowed, nor should a person new to the system be automatically connected to voice mail (especially a public call). Measure the use of each tool against the general goals of the system.

8.2.4.7 SMDR and SMDA

Station message detail recording (SMDR) and station message detail accounting (SMDA) allow larger systems to track and record telephone use and, alternately, produce cost accounting reports reflecting telephone activity. The reports may include sufficient detail to allow assignment of telephone expenses to patient accounts. All system types can support these features to varying degrees. Generally SMDR and SMDA features are run on an optional microcomputer connected to the switching equipment. These are management tools that aid in both monitoring the effectiveness of the system and furnishing a metered service to patients.

8.2.4.8 Automatic route selection

Supported by PBX systems and by some hybrid systems, automatic route selection uses a data reserve to select long-distance call routes that minimize long-distance bills. This feature reflects the need to consider the total system, including utility connections and usage patterns, when analyzing the economy of various systems.

8.2.4.9 ISDN compatibility

Integrated services digital network (ISDN) is a standard interface description for utility connections. It is not commonly used now, but is expected to become more popular because it offers several new features. These include text messages identifying the calling party and better integration of voice and data services. Nearly every large PBX should now be ISDN-compatible.

The communication needs of an institution are likely to change. They will likely include a higher level of data services in the future. The selection criteria of any large PBX should include provisions for data services and compliance with the latest industry transmission and signaling standards.

8.2.4.10 Tandem switching

This is the ability for one PBX to talk with another PBX (usually of the same manufacture) so that they appear to operate as one switching system. This capability can allow an effective growth path and can provide an economical solution to cable plant design in large complexes.

8.2.4.11 Remote diagnostics

On many systems, maintenance and programming assistance can be provided by the system vendor from the vendor's site. The alternative to this is the purchase of a maintenance terminal for a PBX. Some systems furnish maintenance operations through an attendant console terminal. Remote diagnostics are especially effective with mid-sized systems where it may not be economical to purchase a maintenance terminal. The system selection should include a review of maintenance and change procedures in light of ease of use. Some systems come with step-by-step on-screen menus, including all maintenance functions.

The issues of maintenance and reliability blend. Battery backup associated with a telephone switch is generally an inexpensive (and worthwhile) option since the equipment utilizes the battery voltage directly.

Other means of increasing reliability include redundant common control, essentially a duplication of the switch logic circuits. Redundant common control is a pricy option, but it is found on some large PBX systems and on many central office class switches.

8.2.5 Telephone cable plant and support structure

A complete system for telephone facilities in a building includes provisions for the entrance cables, the main terminal and equipment room, the riser cable system, the distribution cable system for each floor, the cable distribution terminals, and the station cabling. Early contact with the building industry consulting service (BICS) at the local telephone interconnect company is advantageous to the designer on all buildings regardless of the specific tenants or type of telephone equipment being proposed.

Subclauses 8.2.5.1–8.2.5.6 outline telephone facilities only, as opposed to communication facilities, which include data, video, and other systems. The space requirements given in these subclauses apply to telephone facilities only.

8.2.5.1 Service entrance cables

This is the means by which the telephone company cables cross the owner's property and enter a building. The type and location of the service depends upon telephone company distribution facilities, local practices, and codes. Service will normally be furnished from underground cables. In most localities service duct will be provided by the owner. Direct buried service may be allowed in some areas. The owner must provide the necessary trench work. Some areas require a utility easement for buried service.

The number of entrance conduits required should be based on the ultimate number of telephone lines. For most systems, a 4 in (10 cm) conduit for every 150 000 ft^2 (1 3935 m^2) of usable floor space with a minimum of two conduits is recommended.

In large or specialized installations provisions for fiber optic cables may be appropriate. These cables are smaller than large twisted pair telephone cables. Fiber cables should be installed in smaller, dedicated conduits or in innerduct (protective tubes) within larger ducts. This may lead to service requirements in addition to the conduits noted above.

A means of bonding and grounding cable inside the building is necessary. The openings for cable entrance should always be kept sealed around installed cable to avoid penetration of water and gas, and to avoid service interruption from flooding or equipment damage from dampness.

Whatever the type of entry, suitable provisions must be made for the appropriate openings through the building structure (with sleeves or conduit) well in advance of the required service date. General recommendations regarding conduit entrances are as follows:

a) Use corrosion-resistant material.

b) There should not be more than two 90 degree bends, and large radius bends are recommended.

c) All ends are to be reamed and bushed, or capped, or both.

d) Sleeves through foundation walls must reach undisturbed earth to prevent shear of direct buried cables.

e) Minimum depth should be 18 in (46 cm) or deeper as required by local codes.

f) Conduit placed on private property must not be terminated in joint-use manholes with electrical cables or equipment.

g) Provide means for locating or identifying nonmetallic buried conduits from above the surface.

Consideration for a dual service entrance provision should be given to hospital facilities.

The local telephone company building industry consultant can be of great assistance in designing the service entrance. Refer to local telephone company guidelines.

8.2.5.2 Main terminal room

The heart of the building's communications system is the main terminal room. It is the main cross-connecting point between the telephone company central office and the riser cable system. The entrance cable usually runs directly to this main terminal room after it is brought into the building.

Conduit should be used from the service entrance to the main terminal. Conduit simplifies future additions and protects the service cable. For some types of cable, codes require metal conduit.

The terminal room should be accessible to communications personnel at all times. It should be located as close as possible to the center of the riser-cable distribution facilities. The room should be well lighted, cooled, ventilated, and equipped with electric outlets. Its floor support must be designed to support heavy terminal equipment. This room should be used only for communication equipment, and it should be capable of being locked for security reasons.

The main terminal room will contain the utility demarcation point. Telephone utility cables from the central office are routed through protective devices and terminated on special jacks called the network interface. These jacks form the boundary between the utility and the premises distribution system. Utility cable terminals and cable protectors (surge protection) are always utility property. Surge protection for data and communications cables may be required within the premises in addition to the utility surge protection. The terminal room may also contain utility-owned switching and transmission equipment. The terminal room contains terminals for the building (or campus) distribution cables, usually labeled the main distribution frame (MDF). The MDF and distribution cables are usually owner property.

For large installations, floor-type main terminals are located in the main terminal room. The space allocated to this room must be adequate to meet the original telephone service needs of the occupants and to provide for later installation of additional terminals for growth. Depending upon communication requirements, batteries may have to be installed in or near the main terminal room.

In smaller buildings wall-type main terminals are commonly used. Each terminal provides connections for the desired number of pairs of cable for voice and data equipment.

Switching equipment [i.e., the private branch exchange (PBX)] may be located in the main terminal room. In this event, the room's environment and electrical services must accommodate the PBX. See 8.2.5.6.

8.2.5.3 Riser systems

The riser system is the backbone of the building's telephone network. It provides facilities for bringing cables from the main terminal room to the various floors of the building.

The riser cables should be fed through riser conduits or sleeves depending upon the relative location of riser closets. Local codes should be checked to determine the responsibility for fire prevention in both used and unused riser facilities.

Telephone cable used for risers is generally multipair #24 AWG copper wire with an overall sheath. Nominal pair counts of 50, 100, 200, 300, 400 and 600 pairs are available. The riser cable should be sized to serve the worst-case scenario for growth and change. Usually health care facilities require less telephones per floor area than office buildings, the exception being a medical office floor where telephone sets (utilized for intercom services) may appear in each exam, conference, and office space. Generally three pairs of riser cable for each 150 ft^2 (13.9 m^2) of gross floor area will handle telephone requirements for a hospital. (If data terminals are connected via the telephone cable plant, additional riser pairs will be required.) So, for example, a closet serving 20 000 ft^2 (1858 m^2) would require a 400-pair riser cable.

Horizontal telephone distribution cable should be four-pair cable, terminated in a standard wall jack and at station terminals (in the telephone closets). Terminals for 100 pairs of cable should be allowed for each 3600 ft^2 (101.9 m^2) of space served by the closet. Our example closet serving 20 000 ft^2 (1858 m^2) of floor area would contain 600 pairs of station terminals. Using typical terminal block materials, our example riser terminals, wire management space, and station terminals require between 1 ft^2 (0.9 m^2) and 2 ft^2 (0.2 m^2) of wall space (without any equipment) for each 100 pairs of station terminals.

8.2.5.4 Apparatus closets

The equipment needed for EKTS services is often housed in the apparatus closets. Locating apparatus in closets eliminates unsightly wiring and contributes to improved appearance. When maintenance or changes are required, communication workers may do their work without inconvenience or distraction to personnel. Physical conditions within the building frequently dictate the number, location, and type of closets. In general one apparatus closet should be required for each 10 000 ft^2 (929 m^2) of usable floor area. This can vary up to a maximum of 20 000 ft^2 (1858 ft^2) of floor area, depending upon access and other layout considerations.

Apparatus closets should be lined with 0.75 in (3 cm) thick fire-resistant plywood to a height of 8 ft (2.4 m) for mounting equipment, terminals, and training cable plant. Floor, walls, and ceiling should be designed in accordance with the fire codes, and proper lighting with switching should be installed. Ventilation is required. One dedicated, 20 A, three-wire circuit and at least two 120 V, duplex receptacles or an electric plug-in strip are required. A #6 AWG copper wire connected to the building ground is required in all apparatus closets.

When data network equipment will be accommodated in the apparatus closets additional power and cooling may be required. When designing integrated communication facilities allow sufficient depths for walk-in closets. Note that spaces containing communication equipment requiring power are often labeled communication equipment rooms (CERs) rather than apparatus closets.

Closets should be sized to provide wall space (measured horizontally) to support terminals, riser cable, and miscellaneous equipment. Plan about 3.5 ft (1.1 m) of clear wall for closets serving up to 10 000 ft^2 (929 m^2) and 6 ft (1.8 m) of clear wall for closets serving up to 20 000 ft^2 (1858 m^2). If equipment is expected, the closet should be 3 ft (0.9 m) deep; otherwise, a 1.5 ft (0.5 m) deep closet is acceptable. Closet doors should open over 80% of the wall space.

8.2.5.5 Satellite closets

Satellite closets (or cabinets) usually do not contain electronic and power equipment. Their primary use is to provide cable terminating facilities; that is, connecting blocks for station wiring.

Satellite closets are often necessary because of the inadequate space of a single apparatus closet to meet increasing needs, or to better serve the physical layout and shape of the building. A length of 2 ft (0.6 m) of wall is required for each 4000 ft^2 (371.6 m^2) of area served, up to the size of an apparatus closet (8.2.5.4).

8.2.5.6 Telephone equipment rooms

In many buildings involving large, sophisticated installations, additional floor area and adequate floor support are necessary to accommodate the complex switching equipment associated with PBX or Centrex telephone services. For early planning purposes, a PBX and main distribution frame should be allotted the larger of an 8 ft × 12 ft (2.4 m × 3.7 m) space or 0.2% of the gross floor area to be served (including expected future growth). This is in addition to the space required for apparatus closets and satellite closets. Since PBX and Centrex services will vary according to the needs of building tenants, each equipment room must be individually designed. Such rooms should be centrally located, well lighted, and ventilated. They may require cooling. They should be equipped with power and grounding facilities. PBX equipment can require as little as a 20 A, single-phase, dedicated circuit or as much as an 80 A, three-phase connection. Power should be provided from the life safety system if it is used for emergency communications, or from the critical system if not. Specific requirements must be investigated in each case and for each supplier who may furnish a system. The room should be as clean as possible, and located in an area not subject to dampness or flood. The PBX supplier should be contacted for advice on designing individual equipment rooms.

8.2.6 Public telephones

While telephone companies will install pre-manufactured telephone booths at suitable locations, built-in booths with a wide variety of designs, finishes, and colors greatly enhance the appearance of the building. Telephone companies are prepared to work with the building designers toward providing facilities that will harmonize with the interior.

Public telephones should be located where they will be readily accessible to the general public and contractors. In many cases, signs harmonizing with the architectural design of the building are desirable to call attention to the telephone locations. Accessibility for the handicapped is now required when designing public telephone facilities.

There is no simple reliable rule for determining the most suitable number of public telephones that should be provided. For help with this design issue, the telephone company's public telephone business representatives can be consulted.

8.3 Intercom systems

8.3.1 Introduction

Intercom systems provide fast, efficient, internal, verbal communication within the health care facility. In addition, loud-speaking intercom systems can provide voice-paging capabilities.

8.3.2 Design criteria for intercom systems

8.3.2.1 General

Statistical investigations made by objective communication consultants have shown that 70% of communication in health care facilities is internal. Other studies have indicated that a loud-speaking internal call via an intercom system takes an average of 30 s to complete, whereas an internal call via a telephone takes 3 min. The internal-external communication ratio may deviate from facility to facility, but even if the ratio in a specific facility should be much lower than the average, the need for a separate loud-speaking system for internal communication is justified by two reasons.

First, using the telephone for internal calls will block external calls, even though voice lines may be available, since a number of telephones will always be busy on internal calls except for EKTSs. It is impractical to use the same telephone instrument to consult with someone else within the facility while using the telephone for an external call.

Second, using a separate loud-speaking intercom system will speed up and improve internal communication. People communicate with brevity and precision when they are aware that others may overhear what is being said. The quick and simple operation of an intercom system stimulates frequent use.

In summary, the installation of a loud-speaking intercom system can improve the overall efficiency of a health care facility. It can also provide a backup internal communications system in case of failure of the basic telephone system.

8.3.2.2 System selection

There are a number of factors that affect the type and size of an intercom system, including the facility's size, the traffic capacity required, and whether the system will be localized by department or consist of one large hospital-wide intercom system with stations located throughout the facility.

8.3.2.3 Local intercom systems

Small localized intercom systems can provide paging and hands-free answer-back voice communications within each department. Local intercom systems are especially suited to areas where there is a central control point for the department, such as a reception desk. Intercom stations can be master stations, which have the capability of calling and receiving calls from any station in the system, or staff stations which, depending upon the system, can only call and receive calls from a limited number of master stations. For example, in a radiology department a master intercom station could be located at the reception desk with staff stations located in each x-ray room. The master station can call each staff station, and each staff station can call the master station, but staff stations cannot call each other.

Local intercom systems are usually installed in radiology departments, laboratory, laundry, dietary offices, loading docks, surgery suites, physical therapy, and other areas required by the facility. In patient care areas, an audiovisual nurse-call system can provide intercom capabilities within a department, and both nurse-call and intercom requirements can be provided by one system. See 8.4.

8.3.2.4 Hospital-wide (multiple master) intercom systems

Depending on the facility's communications requirements there may be several situations in which one intercom station has to be able to call several others located throughout the facility. A standard master-staff intercom system cannot easily satisfy this multiple-station calling requirement, and an all-master intercom system should be installed. In this type of system, most of the stations are master stations with the capability of calling any other station in the system and conversing hands-free at both stations. Staff stations, connected to a dedicated master station, can be utilized in areas that do not require multiple-station-calling capabilities. If the facility has a number of localized intercom requirements with branches to other departments, it may become more advantageous to install one large intercom system to serve both localized and facility-wide intercom requirements.

8.3.3 System types and selection

8.3.3.1 Local intercom systems

Local intercom systems usually consist of one central master station with several staff stations located throughout the department. Ceiling speakers can also be installed to provide local paging in the corridors and in other spaces where intercom stations are not installed. Space for a power supply and control equipment will have to be included in the electrical design.

8.3.3.2 Multiple master intercom systems

These types of systems can be divided into two separate groups: hardwired systems and microprocessor-controlled systems. Hardwired systems operate like local intercom systems with the exception that there are more master stations on the system with the capability of each master station being able to call more than one location.

Microprocessor-controlled systems use a common cabling scheme that reduces the wiring requirements and costs over a hardwired system. They can also offer various programmable features including:

a) *Restricted access.* Any station can be restricted to operate a limited number of functions, such as paging and group calls, and/or be restricted to call only certain other stations. Within this second restriction, groups of stations may be restricted from calling other groups of stations.

b) *Audio program distribution.* Multiple programs such as radio, weather reports, and taped educational programs can be selected from any station. The audio program is interrupted whenever the station is being used for incoming or outgoing calls.

c) *Camp-on-busy.* If the called station is engaged, the caller receives a busy signal, and the call remains camped on the desired party number for up to 120 s. As soon as the called station becomes free, the call is automatically set up with normal call tone.

d) *Automatic recall.* Called station engaged—low-priority call. During camp-on-busy, the caller can request an automatic recall to free his own station for other calls while waiting for the first station to become free. The first call is then established as soon as both stations are free.

e) *Break-in.* Called station engaged—high-priority call. During camp-on-busy, the caller (A) can break in on the engaged station (B) if the call is urgent. Both parties in conversation (B and C) will be warned by call tone and will overhear the break-in call. Caller (A) can withdraw at any time, leaving (B) and (C) in conversation. Caller (C) can also be asked to withdraw, leaving (A) and (B) in conversation.

f) *Break-in immunity.* Any station can be modified to have break-in immunity. Such stations can then not be broken in on. The break-in function can, of course, be completely removed from the total system, if required.

g) *Automatic transfer.* Number transfer. Any station number can be transferred to any other station so that incoming calls are automatically transferred to a location where the subscriber is temporarily located. The instruction can be given from any station in the system. Multiple numbers can be transferred to the same station. This feature can be used for two main purposes:

   1) *Secretarial transfer.* Persons who do not wish to be disturbed for a period, or who are not present, can ask a colleague or a secretary to take their calls. During a meeting a secretary can take calls for all members.

   2) *Follow-me (call forwarding).* Persons who visit other offices can route their calls to any present location. During a meeting all members can route their calls to the meeting room.

h) *Conference.* Additional stations can be interconnected for conferencing.

i) *Group call.* Announcement to a group of stations. A predetermined group of stations can be called from any station in the system, for giving a one-way message. A group call has priority over other calls. Several groups can be formed in the system (standard up to 10), and each station can be a member of several different groups.

j) *All call.* Group call to all stations—emergency call. All stations in the system can be called for giving a short one-way message. This function can be used for paging people. However, this is not advisable, especially in larger systems. Why disturb the complete organization to get hold of one individual? "All call" should only be used for emergency calls.

k)   *Call forwarding.* Backup station. This function allows selected stations to cause incoming calls to be automatically directed to a secretary's/assistant's station.

l)   *Single-digit and reduced-digit dialing.* This feature allows single-digit or reduced-digit dialing of the most-called stations, such as the reception desk, or of any frequently used feature, such as paging system access.

m) *Public-address (PA) access.* Announcements via PA system. The system can be linked to a PA system for giving one-way messages.

n)   *Page reply.* Paging a person on the move. A paged person can answer the page from any intercom station in the system and be connected directly with the person that originated the page.

o)   *Stored-voice message.* The exchange may be connected to a stored-voice message system for voice mail on the intercom system. This system allows callers to leave individual recorded messages both on their own and on other stations to be retrieved when the called party returns.

p)   *Other functions.* Tailor-made functions. For special projects and larger systems any function can be defined in accordance with specified requirements. Standard features cover most needs, and are, of course, less expensive to incorporate.

8.3.4 Design considerations for intercom systems

After the engineer has talked with the facility staff and has determined the type and size of the intercom system that best satisfies the facility's needs, the system can be designed.

a)   *Station locations.* Master and staff intercom stations can be either desk- or wall-mounted. These stations should be wall-mounted whenever possible to provide as much desk space as possible. Avoid locating stations in adjacent rooms in the same stud cavity to prevent potential feedback problems. Handsets may be required in high ambient noise areas. Exterior stations should be of weatherproof construction.

b)   *Station handsets.* Optional handsets can be used for stations located in high ambient noise areas or where confidentiality during a conversation needs to be maintained. Use of a handset should be carefully considered as its use will defeat the primary advantage of an intercom system to provide quick, hands-free communications.

c)   *Station grouping in a multiple master intercom system.* When stations are combined together into different paging groups, the groups should be determined during design so that the system supplier properly installs the system. For example, the intercom stations in the surgery department should be in a separate paging group from those in the laboratory to prevent laboratory intercom paging calls from disturbing the surgery staff.

d)   *Station identification.* In a multiple master intercom system with stations installed throughout the facility, a master index of station extension numbers will be required. One idea is to have the intercom station number the same as the telephone extension number in the same room. This would save printing two separate in-house telephone and intercom directories.

e) *Central controller.* The central controller should be installed in a communications closet. See 8.2.5.6. If the intercom system will be used to provide emergency communications, connect it to the life safety system; otherwise, connect it to the critical system.

8.4 Nurse-call systems

8.4.1 Introduction

A nurse-call system primarily provides a means for a patient to signal the nursing staff that he or she requires assistance. In addition to patient-nurse communication, a nurse-call system can also serve to provide other signaling requirements, such as signaling other departments that a nurse or other staff member needs additional assistance.

8.4.2 Design criteria for nurse-call systems

8.4.2.1 General

Nurse-call systems are required in hospitals, nursing homes, and psychiatric care facilities by health facility regulations. Usually these requirements are minimum standards and the facility's own communications requirements will dictate the type of system installed and the location of the different components to integrate the nurse-call system throughout the facility. Nurse-call systems are not required in medical and dental offices, medical clinics, and residential care facilities (depending on local code requirements); however, some type of signal system may be desired by the staff for more efficient operation. The U.S. Department of Labor Occupational Safety and Health Administration (OSHA) requires that all nurse-call equipment be certified by a nationally recognized testing laboratory. One industry standard is UL 1069-1989. Nurse-call systems are primarily divided into two basic groups: visual systems, which utilize light and tone signals for annunciation of calls, and audiovisual systems, which provide voice communication in addition to the light and tone signals. By utilizing the right components, an audiovisual system can satisfy the interdepartmental intercom requirements and provide voice communications with other areas in the facility.

8.4.2.2 Programming

Before an engineer completes the design, he or she should confer with staff members to find out how the particular department will operate and determine their specific communications requirements. In order to effectively conference with the staff, the engineer should have a basic understanding of the different systems available and their limitations so he or she can help the facility choose the type of system that best meets their needs. For example, one of the requirements in a radiology department may be to have a signal system from the dressing room to the x-ray room to indicate when the patient is ready for examination. A visual nurse-call system would satisfy this requirement; however, if voice communication for each x-ray room to a central reception desk is also requested, both functions could be served by an audiovisual nurse-call system. If each x-ray room needs to be able to call other rooms besides a central location, a separate intercom system and a visual nurse-call system would have to be installed because audiovisual nurse-call systems are limited in the number of other locations each staff station can call.

Some of the basic questions that an engineer needs to answer before designing a nurse-call system include the following:

a) How large is the department? Will a visual nurse-call system satisfy the requirements or would an audiovisual system be a better choice?

b) Which rooms or areas need to communicate with each other? Can this communication be accomplished by telephone or would a loud-speaking intercom system be a better choice? Do rooms in the department need to be able to talk with each other or just to a central location? The intercom capabilities of an audiovisual nurse-call system can satisfy the latter requirement provided each room does not need to talk with more than one master station. Combined intercom/nurse-call systems can provide intercom communication to multiple rooms as well as nurse-call annunciation at the central nurse station. Patient room to patient room intercommunication may be desirable in intensive care/coronary care units or in birthing rooms where the nurse is located in the patient's room and needs to communicate with other nurses/ staff without leaving the patient.

c) In a hospital, are there any swing rooms that have to be connected to different nurses' stations at different times depending on the bed requirements in each nursing unit?

d) In a hospital or psychiatric care facility, which areas require nurse assist or other emergency calls and where should these calls be annunciated?

e) In a hospital, are other nursing stations to provide backup help in an emergency or when the primary nurses' station is left unattended?

f) Will the nurse's station be staffed all the time to receive incoming nurse calls? If not, can the incoming calls be automatically forwarded to the nurses' location or can the calls be transmitted to the nurse via a pocket paging system?

8.4.3 System types

8.4.3.1 Visual systems

A visual nurse-call system provides audible signaling and visual annunciation of patient calls. Two call priority levels are possible: normal calls and emergency calls from toilet emergency stations. Visual systems are used primarily in hospital ancillary areas such as physical therapy, radiology, hydrotherapy, and emergency departments or other treatment areas where patients may be left unattended and where voice communication to a central location is not required by the staff. A visual nurse-call system can be utilized on small nursing units where a more expensive audiovisual system with intercom capabilities does not provide a distinct advantage. Visual nurse-call systems can also be utilized in nursing homes and residential care facilities.

a) *Patient bed station.* A patient can originate a call on the system by depressing a call button on a cord. These calls will continuously illuminate the white section of the corridor dome light and white section of any associated zone dome lights, illuminate the patient call light, sound a fast tone at all duty stations, illuminate the patient's room and bed numbers, and sound a fast tone at the master station annunciator. The call can only be canceled at the originating station.

b) *Toilet emergency station.* A patient can originate an emergency call on the system by pulling a cord. Originating a call from these stations will flash the white section of the corridor dome light and the white section of any associated zone dome lights, flash the patient call light and sound a fast tone at all duty stations, and flash the patient's room and bed numbers, and sound a fast tone at the master station annunciator.

c) *Duty station.* These stations provide audible and visual annunciation of calls placed from any other station in the system, but do not indicate the room number originating the call. Duty stations are usually located in clean and soiled utility rooms, medication rooms, and other areas in which staff members are likely to be when not at the nurses' station.

d) *Master station annunciator.* When a call is placed on the system, the room and bed number are flashed or steadily illuminated depending on the priority level of the call. A call tone is also generated with a distinct difference in signal rates between normal and emergency calls.

8.4.3.2 Audiovisual systems

An audiovisual nurse-call system provides audible signaling, visual annunciation, patient-to-staff communication, staff-to-staff communication, and intercommunication between master station annunciators. An audiovisual system has some distinct advantages over a visual nurse-call system. Minor patient requests such as "What time is it?" can be answered much more quickly; also, it is more reassuring for a patient to be able to talk with the nurse at the nurses' station.

Audiovisual systems can be divided into two basic groups: basic hardwired systems and microprocessor-controlled systems. Microprocessor-controlled systems can provide more levels of calls on the system, can be programmed for swing room and call transfer, and have reduced cabling requirements over hardwired systems. Microprocessor-controlled systems also provide interface to pocket page systems, record system activity, and facilitate day/night transfer of calls between nurses' stations. The overall size of the system, number of swing rooms, and number of master station annunciators required will determine which system is the most cost-effective to meet the hospital's needs.

8.4.4 System components

8.4.4.1 Patient bed station

A patient can originate a call on the system by depressing a button on a pillow speaker or cord set. Most systems have a call selector switch that determines the type of call that is placed on the system. For microprocessor-based systems, the level of call can be programmed at the master station annunciator. The various types of patient calls are as follows:

a) *Normal calls* illuminate the white section of the corridor dome light and white section of any associated zone dome lights, illuminate the patient call light, sound a tone at all duty stations, illuminate the patient's room number and bed number, and sound a slow tone at the master station annunciator. These calls are canceled after they are answered at the master station.

b) *Personal attention calls* perform the same functions as a normal call except they are only cancelable at the patient bed station.

c) *Priority calls* flash the corridor dome lights and associated zone dome lights, flash the patient call light, sound a fast tone at all duty stations, flash the patient's room and bed numbers, and sound a fast tone at the master station annunciator. Priority calls can only be canceled at the patient bed station. Voice communication is established upon answer of the call at the master station.

As an option, a privacy switch can be provided in the patient bed station that will prevent conversation within the room from being monitored from the master station. This switch does not interfere with the placement of a call to the master station, and the master station can still speak to the bed station. Unless this option is desired by the nursing staff, it is not recommended that it be included because it can create some confusion for the patient if it is inadvertently activated. On some microprocessor-based systems the privacy feature is controlled at the master station annunciator so the patient cannot inadvertently place his or her station into privacy.

8.4.4.2 Patient station cord set

Several different interchangeable cord sets are available for the patient's use to place a call. The pillow speaker is the most widely used device when television sets are located in each patient room because it may also contain controls to turn a TV set off and on, change the TV channel, and regulate the TV volume. Switches can also be provided to control the patient reading light via a low-voltage relay, and/or select between several different radio stations. An option on many patient stations is to mute the television or radio audio and transfer the nurse-call audio to the pillow speaker when the nurse is communicating with the patient station. This is a desirable feature since it keeps the patient and nurse from having to compete with the television audio in order to communicate. If patient televisions or radio sources are not provided, a standard call button and cord set should be used. A few pressure-pad cord sets should be specified for those patients who are unable to use a push button. Cord sets designed for use in oxygen atmospheres are also available.

8.4.4.3 Built-in bed controls

The nurse-call system can be interfaced to built-in bed rail controls that allow the patient to place a call, turn a TV set off and on, change the TV channel, and regulate the TV volume. Two-way voice communication is carried on over the speaker in the bed rail. An outlet box behind the bed has to be provided for the multipin receptacle furnished by the bed manufacturer with a raceway to the nurse-call station. Additional backbox space and termination provisions need to be included at the patient station to terminate the wiring from the multipin receptacle.

8.4.4.4 Toilet emergency station

These stations usually flash the white section of the corridor dome lights and associated zone dome lights, sound a unique tone at all duty stations, illuminate the station's call-placed light emitting-diode (LED), display the room number and call priority, and sound a rapid tone at the master station. Voice communications to the master station may be possible via the associated patient bed station. Toilet emergency calls can only be canceled at the calling station. These stations are equipped with a pull cord and are located in toilet, shower, tub, and hydrotherapy areas. Some of these stations are UL-listed as water-resistant and can be exposed to water spray in a shower area.

8.4.4.5 Staff station

Calling facilities and two-way voice communication to the master station can be accomplished from the staff station on a hardwired system. These calls are annunciated at the master station the same as normal calls from a patient station, whereas a microprocessor-based system displays staff calls as a different priority level than other calls. Staff stations can be located in offices, staff lounges, and other areas that need intercom capabilities to the nurses' station.

8.4.4.6 Duty stations

Calling facilities and two-way voice communication can be accomplished from a duty station. Calls are annunciated at the master station in the same manner as calls from a staff station. In addition, the duty station provides audible and visual annunciation of calls placed from other stations in a particular area of the nursing unit or the entire nursing unit. Normal and emergency calls are distinguished by a distinct difference in signal rate. Duty stations should be located in clean and soiled utility rooms, medication rooms, and other areas staff members are likely to be when not at the nurses' station.

8.4.4.7 Master station annunciator—Basic hardwired system

The master station annunciator can be used to call or receive calls from patient stations, staff stations, duty stations, or other master stations. Toilet emergency station calls are also annunciated at the master station.

When a call is placed on the system the room number and bed number are flashed or steadily illuminated depending on the priority level of the call. Answering a call is accomplished by depressing the station button on the master station annunciator corresponding to the calling station. Two-way voice communication can then take place via the speaker microphone utilizing the talk-listen bar or via a handset. If calls are not answered immediately, the tone signal is repeated unless the nurse is in the process of answering other calls.

If the patient stations are equipped with a call selector switch, switches should also be provided in the master station to indicate by bed which stations have the call selector switches placed in the "patient priority" and "personal attention" positions.

Zone monitoring and paging of several stations simultaneously can be accomplished from the master station. When the system is installed patient stations should be grouped separately from staff and duty stations on the annunciator key bank so staff areas can be paged separately from patient areas. Master stations in other areas can be connected together to provide intercom capabilities between them.

8.4.4.8 Master station annunciator—Microprocessor-controlled system

The master station annunciator can be used to call or receive calls from patient stations, toilet emergency stations, nurse assist stations, code blue stations, staff stations, duty stations, and other master stations. When a call is placed on the system, the room number and bed number are displayed on the master station along with a priority name, letter, or word. When there is more than one call on the system, the calls are automatically sequenced in order of importance and time of placement. Answering a call is accomplished by lifting the handset and either pressing a touch point on the master station or pressing the push-to-talk button. Two-way voice communication is then established and may continue through the handset or the speaker/microphone in the master station. If calls are not answered immediately, the tone signal repeats unless the nurse is already communicating with other stations.

Selective station monitoring or paging of several or all stations simultaneously can be accomplished from the master station. When the system is programmed, patient stations should be grouped separately from staff and duty stations so that staff can be paged separately from patient areas. Master stations from the same system or other systems can be connected together to provide intercom capabilities between them. The assignment of stations to zones for paging or monitoring is totally flexible and can be programmed on-site.

8.4.4.9 Nurse assist button

These wall-mounted push-button stations should be located in intensive care units (ICUs), coronary care units (CCUs), surgeries, recovery rooms, and other hospital areas in which the staff may need to request additional assistance in a hurry. Depending on local codes and the facility's requirements, it is recommended that this level of call be annunciated differently than a standard patient or toilet emergency station call. A basic, hardwired, nurse-call system may require the installation of a separate power supply and annunciators to achieve this differentiation. Most microprocessor-controlled nurse-call systems provide at least nine distinct levels of call and separate power supplies and annunciators are not required. Nurse assist calls shall be annunciated at the unit's nurses' station and optionally at adjacent nurses' stations from which additional help can be obtained.

8.4.4.10 Code blue button

See 8.5.2 for design criteria. These stations may be part of the nurse-call system to initiate the highest level of call within the hospital to signal the resuscitation team that a patient is in cardiac or respiratory arrest.

8.4.4.11 Dome lights

Locate dome lights in the corridor above the patient room door or above the patient's bed in recovery and holding areas. These lights indicate which room, or bed, initiated a call and the level of that call. Dome lights can be multisectioned (maximum of four) with different colors to indicate different types of calls from each room. For example, a four-section, four-color dome light on a basic, hardwired, nurse-call system can indicate the following calls from each room:

Call type	Priority level	Dome light indication
Code blue	1	Flashing red
Nurse assist	2	Flashing white, steady green
Toilet emergency	3	Flashing white
Patient—Priority	3	Flashing white
Patient—Personal attention	4	Steady white
Patient—Normal call	4	Steady white

A microprocessor-controlled system can provide more levels of indication. For example, a four-section, four-color dome light on a microprocessor-controlled system can indicate the following calls from each room:

Call type	Priority level	Dome light indication
Code blue	1	Flashing red
Nurse assist	2	Flashing white, steady green
Toilet emergency	3	Flashing white
Patient—Priority	4	Flashing white
Patient—Personal attention	5	Steady white
Patient—Normal call	6	Steady white
Stat service	—	Flashing green, flashing amber
Nurse service	—	Flashing green
Aide service	—	Flashing amber
Nurse present	—	Steady green
Aide present	—	Steady amber

These colors may vary depending upon the scheme established in the facility. The same dome-light color scheme should be utilized throughout the facility.

8.4.4.12 Zone dome lights

Similar in appearance to dome lights, these devices should be located at corridor intersections to indicate the areas or zone that the call is coming from.

8.4.5 Nurse-call system options

There are several optional features that are available on most nurse-call systems. The options that are included will depend on how the hospital intends to operate and staff the nursing unit. Some of the optional features are described in the following list:

a) *Nurse service.* This feature, which is standard on most microprocessor-controlled nurse-call systems, allows the nurse at the nurses' station to answer a patient's call and if the nature of the call cannot be satisfied from the nurses' station, i.e., the patient requests a glass of water, then a nurse or aide service reminder can be initiated at the master station annunciator. Depressing the nurse service button will flash the green section of the corridor dome light and flash the green section of any associated zone dome lights. Depressing the aide service button will flash the amber section of the corridor dome light and flash the amber section of any associated zone dome lights. If service is not provided by the circulating nurse or other staff member, and the nurse service call is not reset at the patient bed station within an adjustable time period (3–10 min) another patient call is automatically initiated. This feature allows the staff member answering calls to remain at the nurses' station while the patient's needs are being satisfied by others.

b) *Staff locator.* This feature utilizes buttons in each patient room that are activated whenever the staff member enters the room. A switch on the master station annunciator will illuminate the room numbers in which nurses or aides are located. The nurse at the nurses' station can then locate the closest staff member that can respond to a nurse call from an adjacent room and direct him or her to it. This feature provides for more efficient use of staff members; however, it may not always be desirable because it requires staff members to check in and out of each room, and patients trying to rest may be disturbed by calls from the nurses' station directing staff members to respond to calls from another room.

c) *Nurse follower.* During night and off-peak hours the nurse at the nurses' station may transfer calls to another location in which he or she intends to be. When this feature is used in conjunction with the staff locator feature, the call-in tones will only be sent into rooms where staff members are registered. Some nurse-call systems allow the nurse to answer the call from the patient station. Other systems provide an interface to the telephone system to permit the staff member to use the patient's telephone to answer a call from another patient. This feature allows the staff more mobility because they do not have to be at the nurses' station to answer nurse calls; however, transfer of all nurse calls to a patient's room may be disturbing to the patient in that room.

d) *Pocket page interface.* A nurse-call system can interface with a pocket page system so that calls from patients are sent through the pocket page system to the appropriate staff member. This feature may be fully automatic so that it is transparent to the patient. This mode of operation is most useful during low staff periods (e.g., nighttime or lunchtime). In the semiautomatic mode of operation, a ward clerk or secretary answers the patient call and then determines whether or not to send the call over the pocket page system. In this mode, the calls can be screened, and only those calls requiring a nurse response are sent to the pagers. Finally, the manual mode of operation allows an operator to locate a particular nurse by manually dialing his or her pager number. This approach reduces the noise pollution in a hospital that is generated by constant overhead audio paging.

e) *Call transfer.* In some units there may be a requirement for nurse calls to be transmitted to different nurses' stations at different times. For example, there may be swing rooms that can be a part of two adjacent nursing units depending upon the number of beds required in each unit. Calls from these rooms must be transferred from one nurse's station to another on an individual room basis. Entire groups of rooms may also be transferred between two nurse's stations.

Call transfer may be accomplished several different ways depending upon the sophistication of the nurse-call system. A hardwired basic system requires transfer switches in each swing room or a bank of transfer relays activated by a switch at the nurses' station. A microprocessor-controlled system can be programmed from the master station to assign patient rooms to a particular nurses' station on an individual room basis.

8.4.6 Centralized nurse-call system

Some hospitals or nursing homes may want to have all patient calls for the entire facility answered at a central location, either on a full-time or nighttime basis. When the nurse-call systems for each nursing unit are interconnected with the other units, the calls from several systems may be answered at one location. This feature is useful at night when the number of patient calls is reduced and calls from several systems can be handled by one person. The staff locator feature is desirable in a centralized nurse-call system so the person answering calls can locate the staff members closest to the room initiating the call and direct them to the correct room. Staff members can also be directed to the calling room via a pocket paging system. See 8.6.4.

8.4.7 Central processor controlled system

The more sophisticated nurse-call systems can provide information storage and retrieval capabilities that can record patient information and nurse-call system activity. Printers can also be included with these systems to provide a hard-copy printout of patient data and traffic patterns on each nursing unit that can be used to determine staffing requirements.

8.4.8 Psychiatric nurse-call system

The nurse-call system for psychiatric patient facilities serves a different role than those installed in a general care nursing area. In a psychiatric unit the nurse-call system usually serves primarily as an alarm system for staff to request additional assistance in a hurry as well as providing for standard patient calls.

a) *Room entrance station.* In a basic psychiatric nurse-call system, room entrance stations are located in the corridor outside each patient room. These stations contain one or more keyed switches that can be used to activate or deactivate the patient station and nurse assist station within the room. When these switches are in the off or deactivate position the patient cannot initiate nuisance calls on the system. Room entrance stations can also be used to signal the nurse at the nurses' station that a staff member is about to enter the patient's room. The nurse at the nurses' station can then monitor the conversation within the room and send assistance if required.

b) *Nurse assist.* Some systems originally developed for installation in prisons may satisfy the nurse assist requirements. These systems utilize a receiver in each room and an initiation device that the staff members carry with them at all times. If a staff member requires help, he or she can initiate an alarm by actuating the initiation device. The signal is picked up by the receiver and the call is annunciated at the nurses' station to indicate the room location. This type of system has some advantages over a standard psychiatric nurse-call system in that staff members always carry the initiation device with them and it is never deactivated like a fixed nurse assist button.

8.4.9 Medical and dental offices and clinics

Variations of a visual nurse-call system can be utilized in clinics and offices to provide a variety of signals. Some examples include the following:

a) *Exam room status system.* Multisection-colored dome lights are located above the corridor door into each exam room with corresponding switches in each room. One illuminated color may signal that the patient is ready to see the doctor. Another color may indicate the room is vacant and needs to be prepared for the next patient and/or another color may be used to signal the room has been prepared and is available for the next patient. A central annunciator may be located at the reception desk to indicate the status of each exam room. Microprocessor-controlled systems can indicate where the doctor's "next patient" is located by flashing the appropriate dome light and can track patient and staff flow throughout the office or clinic.

b) *Doctor and dentist offices.* Different-colored lights may be used to provide rapid, discrete interoffice communication between the doctor and his or her staff. Messages will vary between offices, but some typical messages are "doctor's next patient has arrived," "doctor is wanted on the telephone," "doctor would like to see his assistant or laboratory technician," "hygienist wants doctor to check patient."

8.4.10 Assisted-living facilities

Residents in assisted-living facilities may need to summon assistance if they experience a fall or other emergency. A visual nurse-call system should be installed with emergency stations in the bathroom and at a central location in the living area. A central annunciator can be located at the lobby reception desk or other continuously monitored location. One limitation of utilizing a conventional visual nurse-call system in an assisted living facility is that the residents are usually mobile (not confined to a bed) and may not be able to reach an emergency pull station if they should have to obtain assistance.

Several available wireless systems can be activated by a transmitter carried by each resident. Receivers should be located in each living unit and in common areas to provide facility-wide coverage. Optional features of these types of systems include interconnection with the telephone system to enable direct voice communication to the resident, and/or a computerized data base to automatically provide the resident's name, doctor, and other pertinent information at the central monitoring location.

8.4.11 Design considerations for nurse-call systems

After the engineer has talked with the facility staff and has determined what type of nurse-call system best meets the hospital's needs, he or she begins to lay out the final system.

a) *Patient bed stations.* Mount these stations in the wall behind the patient bed, in a patient headwall unit, or in the patient's bedside cabinet. The station should be located to allow the call cord to be draped to the patient bed. Locating the patient station in the bedside cabinet may not be the best location because this would inhibit changing the furniture later, and the multipin receptacles required for bedside cabinets with nurse-call stations can be a maintenance problem.

b) *Toilet emergency stations.* Position these stations so they can be activated by a patient seated on the toilet and/or by a patient who may have fallen forward on the floor. In combination toilet/shower rooms, one station may be sufficient provided it meets the location requirements described above and the cord is long enough to drape into the shower to a maximum of 6 in (15 cm) above the floor.

c) *Staff and duty stations.* Sometimes rooms such as staff lounges and utility rooms serve more than one nursing unit. If so, two or more duty or staff stations should be installed and connected to the nurse-call system for each unit. Identify each station's nursing unit.

d) *Master station annunciator.* These stations can either be wall-mounted or desk-mounted. It is recommended that visual system master stations be wall-mounted to provide as much desk space as possible. Audiovisual system master stations should be desk-mounted to allow some flexibility in the location of the nurses who are answering calls. Room numbers on the master station must match the final room numbers assigned to each room by the facility.

e) *Psychiatric patient stations.* These stations, installed in ambulatory patient rooms, must be tamperproof for the patients' safety. Call cords should not be located in patient bedrooms, and tamperproof push buttons should be used in toilets in lieu of pull cords.

f)   *Central equipment and power supplies.* Nurse-call systems shall be connected to the critical branch of the emergency distribution system in hospitals or to essential emergency power systems in other health care facilities. Coordinate ventilation, wall space, and wall depth required for these cabinets.

8.5 Code blue systems

8.5.1 Introduction

Code blue alarms are the highest level of emergency call in a hospital. When a cardiac arrest or other emergency occurs, the system alerts the person responsible for the delivery of the crash cart to the point of need and notifies the resuscitation team as to the room or area that initiated the alarm. Different hospitals may call this alarm level something other than code blue, such as code 199, code 99, Doctor Heart, crash unit, etc.

8.5.2 Design criteria for code blue systems

Hospital regulations require a code blue alarm system. Typically, code blue buttons (or other initiation devices) are located in intensive care and coronary care patient rooms, emergency rooms, recovery rooms, labor and birthing rooms, surgery suites, and other areas required by the hospital. Annunciators should be located at the central control center so the telephone operator can announce the code blue alarm either via the public address system, by radio paging, or both. Annunciators may be located at adjacent nurses' stations, the anesthesia office, and the nurse supervisor's office. In some hospitals the staff members may want the code blue alarms from the patient's room to go to the local nurses' station. If the alarm is a true code call and not a false alarm initiated by a visitor, the nurse at the nurses' station can forward the alarm via the telephone or separate code blue button.

8.5.3 System types and selection

a)   *Nurse-call system.* A separate hardwired visual nurse-call system with code blue buttons and annunciators can be installed to serve the code blue system requirements. Microprocessor based nurse-call systems can be interconnected so that a code blue call on any local system is also automatically displayed at the central control center. Many microprocessor-controlled code blue systems can supervise the individual code blue station for electrical shorts or opens in the wiring or burnt out or missing lamps in the corridor dome lights. A supervised code blue system assures that every code blue station will operate when required.

b)   *Telephone system.* A code blue call system can be set up as a separate direct line to the central operator via the hospital telephone system. The major advantage of this type of installation is that a code blue alarm can be initiated from any telephone within the hospital. If the particular phone system is equipped with direct access paging, the code blue alarm can be directly annunciated via the public address system, thus bypassing the telephone operator. Code blue pages must have priority over all other paging calls.

c) *Radio paging.* Code blue alarms can be transmitted to the resuscitation team members via the radio paging system, provided the system has the capability of grouping paging calls together so the proper people are notified with just one call from the telephone operator. Microprocessor-controlled nurse-call systems can be interconnected with the radio paging system to automatically initiate code blue calls to the code team members whenever a code blue call is initiated.

8.5.4 Design considerations for code blue systems

A code blue alarm system should always be designed with system reliability in mind. The power supply for this system must be connected to the critical branch of the emergency distribution system.

8.6 Paging systems

8.6.1 Introduction

The objective of the paging system is to aid in locating persons who do not have a fixed location within the facility or who are away from their normal workstation. It generally augments the telephone system, in that it may notify persons who are not at a fixed telephone number to contact another person inside or outside the facility. In order to be effective, it should reach most locations where these people are likely to be.

8.6.2 System types

Paging systems can increase the efficiency of communications in most health care facilities. There are three types of systems:

a) *Voice paging system.* Voice paging [public address (PA)] systems are used to make general audio announcements. Voice paging systems employ transducers, electronics, and cable plant to reproduce local audio signals over large floor areas. Voice paging systems serve as a general PA system for a less specific audience, and usually support a broader range of messages than radio paging systems. Besides voice signals, paging systems may transmit background music, sound masking noise, security tones, or recorded fire alarm system announcements. The voice paging system may be interconnected with the building telephone, intercom, or visual annunciator systems as part of an overall building communication system. Voice paging systems may be required for issuing instructions in response to emergency conditions including code blue alarms.

A voice paging system can become a distraction that outweighs the advantages of its use. This may result from poor design or from abuse. General voice paging should be directed toward specific audiences with content suitable to concise messages.

The nature of communications and the audience addressed via the voice paging system must appropriately reflect the size of the facility and the impact on people who do not belong in the selected audience. This should not suggest that a lunch menu announcement is necessarily inappropriate. However, a voice paging system utilized once each minute distracts a large number of people.

The policy directing the use of a voice paging system must impact the system design. Multiple zoning can insulate parts of a facility from constant announcements. In hospitals, for example, a separate zone (or the exclusion of voice paging speakers) is appropriate for surgery, delivery, recovery, ICU, and other patient rooms. See 8.6.3.

b) *Radio paging system.* Radio system paging transmits voice or digital messages over a radio frequency channel and is preferred where cost is not an obstacle. Coded signals can be used for messages, or one-way or two-way voice transmission can be provided. Installation costs are low, no corridor wall space is required, and there is minimal disturbance to other personnel. Radio paging is effective in many areas where visual or voice paging is not practical; for example, it often covers rest rooms, utility spaces, and nearby outdoor areas with its radio signal. However, equipment is costly and maintenance costs can be high since pocket-carried receivers are subject to damage. Radio paging can be tied into the telephone system so that paging can be initiated by staff members other than the telephone operator. See 8.6.4.

c) *Flashing annunciator paging.* This system provides a silent, visual, coded message by repeatedly lighting numbers on annunciators located throughout a facility. It is not recommended because of the excessive number of annunciators required before the coverage provided is comparable with other types of paging.

8.6.3 Voice paging systems

8.6.3.1 Design criteria for voice paging systems

8.6.3.1.1 General

Audio components (amplifiers, equalizers, mixers, etc.) are almost all solid-state devices. Performance is not measured by broadband or hi-fi principles, but rather in terms of reliability, control of signal sources, and correct distribution and syllabic articulation of voice. The system need not reproduce the entire audible spectrum for satisfactory results, and quite often compromises with performance are required in order to justify economics.

8.6.3.1.2 Priority

Voice paging systems often feature several audio sources (microphone, tape deck, tone generator, etc.). Operators generally have manual control of most sources while links from other communication systems (e.g., telephone and intercom) are automatic.

In both small and large voice paging systems, the relative signal priority determines the control requirements. A paging system with background music and one paging microphone location will probably mute the background music when the microphone is activated. When several paging sources or a paging source and an emergency signal source are used, a priority system must be set up to accommodate each source's level of importance.

The audio volume may be changed to suit varying work conditions, changing personnel, background noise, etc. Also, it may be changed with each change of source signal. In a paging system with background music, the listener may want local control of the music volume but retain full-volume paging signals. The various volume levels should be consistent with each signal's priority.

8.6.3.1.3 Zoning

In large installations, and in small installations where specific activities vary from area to area, the public address system should be zoned. Each zone may require local volume and paging controls. Priority controls for both source selection and volume are designed to accommodate both zone paging and local sources. In some installations, local pages are given priority and, in others, general pages have priority. Each installation must be programmed individually.

8.6.3.1.4 Talk-back

Single-zoned systems may include talk-back. Either by push-button control or by automatic means, talk-back allows the listener to respond to the operator via the PA system. Talk-back complicates the electronics of a PA system, especially when it is employed in multizoned systems with several signal sources. An alternate means of listener response (telephone, intercom, etc.) usually provides a more efficient system in large installations. Talk-back from speakers in large rooms is usually not very effective unless the person is close to a speaker. Public areas should not have talk-back.

8.6.3.1.5 Distribution

In music and paging systems, there are several ways to distribute audio signals. The simplest involves one set of audio lines run to each speaker zone with background music and paging levels set at the main amplifier.

When local control of music volume is desired, the audio lines may be run to a local volume control equipped with a bypass relay (priority relay). The relay coil is connected to a priority control pair to bypass the volume control for paging announcements.

8.6.3.1.6 Muting

When two sources, one with priority, are available in a voice paging system, two common methods can accomplish the required signal level changes. First, the priority signal may be set to a higher volume than the other signal. This method is limited to circumstances where the nonpriority signal is at a low volume so the priority signal need not be too loud. Second, the initiation of the priority signal may mute the nonpriority signal either by relay contacts or solid-state devices. The same circuit may drive the priority relay at local volume controls. The second is the standard method used in most PA systems. Some components employ automatic circuitry that mutes a signal input when an audio signal is detected on a different input or inputs. Automatic electronic muting often eliminates an objectionable pop caused by relay contact closures. Electronic muting is the preferred method.

8.6.3.1.7 Volume

The required audio volume determines electronic component ratings. The system should be louder than the ambient noise. Sound with a signal-to-noise ratio of at least 10 dB with an appropriate frequency response and distortion below 5% generally provides audible signals. Room acoustics should be considered. Small rooms with low ceilings consisting of acoustic tile are usually not a problem. Rooms with acoustically hard surfaces (plaster walls and ceiling, and tile floor, for example) have a high reverberation time that will contribute to poor intelligibility. To accommodate variations in acoustics and ambient sound levels, provide an audio sound level to average ambient noise level ratio of 20–30 dB, and an overall audio signal distortion of less than 2%.

8.6.3.1.8 Frequency response

Many paging systems, especially those using a telephone system as the audio source, do not require frequency shaping electronics because the electronics and speaker system will present the full range of telephone or microphone frequencies to the listener. Where particular rooms present acoustical problems or where music or a natural sounding voice page is important, an equalizer might be used.

8.6.3.1.9 Compression

Audio signal volume varies from one source to another (i.e., from one person to another). Different paging announcers may produce a difference in voice levels greater than 20 dB depending on their voices and how they use the microphone or telephone. Variations in signal levels of 20 dB are annoying to many listeners. Audio signal compressors may be employed to help reduce sound level variations. They are usually used to control microphone and telephone/intercom/paging interface inputs because the volume of these sources varies the greatest. Pre-recorded music sources, radio receivers, tone generators and noise generators usually produce a consistent signal/level or have their own compressors (i.e., automatic gain control). Where paging signals consistently originate from trained operators, compression might not be required.

8.6.3.1.10 Source

A voice paging system signal is never better than its source. Pre-recorded messages, music sources, and radio receivers are satisfactory sources; however, the quality of microphone sources should be considered. The quality of the microphone itself is usually satisfactory, but the location should be considered. Placing the microphone close to the announcer's mouth (several inches) helps reduce problems of room noise and reverberations. Telephone handsets and headsets with an interface to the paging system provide both efficient operator access and close microphone use for noisy environments. When an operator must address a microphone from more than 12 in (30 cm) away, noise and room echo are likely to be problems.

8.6.3.2 Design considerations for voice paging system

a) *Interfacing.* Telephone, intercom, and tone generating systems may be connected to the voice paging system. The priority and zoning of each system must be determined. A telephone or intercom system may utilize several interconnecting lines to provide both general and zone paging. Alternately, a telephone paging interface unit is available that decodes a touch-tone and selects a paging zone. The drawback of this unit is that the operator must dial the paging system, wait for a paging system tone, and press the zone code before a page is made. This is one step more than simply dialing a paging number.

b) *Coverage.* Generally, voice paging systems utilize a distributed speaker system. A distributed speaker system (typically recessed ceiling speakers) should provide even coverage of direct sound at the proper frequencies and at sufficient volume to be heard above the ambient noise. High-volume distributed systems (usually horn-type speakers) are required in noisy areas. Most applications involve low-level, closely spaced, recessed, ceiling speakers. Even the best recessed ceiling speakers have a narrow, high-frequency, dispersion angle. With 9 ft (2.7 m) high ceilings, speaker spacing of 12–16 ft (3.7–4.9 m) centers is typical. This spacing may be increased somewhat for higher ceilings and in narrow corridors. The closer the speakers are, the more even the sound volume and quality will be.

c) *Equipment.* Voice paging equipment can fill a small cabinet or a small room. Its location is flexible but the equipment requires access and cooling or ventilation. Speaker wiring requires one pair of conductors for a single-zoned page-only system, two pairs for a single-zoned music/page priority system, and many pairs for a multizoned multiple-page priority system. Priority logic pairs will often be #22 AWG and audio signal pairs will be anywhere from #20 AWG to #14 AWG.

d) *Installation.* Nearly all sound-system components on the market today exhibit low noise, low distortion, flat frequency response, and high continuous power ratings. The performance of sound systems is rarely limited by individual component ratings. The components must be selected and assembled for the final system functions and desired performance.

Solid-state audio components are manufactured for specific input and output levels, so cascading components (for example, a mixer, an equalizer, and a power amplifier) require that the output level of each unit match the input level of the next unit. A mismatch of audio signal levels will degrade the overall system signal-to-noise ratio or reduce its maximum output.

Audio signals are generally transmitted at three levels: microphone level, line level (for lines between various pieces of equipment), and high level (the output of the power amplifiers used to distribute audio frequency energy to speakers). The microphone and line level signals are susceptible to pickup of hum, noise, and crosstalk from higher level lines and power cables. Microphone level lines should never be run in the same raceway with other audio lines or power cables, and each type of audio line should be bundled separately in each equipment rack. Microphone and line level cables should always employ an overall metallic shield within the cable jacket.

When an audio system includes an equalizer, the frequency response of the system must be properly measured and corrected to match the desired response curve. Improper system response may cause a loss of speech intelligibility or make the system sound unnatural.

Proper use of a voice paging system is as important as its initial installation. People familiar with the equipment should instruct operating personnel in the system's use. Often this instruction is specified as part of the system installation.

e) *Reliability.* Backup inputs (a second microphone or a microphone as backup to a telephone system) and backup electronics (amplifiers, etc.) may be included in a system where reliability is a must. Many components permit battery-powered operation. Battery operation is acceptable for loss of power situations, but the system should be powered from an emergency ac power system to reduce maintenance requirements.

8.6.4 Radio paging systems

8.6.4.1 Introduction

Radio paging systems transmit messages over a radio frequency channel.

8.6.4.2 Design criteria for radio paging systems

Refer to 8.6.2 item b) for a description of radio paging systems. The following functional factors should be considered to define radio paging system performance: number of active radio pager users, average system call rate, desired grade of service, average input waiting time, and maximum message storage time. The equipment factors discussed in 8.6.4.2.1–8.6.4.2.6 should be considered when designing radio paging systems.

8.6.4.2.1 System input or encoder

On-site and off-campus paging systems are often interfaced with one or more of the telephone, intercom, staff register, nurse-call, and code blue systems. Telephone interconnected systems provide almost unlimited access to the paging system. With voice messages, voice message storage equipment may be required to increase system voice traffic capacity. Display message systems may also use message storage. This and high-speed message transmission can provide high system pager capacity. Smith 1980 [B10][2] discussed this difference. Interconnection with staff in/out register systems, intercom systems, and nurse-call systems is unique to each supplier and should be reviewed in detail with their representatives.

An encoder or paging terminal may be any kind of device, manual or automatic, from which a radio paging message may be originated. The following is a typical list of such devices:

a) *Manual desktop (or flush-mounted) keyboard console.* (Frequently located at the telephone operator position, although parallel units may be located at several sites throughout the facility.)

---

[2]The numbers in brackets correspond to those of the bibliography in 8.22.

b)   *Telephones.* Dial or touch-pad type, and either dedicated or part of the facility's telephone system.

c)   *Intercom stations.*

d)   *Automatic alarm stations.* (Any contact opening or closing device may be utilized to initiate an emergency or routine radio page message. This includes such functions as elevator stoppage, security door openings, boiler temperature limit switches, chiller failure, oxygen low pressure, etc.)

8.6.4.2.2 System type

On-site pagers for the special emergency radio service (SERS), like the systems that control them, come in many different types. Pagers may be classified by type of modulation (AM or FM); frequency band (VHF lowband, VHF highband, UHF, and 900 MHz); type of encoding (two-tone or five-tone analog and digital); and type of message capability (tone, voice, LEDs, LCDs, digital display, and alphanumeric display).

Generally speaking, there has been a gradual shift from inductive loop paging to AM and then to FM paging technology. Inductive loop paging is a low-frequency radio technique, and its employment has largely been discontinued in favor of AM and FM radio equipment for reasons of better coverage both within and throughout a hospital complex of buildings. The recent development of display pocket pager technology has added to the tone-only and tone-and-voice types of paging systems. The availability of this new technology and additional frequencies in the 900 MHz band increase the variety of systems available for on-site and off-campus radio paging system implementation.

8.6.4.2.3 Frequency selection

For on-site systems, the frequency selected is largely a matter of determining which available frequency is the least crowded; although, in an on-site mode, carefully designed systems on the same frequency can operate without any interference with each other, even when only a very few miles apart. In SERS, the VHF lowband and UHF bands are the least crowded. Transmitters for on-site radio paging systems are either AM or FM and set to the FCC assigned frequency of the system. The FCC has set aside 11 one-way paging frequencies in the SERS for which all hospitals are eligible. Business frequencies may also be used; these include four VHF high-band frequencies and nine UHF frequencies for paging only. The paging-only frequencies in the business service are coordinated by the National Association of Business and Education Radio (NABER) users. The FCC has also authorized paging frequencies in the 900 MHz range for which all hospitals are eligible. Frequencies in the 900 MHz range are also coordinated by NABER.

The VHF lowband frequencies and UHF frequencies are generally much less congested than the VHF highband frequencies and, therefore, represent a better potential for fewer problems in sharing the frequency. The FCC does not coordinate the SERS frequency assignments and will authorize whatever is requested. It is suggested that frequency monitoring equipment be used to monitor the frequency band selected. The equipment may be rented or a contractor may perform the monitoring and report the results—or if hospitals in the area have formed a frequency coordinating committee, the best frequency can be determined by contact with such organizations. Note also that the 157.450 MHz frequency is limited to 30 W maximum. On-site radio paging systems, however, particularly for tone-only or display messages, require much less power than voice or wide area paging, and 30 W may be entirely adequate. Note that transmitters may only be set up, serviced, and adjusted by persons holding an FCC commercial license.

8.6.4.2.4 Type of encoding

Again, the gradual shift from two-tone and five-tone to digital encoding has paralleled the growth of radio and electronic technology. Most equipment installed today is either two-tone or five-tone, but new paging systems are more and more likely to use digital encoding. Digital encoding is extremely fast; that is, approximately 1-1/2 s for the transmission of a battery saver preamble and alerting signal, and approximately 1/3 s for transmission of the alerting signal versus as much as 5 s for two-tone systems. In a low traffic, small paging system, the latter would be no problem. But with today's larger systems, high-traffic loading dictates that transmission time be as short as possible. Digital encoding also permits multidigital and alphanumeric display paging messages, and these too can be transmitted in a total of 2 s or less. Voice messages generally require at least 5–10 s, depending upon the operator. Traffic capabilities in display message systems can be up to ten or more times that of voice systems. Digital encoding, because of high-speed multiple transmissions and built-in code checking techniques, reduces "falsing" (pager receives a message designated for someone else or pager receives a false alert tone where no message was transmitted) to an absolute minimum.

8.6.4.2.5 Message type

Radio paging messages may consist of tone(s), light emitting diode (LED) or liquid crystal display (LCD) signals, voice, vibrations, digital display (one or more) and alphanumeric display (up to eight or even eighty characters—and combinations of all of these). Which one or ones you select will depend upon how the paging system will be used, the number of pagers (and the need always increases), the expected message traffic and your budget. A few guidelines for each type may be helpful. Tone-only pagers should not be ignored. Staff members who will receive a minimum number of messages can effectively use a tone-only pager. For example, one tone would mean "call your office," and another tone might mean "return to your workstation." A change in the tone may signify the level or urgency. More sophisticated tone-only pagers may have multiple addresses; that is, one address number for individual calls and one for a group call and display signals to visually indicate which address number has been called. Many different message types may be transmitted in this way. Voice pagers provide unique message content. Although most paging messages contain number information such as "call extension 386," some emergency messages may be difficult to transmit without voice. Display pagers, particularly those with eight or more digits or alphanumeric characters, can provide surprising amounts of information, and all display pagers on the market today have message memory. If a seven-digit telephone number is transmitted, it will be stored in the pager's memory for recall. This provides high message accuracy and confidence during busy times, and eliminates the need to call the operator for verification. Display message systems may need message storage equipment, and messages may be printed on a logging printer together with the time of transmission and the pager address.

Vibration alert or "wiggler" pagers are becoming more widely used because of the silent alert, and because they are a natural adjunct to the inherently silent nature of the display paging. Night shift personnel carry such pagers to avoid noise on patient floors.

8.6.4.2.6 Pager batteries and chargers

There are two types of batteries: disposable batteries and rechargeable batteries with various types of chargers.

The decision between the two types is a function of battery life for the design of the pager selected, the average number of calls per pager per day, average call duration, and the type of message, (i.e., tone, voice, display, etc.). The longer the expected life, the more practical it is to use disposable batteries. A pager with a battery life of 1500 h would strongly suggest the use of disposable batteries. Factors that reduce battery life are average message duration of 10–20 s, voice messages, more than eight to ten calls per day, vibration alert, and whether or not a pager is left on during hours when it is not used. "Battery saver" circuits are effective in some pagers, but this benefit decreases as more pagers are added to the system. The choice between disposable batteries and rechargeable batteries should be based on the type of usage and the economics over a significant period of time, for example, a week, month, or year. Convenience and cost must be balanced by the user. The alternative is to charge batteries in a rack or in individual chargers. This requires someone with the time and expertise to switch the batteries. In some installations, secure storage of pagers in a rack is combined with the charging function. A keypad or magnetic card reader provides access to the secured pager storage rack. This function is sometimes linked to a staff in/out register system.

8.6.4.3 Design considerations for radio paging systems

8.6.4.3.1 Encoder location

Locations of telephones, intercom stations, or automatic alarm station type encoders may be almost anywhere in a facility. However, FCC regulations require that there be one so-called control point in every radio paging system from which the entire system is monitored and controlled. This particular encoder or paging terminal is most commonly located at or immediately adjacent to the telephone operator's position. This location is generally the focal point for radio paging and other types of message functions and is the recommended site for the control point.

The control point encoder generally consists of the following: a keyboard to enter the address of the pocket pager to be paged (may be a telephone dial or standard 12-button keypad or other button configuration), an emergency switch to interrupt a message placed from another parallel encoder (required by FCC regulations), an emergency message button or capability, a microphone with hand or foot switch (if voice messages are to be provided), a small loudspeaker with volume control (part of a frequency monitoring system to allow cooperation in the use of the FCC assigned transmitting frequency), and an "in-use" or "busy" signaling lamp (illuminates when other encoders or input devices are using the system). Depending upon the particular brand of encoder selected, a variety of other special control buttons, lamps, and displays may also be provided. Parallel encoders (that are not a control point), if provided, will omit the emergency interrupt switch.

8.6.4.3.2 Base station configuration and location

The base station may include a computer or central processor unit; voice or display message storage capability; an automatic paging terminal; pager address translation circuitry and other special circuits depending upon the system supplier. The central unit of a radio paging system contains the control circuitry of the system. All manual or automatic encoders (sometimes both types) normally terminate at the central unit. Also connecting to the central unit may be inputs from a telephone system or intercom system and an output to the system transmitter.

The location of a central unit is largely a matter of choice, but it is usually preferable to select an air-conditioned space that may be key-lock secured. Systems with tape recorder voice storage capability may require especially clean or dust-free space.

Central units are commonly housed in a 19 in (48 cm) rack mount or other similar configuration. Computer bus technology with a motherboard and plug-in printed circuit boards (PCBs) are currently state-of-the-art. PCBs are provided for control of sequencing and prioritization of connected encoders, automatic alarm devices, intercom stations, and telephones if the system is interconnected. The motherboard also accepts PCBs with features for speech-enabling circuitry, display message control, automatic system supervision or diagnostic circuitry, and interface of staff registration and message management systems. Power requirements are normally nominal, usually requiring only a 117 Vac, 60 Hz, 20 A circuit. If voice-message storage or automatic paging terminal equipment is included, power requirements may need to be increased. The engineer should check carefully with the supplier to ascertain exact requirements. It is strongly suggested that the selected system includes a battery-backup capability or be connected to the facility's emergency power system. Radio paging systems with either multiple dispatch points or with interconnection with the hospital's telephone system will include a monitoring circuit with output to the control point encoder. This allows the telephone operator to meet the FCC requirement of monitoring all dispatch points' transmissions and to be able to interrupt such transmissions for priority page messages or to prevent illegal transmissions.

8.6.4.3.3 Transmitter location and configuration

Transmitters are generally located as close to the antenna as possible to reduce signal losses. However, consideration is also given to location for easy service access, security, and generally, air conditioning. Regarding the latter, it is important to consult with the supplier's technical staff or to review technical literature, or both, to determine the requirements. On-site systems utilizing slotted, radiating coaxial cable for the antenna system may require central transmitter location to provide equal cable runs to all parts of the building.

A wide range of transmitter configurations are available based on particular supplier requirements, range of coverage, type of antenna, and method of signal coverage within the building(s) and hospital complex. Transmitters are frequently mounted in a 19 in (48 cm) standard rack with a secured door. Transmitters generally contain the following modules: a power supply (connected to the building emergency power system); the transmitter itself, an automatic carrier-operated relay circuit (inhibits transmission when carrier signal is detected from another transmitter on the same frequency and assures compliance with the FCC requirement to cooperate in the use of the assigned frequency); and an automatic station identifier (eliminates the need for the telephone operator to transmit the station call letters periodically as required by the FCC). An automatic station identifier (ASI) may transmit either a voice message or Morse code, the former being more common in new systems. The ASI makes the identification at prescribed intervals, but it will not interrupt a transmission to make such an "announcement." While primary power requirements vary depending upon transmitter power, generally one 117 Vac, 60 Hz, 20 A circuit is adequate.

Improved "coverage" of an on-site system is obtained by some suppliers by the use of master and slave transmitters. This technique accomplishes several things: lower total radiated power (reduces interference with other possible users on the same frequency and reduces the possibility of interference with sensitive or unshielded biomedical electronic equipment), more even signal coverage within the building(s), improved coverage of a multiple building complex, and better coverage of below-grade floors.

8.6.4.3.4 Antenna systems selection

The conditions governing the installation of an on-site paging system antenna are quite different from those applying to a mobile radio system. The main objective is not to cover as large an area as possible but to ensure full and uniform coverage within the defined paging area.

Ideally, signals are dispersed uniformly in all directions and decrease linearly at increasing distance from the antenna. In practice, however, antenna radiation is not uniform, which is primarily due to attenuation caused by screening or reflection.

To a certain degree, radio waves are attenuated by all sorts of materials, but antenna radiation is affected most by metallic objects between the antenna and the receiver, such as in steel-reinforced concrete buildings. It is obviously undesirable to place the antenna on the roof of such a structure, in all instances, as the radio waves might have to pass through several screening floors before reaching the receiver. Also, the signal strength is generally at its lowest directly below the location of most antennas.

When radio waves reach a surface, part of them will pass or be absorbed, while others will be reflected. When the reflected radiation mixes with the direct radiation, interference will occur, which may amplify the signal at some places but weaken and perhaps extinguish it at other places. A special risk of such dead zones is present at elevators or stairwells or between thick pillars. Dead zones may be eliminated through change of antenna location or type, but may then arise at other places instead.

The on-site paging receivers are generally designed for best reception of vertically polarized radiation. The choice of transmitter antenna is influenced by many different factors, such as the size and shape of the area that is to be covered, the construction of the building where the paging is to be performed, etc. For these reasons, there are several different types of antennas in use. The tuned antennas include the following:

a) Ground plane
b) Dipole
c) Aperiodic antennas
d) Twin-lead with folded dipole
e) Radiating coaxial cable

The first two are used as regular directional antennas while the last three are used as extra antennas. The last three are used to improve the reception at places that are out of reach of the radiation of the regular antenna.

It should always be observed that the antenna height should be reduced as much as possible and only cover the required area, thereby reducing the risk of interference with other installations.

The following general remarks may be of assistance in choosing antenna type and location.

The quarter wavelength ground plane antennas are used where wide and mainly circular coverage is desired. Due to the construction, a free area with a radius of about 10 ft (3 m) around the antenna is required for the ground plane elements at the place of installation.

If possible, the antenna should be located above nearby steel or concrete structures and above other antennas that lie within a radius of wavelength. If the antenna is to be installed on a roof, for example, and there are no obstacles nearby, it is, as a rule, sufficient to mount it on a steel pipe at least 15 ft (4.6 m) high in order to avoid lobe-lift, which will decrease the field strength at ground level. Ground plane antennas, because of their radiation pattern, are frequently best located close to the edge of the roof.

Antenna(s) must always be mounted a minimum of 15 ft (4.6 m) above the ground or roof. The horizontal distance between ground plane antennas and building sides must be at least 50 ft (15.2 m), this with a view to prevent both reflection and permanent-wave patterns.

In a large building made of reinforced concrete, for example, it may happen that the signal from the regular antenna is so strongly attenuated in one or more parts of the building that reception there becomes unsatisfactory. To improve reception in a single place, a slave transmitter (or multiple slave transmitters) connected to an internally located aperiodic antenna may be installed at the place in question.

Lightning protection for all antennas should be provided; however, the potential for lightning damage is one that is often misunderstood. If a radio antenna suffers a direct hit from lightning, no built-in protection will save it, nor possibly its transmission line nor base station, from substantial damage. The 100 000 A current and great surge current encountered in a direct lightning hit will destroy an antenna used in normal radio installations.

Antenna design features that offer lightning protection actually minimize damage from nearby lightning strikes as well as damage and static that can be caused by various other electrostatic charges in the air. Spark gaps and grounded elements within the antennas themselves are used to provide this important feature.

8.6.4.3.5 Requirements and licensing procedure

In order to operate a radio paging system, the owner/user of the system must obtain a license for the system and be assigned call letters to identify the station.

An important part of planning a radio paging system involves conforming to the FCC requirements regarding radio system control, and obtaining the station license. The following material discusses both the FCC requirements and licensing.

Since paging systems utilize radio transmission, these systems will be governed by FCC Rules and Regulations (see CFR in 8.21). Therefore, an operator's license is necessary to test, adjust, and maintain a system. A "Radio Station Authorization" is a license issued by the FCC that authorizes the operation of radio paging systems.

A copy of the appropriate part of the FCC Rules and Regulations should be available at each control point. Part 90 is contained in Volume V of the FCC Rules and Regulations. A copy of the applicable FCC Rules and Regulations should be kept on site during radio equipment operation.

The FCC defines a control point as an operating position under the control and supervision of the licensee where the person immediately responsible for the operation of the transmitter is stationed and where monitoring facilities are located. Authority must be obtained from the FCC for each control point. Every system must have at least one control point.

A dispatch point is any point from which messages may be transmitted under supervision from a control point. Dispatch points may be installed without authorization.

Each control point must have the following facilities:

a)   A visual indication of a "transmitter-on" condition—either a light or a meter

b)   Facilities to permit the operator to turn the transmitter on and off

c)   Equipment to permit the operator at the control point to monitor all transmission by dispatch points under his or her supervision

d)   Facilities to permit the operator at the control point to take transmitter control away from dispatch points (priority or supervisory control)

Any operator must be able to monitor the channel to see if it is clear before transmitting.

These regulations determine, to a great extent, what equipment the facility must have in any given system. For example, a special requirement in the FCC license to monitor the channel prior to transmitting means that the system must have either a receiver/monitor or a method of indicating detection of the carrier transmission by others on the same frequency, or both.

No "on-the-air" testing may be started until the station license is granted and Form 456 has been completed and forwarded to the FCC regional office.

A station log must be maintained in accordance with the part of the FCC Rules under which the station is licensed. Initial frequency and power measurements must be made and entered in the station log and signed by a technician or engineer holding a radio-telephone operator's license.

Paging systems with voice capabilities must be identified with station call letters every 15 min in standard services and every 30 min in the Public Safety and Special Emergency Radio Services [FCC 90.425(a)]. However, if there are no transmissions over a 30 min period, the station may be identified at the end of the next transmission. Stations are not required to go on the air solely for identification. Morse code station identification is now acceptable by the FCC.

When making a change to the system, that is, adding a second control point, the customer may be required to change his or her license. Any time the user has two (or more) operating points, neither of which has priority, he or she must obtain authorization from the FCC and specify the number of control points in the license.

8.7 Physician and staff register systems

8.7.1 Introduction

Physician and staff register systems are information systems used to locate specific doctors, provide telephone and pager numbers to the operators and others, verify the availability of needed specialties, and provide meeting reminders. Some systems provide printed patient lists. Messages received before the physician or staff has arrived are stored and then displayed to the intended recipient upon arrival. Since these systems are sometimes used by both physicians and allied health professionals, they will be referred to generically as staff register systems.

8.7.2 Design criteria for physician and staff register systems

8.7.2.1 General

Staff register systems are not required by the codes. Hospitals (and occasionally their medical staffs) purchase systems for a number of reasons. Doctors want a means of advising their own presence and of knowing which other physicians are in-house. This is due to the frequent need for consultation between generalists and specialists. By knowing which doctors are in-house, annoying voice paging is reduced. Some costly legal actions have been lost due to the inability to locate or verify the presence of a particular specialist who was actually in-house at the time of critical need.

The number of functions to be accomplished by a register system depends on several factors:

a) *Message traffic.* With increasing hospital size, message traffic becomes a real problem for the telephone operator. Some facilities try to solve this problem by refusing to handle messages for physicians when the messages are related to private practice matters. In the long run, this distinction proves difficult to make and often competes for physician's services. If facility "A" provides good message service, and facility "B" does not, facility "B" may be at a disadvantage. Some modern register systems are actually "options" provided as part of a computerized telephone answering system. Facility size also creates problems in locating staff members for both emergency and routine messages. The bigger the facility, the more likely it is that people are going to be away from the "assigned" workstation. For example, few facilities can afford to equip every staff member, plus the roster of outside physicians, with pocket pagers. Overhead loudspeaker paging can become almost continuous background noise pollution for both patients and staff. The display of staff location information on video monitors throughout the hospital in key locations can greatly reduce these problems. Register systems are generally agreed to reduce overhead paging by at least 80%. The balance of the paging represents information of an emergency or general nature not suitable for register system use. Monitors can also display, via special symbols, the location of a particular member, their pocket pager number, and the presence and urgency of waiting messages.

b) *Number of hospitals in proximity.* In larger metropolitan areas, where physicians often see patients in several hospitals, the location problem for routine, urgent, and emergency messages becomes critical. Where did Doctor Davis go when he left City General? Did he go to Einstein or St. Anthony's? Microprocessor-based register systems can store and display this information quickly and easily. The physician leaving a facility is given several destination choices as part of the registering out procedure. The information is stored in the system's memory and can be retrieved by a telephone operator in seconds.

c) *Specialization.* If 80 doctors are in the hospital and a particular specialist is needed in the emergency room, the question becomes, "Is there a neurosurgeon in the house?" If so, what is the name of the neurosurgeon and where is he? With a well-designed register system, these questions can be answered quickly, and the proper person can be located.

d) *In-house staff location.* In teaching hospitals, it is often the in-house staff that must solve the problem of locating and assembling the best team of physicians. This can be greatly facilitated by a register system that identifies who is in the hospital and who is on call. Some hospitals have display monitors that list outside physicians currently in-house and staff members separately to simplify this process.

e) *Incentive to use.* Because the technology now allows innovative solutions to long-standing problems, needs not previously recognized or addressable can now be satisfied. However, the overriding need is simplicity. If entry/exit stations in particular are difficult to operate, they won't be used. At entry/exit stations, directions and function labels must be simple, clear, concise, and familiar. Displays must be very readable. The entry/exit procedure must be quick and easy to remember. The consulting engineer should ensure that the physicians are directly involved in the selection of the system. Unless physician acceptance is assured prior to final selection, there is no guarantee that the system will be well-utilized.

8.7.3 System types and selection

8.7.3.1 General

In its simplest form, the lighted annunciator types of system, with toggle switch by each name, has been with us for at least 60 years. Annunciator systems continue to be sold and used effectively by small hospitals, nursing homes, and clinics.

The development of microprocessors, personal computers, and mainframe computers has allowed for the expansion of the registering in and out concept to extremely sophisticated systems. A single system can serve thousands of physicians and staff members with special functions for message management, voice synthesis, internal and external destination information, location of staff by title or specialty, radio paging, telephone interconnection, multiple video monitor display or staff registration information, displays of code blue or disaster alerts, staff profiles [listing telephone number(s), pocket pager number, date/time last in hospital], system diagnostics, message printers that may include a list of the doctor's patients and those of his group, logging printers, etc.

8.7.3.2 Lighted annunciator panels

Lighted annunciator panels are recommended for small facilities. A basic system will consist of a minimum of two panels, one usually in front of the telephone operator position and the other at the doctor's entrance point. Both panels have a switch opposite each backlighted name slot. A staff member or doctor indicates their presence by turning on the switch opposite their name. This in turn lights the appropriate name in each panel. Many of these systems have a light flashing circuit activated at the telephone operator position that advises the entering or exiting physician of a message waiting. Often, a private telephone or two-station intercom system is provided to obtain messages from the operator.

The installation requires a minimum of a pair of wires for each name to be annunciated. Therefore, a panel for 50 persons requires a minimum of 100 wires and 200 terminations. The disadvantage of lighted annunciator panels appears when more names must be added and/or the system must be expanded to add or relocate entry/exit stations. For example, adding one doctor's name (assuming space is available on the panel) requires moving every name in the alphabet beyond the initial letter in the name to be added. If changes occur regularly—and they tend to—this can be a time-consuming process, multiplied by the number of panels in the system. Adding stations requires more wire, conduit space, and multiple terminations. Moving a station is the biggest problem because of the electrical conduit and cabling, all of which may have to be replaced or extended via a large junction box with terminal strips. Large systems require a cable bundle with a diameter as large as 6 in (15 cm). Lighted annunciator panels are simple to use and are generally reliable. However, they don't offer the users much incentive to register in and out, and it is expensive to display the data in more than a limited number of locations in rather close proximity. Relocating a medium-sized (200 name) panel, with its corresponding raceway, wire, and labor needs, can be as costly as an entire modern microprocessor-based system.

8.7.3.3 Keypad or coded button-operated register systems

This type of system began replacing annunciator panel systems 30 years ago. The stations became much smaller since the annunciator panel with names is eliminated at both the entry/exit station and the switchboard.

In use, the staff member enters an assigned multidigit registration number in the keypad. The entered digits are displayed via LEDs in a display window for verification. Then, an *in* or *out* button (sometimes within the keypad and sometimes separate) is pushed to complete the registration. If a message is waiting, a *message* light will illuminate, and the user can then call the operator with the provided handset. A *message cancel* button is sometimes provided. Due to wiring simplicity, multiple entry/exit stations can easily be installed at various entrances and other key locations.

8.7.3.4 Microprocessor voice synthesizer systems

A number of voice synthesizer systems are on the market, all of which are quite similar in their functions. A staff member registers into the system from either a dial or touchtone type telephone. First, a multidigit system access number is dialed; access is indicated by a connection tone. Then, the assigned staff member's number is dialed into the system. The voice synthesizer in the system responds by repeating the digits dialed and then saying the words "in" or "out," depending upon the current status of the staff member. The staff member then dials, for example, the number four to register "in" (GHI) or six (MNO) to register "out." Messages stored in the system can be tagged with the extension number of internal departments trying to reach the registering staff member. Depending upon various option selections, these "extension calling" messages may be entered either from the operator position or from any telephone within the hospital. Special number codes are utilized to accomplish these functions. Voice synthesizers can include a number of canned messages, such as "call lab," "call office", and "call records." Video display monitors may be added wherever desired in the hospital and will display staff members' names, pocket pager numbers, location in the hospital, alternate covering physician number, specialty codes, and message insertion and retrieval from outside telephones. An option is available from some suppliers for dedicated telephone "terminals" that do not require the initial dialing of an access number to use the system.

Components of these systems are as follows:

a) A telephone operator 12-button keypad with video monitor
b) Video display monitors throughout the hospital
c) A microprocessor controller
d) Entry/exit stations that might consist of dedicated telephones, Telco network telephones, and/or hospital telephones
e) FCC approved telephone interconnect device
f) System cabling (generally two twisted pairs)
g) Message printer option

8.7.3.5 Microcomputer system

Microcomputer-controlled registry systems are now available from five or six suppliers. These systems provide all of the functional capability of prior systems plus new and useful functions relating to management of the message-processing function at the telephone operator position, and related record keeping and staff services. Functions, instructions, user terminology, nomenclature and vocabulary, display formats, message content, and many other variables can be customized for each installation. The better systems allow most of this flexibility to be in the hands of the hospital user. Suppliers provide in-service training in system operation, set-up modification, and testing.

A printer for messages received at registration, and a logging printer with its system data activity printing capability for legal records free the telephone operators from the enormous chore of logging all page and message information. Some systems can display special alert messages on all video monitors, such as disaster alerts and code blue information. Messages for staff members may be personal ("Your garage called: your car is ready."), departmental (Department/Pediatrics meets 9:00 A.M., Nov. 14, Conference Room "A"), or general ("CME Program, June 4th, routine, doctor's dining room").

Physician information available to the PBX operator position in regard to each physician can vary from the pager number and several telephone numbers, to a full profile of demographic data that includes office addresses, backup doctor, mode of payment accepted, whether board-certified, etc.

8.7.4 Design considerations for physician and staff register systems

a) *Entry/exit stations.* Entry/exit stations should be located at major physician entrances and should include video monitors listing in-house doctors. The intent is to provide entry/exit station users with a practical, useful, and compelling incentive to use the station. Well-designed systems provide personal, general, departmental, and emergency messages. Hospitals with such systems report high utilization.

b) *Central control equipment.* Control cabinets and power supplies need the same type of environment as other communication control equipment. Operator consoles are located by the telephone operator. Well-designed systems use off-the-shelf video and radio frequency (RF) monitors or both. The microcomputer selected should be a well-known national brand with a trackable service history.

c) *Cable plant.* Installation of these systems normally requires no more than two twisted pairs of #22 AWG or pencil-sized shielded cable for connection of entry/exit stations to the computer, and coaxial cable for the monitors. Battery backup for the central processing unit (CPU) is required in regions where momentary power losses are common. Computers are susceptible to spike or surge damage to chips and other circuitry. It is recommended that quality surge protector units be purchased to protect all locally powered components.

d) *Software considerations.* Good programming is required to provide simple user-friendly displays and instructions. For a staff registration system, this is essential for personal comfort in operating the system. If any portion seems awkward, it will be difficult to use, inflexible, and staff members will avoid it. The development of quality software programs requires several years or more of intensive work with customers. A supplier with an excellent track record should be chosen. Start-up of the system requires input of all the roster data plus the pre-established message content and other user variables. The system supplier should be required to teach the operating personnel not only how to run the system, but how to change all the variables, modify the data base, and furnish technical support.

8.8 Dictation systems

8.8.1 Introduction

Dictation systems are recording systems used for storing voice signals (dictation) for transcription. They are used by medical staff for the production of patients' medical records and for administrative functions.

8.8.2 Design criteria for dictation systems

8.8.2.1 General

Health care facilities are required by federal and state laws to maintain a medical record for every individual who is evaluated or treated in a facility. Individuals write more slowly than they speak and memory retention decreases over time; consequently, producing medical records from dictation systems, which are based on spoken records, is more efficient and more accurate than producing them from medical staff notes.

Systems should be selected based on performance, which is measured by turn-around time of important dictation, ease with which the system is used (i.e., ease of training), and dependability as well as overall throughput. System selection criteria is discussed in 8.8.2.2–8.8.2.7.

8.8.2.2 System capacity

An effective dictation system eliminates bottlenecks. The system capacity should be determined by a survey of the dictating load, with consideration being given to the number of persons dictating, amount of dictation, and dictating habits. All systems should allow dictation positions and recording machines to be economically added as system usage expands. While the same amount of dictating may be done, more recording capacity will be necessary where dictation cannot be scheduled or occurs during limited peak periods.

8.8.2.3 Recording machines

Cassette, microcassette, loop, and digital recording devices are employed in dictation systems. The details of the recording devices are less critical than in the past due to an increased effectiveness of digital management systems. There is one caveat. Portable dictation stations often add flexibility to the overall system. Thus the central equipment must have an effective means of reading (and handling) cassette tapes generated by portable devices.

8.8.2.4 Record keeping

Most dictation systems used in health care facilities are computer-based equipment. The label "digital dictation system" is appropriate. These microprocessor-based systems keep records for each dictation. The information may include location of priority dictation; length of dictation recorded with system totals; production history of each transcriptionist; doctors' code, patients' code, and length and type of each dictation. The particular information recorded varies from system to system and can be tailored to each installation. In high-volume installations, this record-keeping capability is necessary.

8.8.2.5 Supervision

The supervisor helps both dictation authors and transcriptionists. The supervisor should have control over each recorded dictation and over related information and should have access to intercom or telephone sets (for speaking with authors and transcriptionists). The supervisor's console often includes a VDT, printer, keyboard, and central processor.

8.8.2.6 Transcription

Transcription controls include recorder transport functions and controls for tone, speed, and intercom (for speaking with the supervisor). Transcriptionists' terminals are typically equipped with a word processing system.

8.8.2.7 Dictation station comfort

A good dictation station makes it easy for an author to record, review, and edit his notes. Each dictation station (or telephone handset) should have controls (or codes) for rewinding, fast forwarding, quick reviewing, full playback, editing, and signaling the operator. Automatic start/stop controls make the system more efficient by eliminating pauses in the dictation. Comfort can affect the efficiency of dictation systems. User-friendly terminals include features like signal muting during fast forward and reverse, automatic gain control, and clear indication of system functions.

8.8.3 System types and selection

a) *Portable.* A small dictation system may consist of portable tape machines and tape players equipped as transcription terminals. Recorded tapes are carried from the dictation author to transcriptionist.

b) *Central system—independent.* A central dictation system allows dictation at any time at various points convenient to the medical staff. Dictation and relevant data is transmitted to a central location for storage until material can be transcribed. An independent system requires a separate cable plant and dedicated dictating sets. These sets are similar to a desk telephone, with push buttons to record, playback, rewind, etc. Dedicated dictation sets are designed specifically for their task and will be labeled accordingly. This can help reduce training time and improve ease of use [over telephone system access—see item c)].

c)   *Central system—telephone access.* Used with telephone systems, a central dictation system receives dictation via the telephone system through telephone instruments. Central recording is connected to the telephone system via a trunk line. The author can record, listen to playback, etc. Note that these dictation codes must be learned or posted (and interpreted) to effectively use the telephone instrument. Interconnection to the telephone system has the advantage of greater system flexibility and wider system access [than dedicated dictation sets—see item b)]. Telephone system interconnection can allow off-site access.

d)   *Digital dictation systems.* Most dictation systems supplied to health care facilities provide close integration of record keeping and transcription control. Any dictation piece can be accessed in any order. It can be identified by doctor's name, dictation type (priority), patient number, time entered, etc.

8.8.4 Design considerations for dictation systems

a)   *Dictation stations.* The effectiveness of a dictation system will depend on both the flexibility of the system and on the way the staff uses the system. Simple systems, effective training programs, and operator assistance help improve performance. Pre-recorded instructions, available each time a system is used, will be useful where staff may work at several facilities and might need a reminder of operating codes each time they relocate.

Locate stations for convenience and so staff wishing to dictate can do so with access to all relevant source material. This includes charting areas at nursing stations, operating and delivery suites, control areas, radiology reading rooms, and pathology analysis areas.

b)   *Portable recorders.* Portable recorders must be compatible with central system transcription machines.

c)   *Wiring.* When the recording machines and supervisors' console are in separate rooms, cables are required to connect them. When the dictation system operates through the telephone system, cable is required from the console and recorders to the telephone switch or main distribution frame (MDF).

d)   *Power source.* Although not directly tied to patient safety, dictation systems are necessary for efficient facility operation. In many facilities, the dictation system is protected by an uninterruptible power supply (UPS) system to reduce the economic impact of short power fluctuations, which could interrupt dictation in progress. UPS sizes for this application typically vary from 1.5–3 kVA.

8.9 Patient physiological monitoring systems

8.9.1 Introduction

A patient monitoring system generally provides numeric and waveform displays of one or more physiological parameters at the bedside and at a remote location. The system makes it possible to provide continual monitoring of several patients from a central location for surveillance and recording, increasing the quality and quantity of the information and thus improving the care giver's ability to deliver appropriate care. These systems are typically provided in the ICU, CCU, recovery room [post-anesthesia care unit (PACU)], short-stay surgery, and neonatal intensive care unit (NICU). Fetal monitors are typically installed in labor and delivery suites. Some systems include telemetry for ambulatory patients.

The patient monitoring system consists of bedside monitors, a central station, optional remote monitors, patient computer systems, and the interconnection hardware. Bedside monitors acquire, process, and display patient parameters, such as the electrocardiograph (ECG); pulse rate; respiration waveform and rate; blood pressure waveform(s) with systolic, diastolic, and mean values; temperature; and oxygen saturation. They provide alarms for out-of-bounds parameter values and may provide data storage and vital sign trend analysis. There are a variety of signals, such as the small, millivolt level ECG obtained through skin electrodes and the transduced blood pressure (from a strain gauge excited by the monitor). The monitor may also accept manually entered data obtained intermittently from other sources (e.g., cardiac output). The bedside instrumentation may be a single device, but frequently is a collection of devices. The monitor may be modular with some parameter modules inserted into the mainframe as needed. The signal conditioning input device may be a separate, smaller unit connected to the monitor with an umbilical cable, permitting it to be located close to the patient or on the bed, with only one cable from the bed to the monitor.

The central station provides remote waveform displays, digital values (e.g., heart rate) and alarms for several patients. Continuous waveform recording onto a paper strip can be initiated manually and short recordings of ECG and perhaps other parameters are initiated by certain alarm conditions. Many systems incorporate special- or general-purpose computer systems for signal analysis, display, and report generation. These additional displays and printers may be located at the central station while the computers may be remotely located. Signal transmission in currently marketed systems is often digital.

The interconnection cabling can be a multiconductor for analog or digital signals or coaxial for data or display. It connects the bedside instrumentation with the central station display, the central-station special-purpose computer, or a network, depending upon the complexity of the system. All of the elements of the system are interconnected, often by more than one signal cable and a separate power cable. There may be additional connections to other central stations, to special-purpose computers (e.g., for arrythmia analysis of the ECG), to remote displays, or to a patient data management network.

8.9.2 Design criteria for patient physiological monitoring systems

8.9.2.1 General

Patient physiological monitoring systems as defined here include connection by cable or telemetry to a central station and perhaps to additional instrumentation. Local bedside patient monitors without connection to a central station may be found in a number of places in the hospital, such as the emergency department, recovery room (PACU), delivery room, operating rooms, short stay surgery, and NICU. The bedside instrumentation may be connected at the bedside to recorders or to other devices.

8.9.2.2 Telemetry systems

A telemetry system may be utilized for ambulatory patients. This type of system includes a portable transmitter carried by the patient with antennas located throughout the area. A receiver at the nurses' station processes the signal and displays the patient's heart rate.

If the hospital considers telemetry, the system supplier will generally make on-site field strength measurements to ensure adequate signal coverage. Each installation must be treated on an individual basis as each hospital has specific details of construction, placement of walls, and location of electrical equipment along with other factors that can affect telemetry signal reception.

8.9.2.3 Computers

Special-purpose computers are often a part of patient monitoring systems. Arrhythmia monitoring systems store a patient's heart rate on a hard disk and this information is continuously updated and analyzed to detect abnormal changes in rhythm and heart beat parameters. Future upgrades or replacement systems in larger or more sophisticated institutions will include signal processing and interconnection to other systems. Adequate cooling, emergency power, separation of circuits from sources of electrical noise, and grounding should be carefully considered. Signal junction boxes and conduit are often dictated by the particular system and the location of the various components. Consultation with system suppliers is recommended.

8.9.3 Design considerations for patient physiological monitoring systems

8.9.3.1 General

Technology is introduced and will be replaced several times during the life of the physical plant. The number of circuits, location of receptacles, layout of signal conduits and raceways, size of conduit and junction boxes and their location can make a significant impact upon the initial installation and an even greater impact upon the future installations of monitoring systems. The design should include reasonable estimation of future electrical requirements and, if possible, should minimize the downtime associated with replacement of the system or its components.

Although the power requirements and cabling sizes are reduced with modern digital systems, the number of components and interconnections may be increased. Access to junction boxes and the various components of the monitoring system is important for installation and maintenance. Hospital power systems are noisy, and separate circuits for the monitoring system are considered good practice.

8.9.3.2 Location of equipment

Patient-monitoring central stations are usually located at the nurses' stations of the units where central monitoring systems are installed. The central monitors and recorders are usually located on or above the counter within easy view for continual monitoring. Larger systems with several monitors may be built into custom casework.

Bedside monitors can be located on small tables, on mobile instrument carts for freedom of movement to any desired location, or, ideally, on wall-mount brackets to keep the bedside area as free of equipment as possible. Depending on the number of patients to be monitored by the central station, the system control equipment may be located at the central station or in a separate equipment closet.

Remote monitors may be wall- or ceiling-mounted at any strategic location in the room or in medical staff flow patterns, such as hallways, where monitoring of patient parameters is desired. These allow observation of the patient parameters while staff members are away from the central station.

8.9.3.3 Space requirements

A countertop or other suitable structure to support the equipment at the central station must be provided. A minimum depth of 6 in (15 cm) from the rear of the instruments to the back of the enclosure is required for ventilation and cable access. Ventilation requirements should be discussed with equipment manufacturers. The structure should consist of a surface above and behind the monitoring equipment for protection of the cables and equipment. Custom-built enclosures are often available from the system supplier. Space for the system control equipment and arrhythmia monitoring computer, if required, must be provided either at the central station or in a separate equipment closet. For larger systems (34-bed unit) up to 80 ft^2 (7.4 m^2) of wall space with plywood backing and cooling capacity of 10 000 Btu/h may be required.

8.9.3.4 Installation requirements

Physical space, power, and cooling requirements must be obtained from the system supplier for each specific installation. Interconnection requirements for the patient-monitoring system, including sizes and types of raceways, cables, and terminating junction boxes at the bed locations and central station, should also be obtained from the system supplier. For most applications, a 2-gang-deep outlet box at each patient bed location with a single-gang coverplate should be adequate. Verify with the system supplier whether the coverplates are furnished with the system. Depending on the specific-system requirements, a 0.75–1.25 in (1.9–3.2 cm) raceway from the monitor outlet at each patient bed location to the system control equipment location should be installed. If the control equipment is located in a separate equipment closet or room, additional raceways are required from the control equipment to the central monitor station. Patient monitoring cables may also be run in a cable tray system. To avoid electrical interference, the cables should be located at least 1 ft (0.3 m) away from power lines, air-conditioning units, diathermy units, elevators, etc. The cables should be installed during the construction project prior to the installation of the finished ceilings. For retrofit installations, surface-mounted raceways may be utilized for the interconnecting cabling. If the bedside monitors are to be installed on wall-mounted brackets, adequate backing must be installed in the wall to support the load.

For telemetry systems, signal transmission cabling from antennas and possibly power for remote amplifiers may require conduit for protection, ease of installation, and future changes or for code compliance.

Coordination of the installation is of utmost importance as several different specialties are involved in or affected by the installation of the monitoring system.

8.9.3.5 Power requirements

Each patient bed location should be provided with a hospital grade emergency power receptacle located within 3 ft (0.9 m) of the monitoring equipment. In critical care areas, the receptacle for the patient-monitoring equipment should be connected to the critical branch emergency circuit dedicated to the bed location. Depending on the size of the system, four to ten emergency duplex receptacles connected to the critical branch of the emergency power system should be provided for the control equipment. It is recommended by some system manufacturers that conditioned power be provided at this location. For computerized arrhythmia systems it may be desirable to provide uninterruptible power for the central control equipment. Multiple emergency receptacles are required at the central station sufficient for the number of monitors and recorders to be installed at this location.

8.10 Emergency medical service communications

8.10.1 Introduction

Emergency medical service (EMS) is a system of trained personnel, transportation equipment, and communications equipment that provides pre-hospital medical care to patients at a remote accident scene and during transport to the hospital. Emergency transportation includes ambulances, helicopters, and fixed-wing aircraft. The communications equipment can provide continuous voice communications and cardiac telemetering between the patient's site and the hospital emergency room. The communications equipment may also be used to coordinate the hospital's participation in regional emergencies. The design, operation, and control of EMS communication systems is usually set by state authorities. Special UHF frequencies are set aside by the FCC Rules and Regulations, Section 90.53.

8.10.2 Design criteria for emergency medical service communications

Whenever a health care facility is equipped for emergency care, the engineer should investigate his responsibilities in installation of the EMS communications equipment. Close coordination with the equipment supplier is required.

8.10.3 Design considerations for emergency medical service communications

8.10.3.1 General

There are many different systems available to provide EMS communications, and the equipment locations and power requirements can vary widely from what is described here. The engineer should carefully investigate the system requirements for each design and ensure the reliability of the power supply to this important system.

8.10.3.2 Emergency room control center

The console contains the radio transmitter and receiver equipment, as well as equipment to display the physiological monitoring signals and to route the voice communications to telephone lines.

8.10.3.3 Raceway for antenna conductors

The EMS antennas will normally be located on the roof of the health care facility and the engineer must provide a raceway from the transmitter and receiver to the antennas. The engineer should verify the maximum length of these cables for the system installed.

8.11 Clocks

8.11.1 Introduction

Clocks are required to provide accurate and reliable time indication for legal records, medical procedures, and efficient and safe operation of health care facilities. Clock systems with automatic hourly and 12 h time supervision and regulation features provide accurate and reliable synchronized time indication. Individual non-self-regulating (non-system) type clocks will usually provide reliable individual time indication.

8.11.2 Design criteria for clocks

Clocks are required by health facility regulations.

8.11.2.1 Clock locations

Clocks should be provided in lobbies, waiting rooms, cafeterias, staff lounges, offices, central control centers, and elsewhere where time indication is appropriate. Clocks with a sweep second hand shall be located in nurses' stations, recovery rooms, scrub sinks, birthing rooms, emergency treatment rooms, intensive care rooms, coronary care rooms, operating rooms, and nurseries. Elapsed time clocks may be required in emergency, surgery, and delivery suites, depending on staff requirements.

8.11.2.2 Individual clocks

Individual non-self-regulating (non-system) type clocks will usually furnish reliable individual time indication; however, they have the inherent disadvantage of nonsynchronization and they must be individually hand-set twice a year for daylight savings time changes as well as following power outages. They are recommended only for public areas, offices, and general-care patient rooms. There are two types of individually powered clocks: one type plugs into a 120 V, 60 Hz receptacle and the other type is battery-operated. Battery-operated clock prices are decreasing, and this fact, coupled with mobility, accuracy, and long battery life, makes battery-operated clocks acceptable. The disadvantages are the cost of replacing the batteries and their not being designed for heavy-duty cleaning. Many battery-operated clocks are provided with a quartz crystal regulated motor to provide higher accuracy and longer battery life.

8.11.2.3 Elapsed-time clocks

Recently, digital direct-read displays have become popular, but often these are too small for across-the-room reading. If the readout is large enough [1 in (2.5 cm) is acceptable; 2 in (5 cm) is recommended], digital direct-read displays are preferred over analog dial clocks in the operating and delivery rooms. Digital direct-read clocks are manufactured to utilize two types of displays: LED and LCD. The LCD has the advantage of being more legible from an angle view, but can only be manufactured up to 2 in (5 cm). The LED can be manufactured to virtually any size [2–4 in (5–10 cm) is typical], but is not easily readable from an angle view. The time clock should have the capability of immediate automatic time correction in the event of power interruption. The elapsed-time clock is controlled from a control panel, with settings for start, stop, and reset from zero or resumption. It is desirable to have both upcount and downcount timer capability with audible signal option at the end of downcount.

8.11.2.4 Clock systems—general

The centrally controlled clock system approach provides the advantages of synchronized, accurate time indication throughout the building and allows quick resetting of all clocks for daylight savings time changes or after a power failure.

Clock systems can also be a source of control signals for time-of-day control of building systems, such as heating, ventilating, and air-conditioning (HVAC) and exterior lighting. The clock system control unit serves the function of a number of individual time clocks in this mode. Where employee shift changes are supervised by attendance recorders, the recorders may be connected to the clock system to provide accurate operation at the recorders. Time stamps may also be connected to the clock system.

8.11.2.5 Clock system—wired

There are three types of direct-wired systems: minute-impulse, synchronous, and binary coded decimal (BCD). Minute-impulse systems are obsolete. Wired synchronous systems require three conductors to be run from the master controller to all of the secondary clocks, with the clocks wired in parallel. The three conductors are labeled clock power, correction, and common; and system voltage is either 120 V, 60 Hz or 24 V, 60 Hz. BCD systems transmit a digital signal to synchronize digital clocks and computer systems via an RS-232 port connection.

8.11.2.6 Clock system—carrier current

This system requires connection only to a suitable 120 V, 60 Hz electric circuit, usually the nearest unswitched duplex receptacle circuit. Automatic individual self-correction is provided by carrier current transmitted over the building secondary electrical distribution system. The costs of carrier frequency signal generator equipment makes its use economical only for medium to large facilities and remodels. Sometimes the carrier current causes interference with other systems. For systems having over 100 clocks, where either a wired synchronous or carrier current system is acceptable, the engineer could show the wired type on the drawings and provide the nonwired type as an alternate. For systems of over 100 clocks, the carrier current type system is recommended.

8.11.3 Design considerations for clocks

8.11.3.1 Size and mounting

Clocks are available in a wide variety of sizes, face styles, enclosure styles, and mounting methods. The clocks are most commonly mounted on the wall in a semi-flush or surface-mounted configuration. In either case a flush outlet box is supplied with the clock to support the clock and to accommodate a concealed attachment plug and receptacle to allow quick disconnection of the clock wiring. The plug and receptacle are three-wire grounding type for carrier current systems, but direct-wired system clocks require four-wire grounding type plugs and receptacles.

Clock sizes are determined by maximum viewing distances and relations to architectural designs. Minimum recommended sizes are listed in table 8-1.

Table 8-1—Clock sizes

Viewing distance ft (m)	Clock diameter in (cm)
100 (30)	12 (30)
150 (46)	15 (38)

8.11.3.2 Clock system control unit

The clock system control unit contains the time base for the clock system. The time base is usually a quartz crystal oscillator, which is either synchronized with the 60 Hz power line, or is a completely independent, temperature-compensated oscillator. The signal from the oscillator is used to drive either a master synchronous motor or a microprocessor-based computer. In the mechanical-motor-type units, which are no longer manufactured but found in many existing hospitals, the system control signals are regulated by the rotation of the motor. The microprocessor-based units generate control signals using solid-state counting and signal generation circuits.

One of the main functions of the master control unit is correction of secondary clocks that are displaying the incorrect time due to power failure or changing to or from daylight savings time. Synchronous wired and carrier-frequency-type systems will provide up to 59 min slow and 55 s fast correction at the end of each hour, and will fully correct the clocks within 12 h.

The master time control unit should be provided with a standby feature to ensure retention of the master time during power outages. This device may be either a spring motor or internal battery and should be capable of retaining the master time for a minimum of 12 h.

8.11.3.3 Cable plant

The synchronizing signals originated by the master control unit are conducted to the secondary clocks either by direct (dedicated) wiring or by carrier current signals over the 120 V, 60 Hz building secondary electrical distribution system. If a carrier current system is selected, the engineer should investigate possible interference with medical instruments and monitors caused by the high-frequency carrier current signal. Medical instruments may also backfeed a frequency on the power distribution system, causing the secondary clocks to malfunction; therefore, highly sensitive receivers should be used.

8.12 Fire alarm systems

8.12.1 Introduction

Fire alarm systems for health care facilities ideally should provide early detection; accurate location of the alarm origin; fire department notification; and automatic control of the HVAC systems; elevators and other building systems necessary to make the building safer for its occupants. The engineer must ensure that the fire alarm system is designed to initiate a planned response by the staff and the fire brigade without disturbing patients unnecessarily. The fire must be placed under control quickly, because evacuation of seriously ill patients is not always possible.

8.12.2 Design criteria for fire alarm systems

Fire alarm systems are required by life safety regulations. The engineer should meet with the local fire marshal to determine the legal fire alarm requirements. Although beyond the scope of this standard, building codes require compartmentalization, fireproofing, and sprinklering as essential to adequate fire protection in health care facilities. The electrical engineer is not charged with the responsibility for designing architectural, structural, and fire suppression systems, but he must integrate the fire alarm system design with the overall fire protection plan.

Three building codes generally are used on a wide basis:

— Uniform Building Code™. Used by most cities west of the Mississippi.

— Basic National Building Code [B2]. Used by many jurisdictions east of the Mississippi River.

— Southern Building Code [B11]. This covers most areas in the southeast.

The basic standards of the fire alarm industry are National Fire Protection Association (NFPA), Underwriters' Laboratories (UL), and Factory Mutual (FM). UL and FM standards are equipment testing standards that are used to determine if equipment meets the functional and operational requirements of the appropriate NFPA standards, and to determine that the equipment does not present a safety hazard if properly installed and maintained.

The following standards provide appropriate guidelines for the application, installation, maintenance, and use of fire-protective signal systems:

— NFPA 72-1996
— NFPA 90A-1996
— NFPA 101-1994
— ASME A17.1-1993
— CABO/ANSI A117.1-1992

In addition to codes, the following factors should be considered when designing fire alarm systems:

a) A high percentage of patients in acute care hospitals are not ambulatory. Almost all patients will require staff assistance for relocation or evacuation.

b) Most hospital patients are in a weakened condition, and many have some cardiopulmonary deficiency. Therefore, the effect of smoke inhalation can be devastating in terms of loss of life.

c) Panic or stress resulting from a poor fire management plan can cause shock, heart attack, and stroke—particularly in the critical patient.

d) Heat from the fire or even the absence of environmental systems can jeopardize the sick patient's life. Extremes of temperature are particularly threatening to the critically ill or postoperative patient.

e) Ambulatory patients may be sedated and may not be able to evacuate or relocate themselves.

f)   The high incidence of plastics, volatile liquids, and other combustibles in a hospital present a unique hazard—that of supporting combustion and often producing toxic gases.

g)   At any given time, a significant percentage of patients cannot be relocated or evacuated, because they are undergoing surgery or some other invasive procedure. For example, a 300-bed hospital can have as many as 30 such patients during a typical morning.

h)   The presence of data processing, biomedical, radiological, and other electrical and electronic equipment presents a two-fold problem. First, these items, because of their high use of electricity and combustibles, increase the chances of fire. Second, when a fire starts, the loss of critical, sophisticated, and expensive equipment can be a major financial loss.

i)   Health care facilities have a high incidence of low property damage fires that nevertheless result in loss of lives.

j)   About half of all hospital fires begin in service areas such as kitchens, general storage, maintenance areas, etc. Fires in patient care areas are most likely to occur in patient rooms.

k)   Finally, the Americans With Disabilities Act of 1991 (ADA) contains requirements for device location and alarm intensity (audible and visual).

8.12.3 System types and selection

8.12.3.1 Hardwired

A hardwired fire alarm system consists of a single control panel from which radiate all the building's initiation and control circuits. Each initiation circuit may be one-pair of conductors (single-loop circuit) terminating in an end-of-line resistor, or two pairs of conductors in separate conduits from the control panel, i.e, a reversible or double-loop circuit. Each initiation circuit may contain one or more initiation devices, activation of any one of which will initiate an alarm from that "zone" (or area) circuit. A typical installation of such a system will include one or more fire alarm zones, each with a one-pair detector circuit and a one-pair circuit for each pull-station, duct smoke detector, flow switch, and tamper switch. Control circuits do not need to be zoned, and may be wired to the limits of the system. (See 8.12.4.13.)

Such systems may use mechanical (relay) or solid-state components (older systems in existing buildings), or microprocessors. Microprocessor controls allow for the use of addressable initiation devices, so that a large number of such devices may be wired to the same circuit, and activation of any device will result in alarm from that device in lieu of from that circuit as with traditional non-addressable type systems.

In selecting a microprocessor-based system versus a hardwired solid-state system, the engineer must carefully consider the economics in wiring and precision in alarm location an addressable system offers, as opposed to the extra costs of the addressable initiating devices. Very often, a simple, solid-state, hardwired system is the most cost-effective system.

8.12.3.2 Multiplex

When fire alarm systems are combined with emergency communication and other non-fire-related systems, the number of conductors needed to interconnect all the system components is greatly increased. This has resulted in sharply escalating installation costs. Multiplex systems offer a means of reducing the installation costs, though some of the savings are offset by increased equipment complexity and cost.

Multiplex systems use microprocessor technology to poll various groupings of initiation circuits. Instead of requiring a set of conductors for each alarm initiation circuit, a multiplex system requires a single set of conductors to a remote data gathering panel, which, in turn, serves a number of its own alarm initiation circuits regardless of the number of circuits or risers in the data gathering panels zone(s). In addition to reducing the number of conductors required, a multiplex system also simplifies the method of wiring. Instead of requiring, for the purpose of supervision, that all the wiring for a single zone be installed in one continuous loop without any parallel branching, a multiplex system can be installed using parallel branching at any convenient location. This is made possible because NFPA codes only permit the use of active multiplex systems which report continually the status of each device on a zone within prescribed time intervals, eliminating the need for the conventional method of continuous supervision. Refer to NFPA 72-1996 for requirements.

Because many initiating devices in a multiplex system share a common transmission path and each device transmits its status sequentially, it is not always possible for a change of status indication to be received immediately at the control panel. Codes permit a delay from the time a fire is sensed by an initiating device until it is displayed at the control panel. Since requirements can vary with each application, the acceptability of the system delay time should be determined before a particular system is specified or accepted.

Because multiplex systems offer the advantages of lower installation costs, a greater variety of features, and computer compatibility, they are being used extensively in all types of buildings and should be given consideration in systems with more than 15 zones.

8.12.3.3 Combination systems

Codes now permit fire alarm systems to be combined with other systems not related to fire emergencies. These include security, building management, and combination communications/fire alarm systems. When these systems are used, fire alarm signals must be clearly recognizable and must take precedence over any other signal, even though the nonfire alarm signal is initiated first. The nonfire alarm functions of the system cannot degrade the integrity of the first alarm functions. Circuits and components that are common to fire alarm and nonfire alarm functions shall be installed and supervised in accordance with fire alarm system standards. Combination systems must be listed by a nationally recognized testing laboratory for fire alarm use. When combination systems can meet the above requirements, significant cost savings can be realized when the systems are installed. Because of the importance of the fire alarm system for life safety and property protection, combination systems should be installed and serviced by trained fire alarm personnel.

8.12.4 Design considerations for fire alarm systems

8.12.4.1 General

Both manual and automatic fire alarm initiation should be used in health care facilities. The complete system should consist of ceiling or spot-type smoke detectors, duct-type smoke detectors, manual stations, and sprinkler water flow switches. Heat detectors are used selectively in place of smoke detectors where conditions may tend to cause a false alarm from smoke detectors.

8.12.4.2 Smoke detectors

In terms of sensitivity and number of devices, the smoke detector is the first line of defense in a health care facility. Ceiling detectors should be provided in corridors, and spaced no more than 30 ft (9.1 m) apart or more than 15 ft (4.6 m) from any wall. Various building and NFPA codes govern spacing at doors and dead ends. Corridor detectors serve two purposes. They control the operation of cross-corridor smoke doors, and they provide hospital-wide coverage, detecting smoke from adjacent spaces. Since fire and health codes ensure that no area will be far from a corridor, all spaces are near a detector. In addition to corridors, smoke detectors should be used in high fire risk areas where false alarms are not likely, in areas requiring very early detection such as medical records, electrical rooms, and computer rooms, and in areas without sprinkler heads. As mentioned before, health care facilities should be sprinklered, but sometimes sprinklering areas such as ICUs, electrical rooms, or radiology rooms may be unwise, as an accidental discharge may jeopardize patient safety or expensive equipment. In these areas, the engineer should consider using a smoke-detector-operated pre-action sprinkler system. Similarly, provisions in ASME A17.1-1993 require that power to elevator equipment must be disconnected before the application of water to an elevator equipment room. In this case again, a smoke- or heat-detector-operated pre-action sprinkler system should be used.

The Uniform Building Code™ (1994, Section 308.10) requires a smoke detector in each patient sleeping room of hospitals and nursing homes with annunciation at the local nurse station. Other codes often permit smoke detectors in patient rooms, at smoke barrier doors, and at horizontal exits to be used in lieu of corridor detectors on patient sleeping room floors. When door closers are required, smoke detectors can be provided as a part of a combination holder/closer.

Suppliers of photoelectric-type and ionization-type smoke detectors have long debated the advantages and disadvantages of their detectors for health care facilities. Accepted wisdom has been that hot, invisible products of combustion are detected faster by ionization detectors, and cold, visible smoke from a slow, smoldering fire is detected better by photoelectric detectors. Photoelectric-detector suppliers argue that fires likely to occur in hospitals are of the slow, smoldering type. They also contend that photoelectric detectors are best in large buildings where smoke cools when it must travel great distances before detection. It is accepted in the industry that false alarms from ionization detectors are more likely to occur from cooking fumes, ozone produced by electrical arcing, steam, and engine exhaust. UL 268-1989 now requires all detectors to pass the same fire tests including the slow, smoldering fire test originally used only to test photoelectric detectors. This has improved the performance of the ionization detectors, but for some models it has made the detector even more sensitive and subject to more false alarms. Suppliers of ionization detectors argue that quick-burning fires are more dangerous and do not produce the visible products of combustion needed for photoelectric-detector operation, making their ionization detector the logical choice. Combination photoelectric/ionization detectors are available. The specifier should make the choice based on the above factors, local and state requirements, and the requirements of the particular facility. Detectors selected for use in health care facilities should be listed under UL 268-1989.

8.12.4.3 Door closers

The use of closers on patient room doors is a controversial issue. The Basic National Building Code [B2] now allows their use in order to meet the requirements for detectors in the patient room, though the issue continues to be debated (see the Basic National Building Code, 1610.6.1). The use of closers almost demands that holders be provided, because nurses cannot function with all patient room doors closed at all times. If closers are required, detector control of closers can be handled in a number of ways:

a) The smoke detector can be installed as an integral part of the holder/closer. This location permits detection of smoke in both the room and the corridor, but its position makes for poor detection in either case.

b) A smoke detector can be installed in the patient room. If a fire starts in the room, the door closes and a general fire alarm is initiated, but without annunciation (usually at the nurses' station or over the door) the location of the fire cannot be quickly determined and the patient can be asphyxiated before the fire is discovered. This represents a sacrifice of the patient to impede smoke spread to the corridor. Individual annunciation of each patient room is an alternative and can be provided by addressable-type devices.

c) Holders can be operated from corridor smoke detectors by zone or by individual detectors. Another alternative is to close all patient doors in the building for any general alarm. However, if all doors are closed, a problem with evacuation and relocation of patients is also created.

Because all of the above methods are unsatisfactory, door closers are not recommended for patient rooms, unless in a jurisdiction requiring them under the Basic National Building Code [B2]. Patient room detectors offer an additional measure of protection at increased cost. Corridor detectors, fire-rated trash cans, noncombustible mattresses and fixtures, and vigilant supervision by the nursing staff may provide adequate protection against the patient room fire.

8.12.4.4 Heat detectors

Heat detectors should only be used in lieu of smoke detectors in places likely to provide false alarms due to the normal occurrence of combustion products. The designer should keep in mind that sprinkler heads operate only a little slower than heat detectors and, in addition to extinguishment, provide alarm initiation and general location annunciation through flow switches. The only advantage added by the heat detector is that it can provide better annunciation. Heat detectors, flame detectors, and other special detectors are not used extensively in fully sprinklered facilities.

8.12.4.5 Sprinkler system water flow switch

In a fully sprinklered facility, the next line of protection is provided by sprinkler water flow switches. The importance of flow switches comes from the fact that virtually every space in the building has a heat-actuated sprinkler head. The only difficulty in using the sprinkler system to initiate an alarm, is in providing accurate location annunciation. For several reasons, sprinkler zones may not always coincide with fire alarm or building zones and smoke and fire compartments. Often, sprinkler systems are hydraulically calculated by the fire protection contractor and zoning becomes a matter of optimum water flow and lowest cost, rather than building geography. If sprinkler zones and other zones do not coincide, the engineer should ensure that

    a)   The sprinkler zone on the annunciator coincides with locations of the heads monitored by the flow switch—not the location of the flow switch itself. Sometimes, the sprinkler flow switch and the sprinkler heads it monitors are not located in the same area.

    b)   The limits of the sprinkler zone are properly identified. In all cases, coordination is required among subcontractors to ensure the proper location of annunciation for alarms initiated by the sprinkler system.

8.12.4.6 Duct detectors and fan shutdown

Air-conditioning and ventilating systems can potentially transmit smoke, toxic gases, and fire from one building compartment to the other. They may also provide oxygen to sustain combustion. For this reason, duct smoke detectors are generally installed in HVAC ducts to automatically initiate the exhaust of smoke-laden air or to shut down air-handling equipment and to provide an additional measure of detection. Duct detectors are required in supply and return plenums of air-handling units 2000 ft^3/min (566.4 m^3/min) capacity or larger but can be omitted in systems of less than 15 000 ft^3/min (4248 m^3/min) capacity under certain conditions. The primary purpose of duct detectors is to ensure that smoke-filled air is not recirculated by air-handling equipment. These detectors should also be tied into the fire alarm system to initiate a general alarm. A large amount of smoke is generally required to activate a duct detector, because the smoke-filled air entering the duct from the fire area is mixed with, and diluted by, large volumes of clean air entering the duct from other areas. To provide appropriate warning, then, duct detectors should be used in addition to a complete area-smoke-detection system, never in lieu of it. Duct detectors should be installed in the return duct at a location before the return air is exhausted from the building or mixed with outside air. Duct detectors in the main supply duct should be installed downstream from the last filter (to detect smoke from a filter fire) and upstream from humidifiers (to prevent false alarms). Some local or state authorities require additional detectors in the duct system to detect smoke before it is diluted. Additional supply duct detectors provide little or no additional protection and are not recommended. Additional detectors in the return ducts can provide additional protection when installed at dampers or other strategic locations to detect smoke near the source before the air is diluted by air from collateral ducts. Although providing an additional measure of protection, the additional detectors are not usually worth the additional invest-ment—particularly in a fully sprinklered building or in a building with area smoke detectors mounted on 30 ft (9.1 m) centers in the corridors. Most codes dealing with duct detectors in the duct system (not at air units) are not specific and only imply intent. Therefore, local inter-pretations vary widely.

All detectors (both duct and area) in a system should shut down all fans and close all dampers in the affected zone. That is, facility-wide fan system shutdown is not recommended. HVAC systems not only provide heating and cooling, which are especially important to critical patients, but also humidification and proper air balance, which are crucial to infection control. Moreover, parts of the facility not directly affected by the fire must continue to func-tion normally as patients are relocated and efforts are made to control the fire. The simplest and a reliable mechanism for this purpose is a pneumatic/electric valve used to close pneu-matic smoke dampers. The control panel includes wiring and modules to initiate control func-tions, and this shuts down the fans and closes the smoke dampers. When the fans shut down, they de-energize the pneumatic electric (PE) valve and the dampers close. If the dampers are electric, wiring must be provided from the fan to each damper.

8.12.4.7 Smoke evacuation systems

Smoke evacuation systems are becoming increasingly popular in commercial and institu-tional buildings. These systems use return and exhaust fans to evacuate smoke-filled air with the outside air dampers fully open to provide makeup air. Such systems are not usually appro-priate for health-care facilities (unless required by state or local codes) for the following reasons:

a) Patients may be subjected to sudden, significant changes in temperature from the outside air. As mentioned earlier, the lives of critically ill patients may depend upon favorable environmental conditions.

b) Extremely cold, outside air can freeze coils in the duct system—especially cooling coils unless the cooling coils utilize a glycol mixture.

c) Smoke evacuation systems tend to complicate the HVAC control system.

d) Additional generator capacity may be required to serve the fan loads.

Should such a system be required, warnings about subjecting patients to cold outside air and the potential for freezing the coils should be included on the smoke evacuation control panel.

8.12.4.8 Manual pull station

Manual pull stations provide the final measure of protection in a fire detection system. In addition to those placed at exits and in corridors as required by codes, manual stations should be provided at all nurses' stations. Usually, the nurse will see fire or smoke in the patient care area, or become aware through a call over the nurse-call system. Since the staff must assist patient evacuation, there is no time to walk to an exit door in order to initiate an alarm.

In addition to exits and nurses' stations, pull stations should be installed so that horizontal travel distance to a pull station is never more than 200 ft (61 m). Breakglass stations (stations with a glass restraining rod), double-action stations, or covers over stations may be used in public areas as a deterrent to false alarms. Recent requirements for the handicapped prohibit mounting manual stations out of the reach of children.

8.12.4.9 Alarm signals

When a fire activates the detection system, it will initiate alarms, both audible and visual. Visual systems consist of flashing "fire" lights, and flashing exit signs (CABO/ANSI A117.1-1992). Audible alarm signals can be chimes, small bells, or electronically generated sounds such as the slow whoop. The slow whoop is not recommended for health care facilities because it can frighten patients. Since the fire alarm signal is primarily used to initiate a planned response by the staff, the alarm must be heard in all parts of the building, including mechanical rooms. The requirement might mean the use of different types of audible signal devices in different locations (for example, chimes in nurses' stations, horns in mechanical rooms). However, some authorities require the alarm sound to be the same throughout the system. The engineer should also consider that horns in mechanical areas adjacent to patient care areas may alarm patients unnecessarily. With more reliance being placed on automatic detectors instead of manual stations, the trend in recent years has been away from coded fire alarm systems. Automatic detectors were traditionally coded by zone using transmitters located in the system control panel. Manual stations usually generated a coded signal mechanically utilizing a coding mechanism located within the station. Coded systems require more maintenance than noncoded systems and are more expensive. Some fire alarm engineers and facility personnel still feel a coded system can save additional seconds in responding to a fire because a coded alarm system permits the fire brigade to dispatch immediately to the affected area without waiting for a call from the telephone operator or for paged instructions. All things considered, however, the coded system is not recommended for most health care facilities, particularly if there are more than 10 fire alarm zones. Current microprocessor-board systems are capable of generating codes, but these systems should be used with general alarms, and voice paging to locate alarms. Instead of relying on coded signals to inform the fire brigade of the fire location, these systems generally use a continuously monitored annunciator. The annunciator station has access to telephone, paging, or other communication systems to inform the fire brigade and others of the fire location. Normally, persons responsible for evacuation of patients and in-house fire suppression can be notified within seconds after an alarm is received. Note that both alarm device location, and alarm device requirements (sound pressure, visual intensity) must be in accordance with standards in the Americans With Disabilities Act [B1].

Presignal, zoned voice alarm, and other systems which do not provide facility-wide general alarm signals are not recommended for health care facilities. These systems may be considered for the campus-type facility where there is no chance of a fire spreading from building to building. Facility-wide alarm signals may also be undesirable in the extremely large facility where the number of occupants makes the building-wide evacuation or relocation of patients, visitors, and staff undesirable or the sheer number of automatic devices makes the incidence of false alarms high. The decision to go with something less than a facility-wide general alarm is one that must be taken up with inspection authorities and accreditation agencies.

Presignal systems are no longer common, but voice alarm systems that automatically direct prerecorded messages to selective parts of the building are becoming increasingly popular—especially in high-rise buildings. Most building codes require voice alarm systems for high-rise business and residential occupancies, but do not require them for high-rise institutional occupancies. The voice alarm is intended to relocate or evacuate occupants of a large building one, two, or three floors at a time—thus avoiding a panic situation in crowded stairwells. In order to facilitate fast response by a fire brigade, a software-coded voice-splicing system can be utilized. The system will automatically provide discreet location information via the system speakers (i.e., "Dr. Firestone: Respond to the fourth floor, east wing."). A voice alarm system also assumes that the building's occupants can respond to voice instructions under their own power, which is not true for health care facilities. Since patients must rely on staff help to relocate or evacuate, voice alarm systems are not always recommended for health care facilities that have an adequately trained staff and a well-maintained paging system. If the paging system is used to broadcast instructions during a fire situation the engineer should verify that paging speakers are located in all areas of the facility.

8.12.4.10 Elevator control

Standards for elevator installations in multistory buildings that require that the elevator controller be interlocked with the fire alarm system to provide elevator recall. Although these standards intend for the elevator to be controlled by elevator lobby smoke detectors, many authorities require elevator recall to be initiated by any general fire alarm. As stated before, health care facility fires are unique in many ways. The fire brigade attempts to control the fire while relocating patients to safe areas of the hospital. Although a fire may be burning in one wing of the hospital, operation of the hospital must continue in other areas. Elevators can be very useful in relocating patients and dealing with other emergencies. So, the automatic controlling of elevators from the fire alarm control panel on any general fire alarm is not recommended, but may be required by code.

Requirements for a vertical fire alarm zone, incorporating all of the upper (second floor and above) floor lobby smoke detectors for a particular elevator bank are frequently encountered. With all lobby detectors on a single initiating circuit, elevator recall can be indicated on the fire alarm annunciator. However, the floor of the fire would not be known unless adjacent smoke detectors sense the fire and make the proper annunciation. Therefore, the vertical zone is not recommended unless other detectors connected to the floor zone are installed in the vicinity of the elevator lobby to provide floor annunciation. An alternative to the vertical zone would be to use lobby detectors with auxiliary relay contacts and to place each lobby detector on the same zone with other detectors on that floor. Each lobby detector's auxiliary relay contact would be used for elevator recall. These contacts are connected in parallel with two wires connected to the elevator bank control circuit.

Elevator control systems should be designed so that smoke detected on any upper floor will cause the elevator control circuit to go into the recall mode. All elevators in the elevator bank return to the ground floor and cease operation with the doors open. The elevators can only be returned to operation by means of a fireman's key. If an elevator is on an upper floor when the sequence begins, its door closes and will not be permitted to open until the elevator reaches the ground floor. The car will also stop on the second floor if a first floor lobby detector senses smoke. The system will stop the car on the third floor if the first and second floor lobby detectors sense smoke, and so forth.

8.12.4.11 Emergency communication systems

Emergency communications systems can be useful in high-rise health care facilities. These systems usually consist of a central control station, usually located on the ground floor, portable telephones, and strategically located telephone jacks for firemen's use in stairways, at exit doors, at sprinkler system valves, and at hose connections. In addition, a corridor and lobby paging system is used for transmitting "live" or prerecorded messages to the building occupants. These systems are generally required by building codes for high-rise residential and business occupancies. Although they are not always adopted for institutional occupancies, state authorities frequently require them. These systems can be a valuable tool for firefighters if the firefighters desire to use them and are properly trained in their operation.

8.12.4.12 Annunciation

A zoned, backlighted, graphic, or VDT annunciator should be installed where it can be monitored 24 h/day. This location will usually be the telephone operator location, a nurses' station, or a security office. This location should have access to a telephone and a paging microphone. Duct detectors for each fan system, each manual station, and each sprinkler water flow switch should be separately zoned and annunciated by a separate light on the annunciator. Smoke detectors should have a light for each building zone as a minimum. Graphic annunciators are preferred if the graphics are prepared with sufficient detail and areas of the facility are properly labeled. Graphic annunciators can be confusing if sufficient detail is not included or if the person doing the monitoring is unfamiliar with the facility layout. Graphic annunciators tend to be more expensive than backlighted annunciators and are difficult and expensive to modify when expanding the facility or changing the fire alarm system. If zones are properly labeled, backlit annunciators are adequate for most health care facilities.

8.12.4.13 System integrity

Applicable codes address protection and supervision requirements, so they will not be discussed in this standard in detail. It should suffice to say that all alarm-initiating and alarm-indicating circuits must be supervised to detect a single ground or open fault in the circuit wiring that would interfere with normal operation. Most hardwired fire alarm systems used today utilize single-loop circuits (previously known as Class B circuits) that may not be capable of initiating or sounding an alarm when the initiating or indicating circuit is in a "trouble" condition. Double-loop circuits (previously known as Class A circuits) are designed to deliver alarms even with a single grounded or open conductor and are therefore recommended. This is generally accomplished by using special zone modules in the control panel and looping the circuit conductors back to the control panel instead of terminating it with an end-of-line resistor after the last device.

Health care facilities generally have a large number of area type smoke detectors on ceilings—especially in corridors. Single-loop initiating circuits go into trouble (from an open circuit) when a smoke detector is removed and may not be able to initiate a fire alarm signal.

This is of particular significance if initiating circuits combine several types of devices, such as smoke detectors, pull stations, and flow switches. In a large hospital, there is high probability that at any given time a detector will be out for repair or a circuit will be in a trouble alarm. Combining devices can mean that all alarm-initiating devices in a particular building zone may be incapable of initiating a fire alarm signal when that zone is in trouble. It is recommended that each type of device within each building zone be placed on a separate initiating circuit, so a trouble condition on one circuit will not affect the operation of other types of devices in that part of the building. If devices are to be combined, it is recommended that double-loop circuits be installed.

It is recommended that different types of devices within each building zone and each sprinkler system valve status switch be placed on individually supervised circuits with individual location annunciation. This will increase the speed with which the staff can respond to a trouble condition.

If an annunciator is required to be installed by the authority having jurisdiction, the annunciator must be fully supervised. Supplementary annunciators are not required to be supervised.

8.12.4.14 Power supply

Fire codes require that all fire alarm systems have a primary power supply and a trouble signal power supply (usually taken from a different phase of the power system from the primary power supply using two single-pole circuit breakers). If systems are used to automatically notify the fire department, a secondary power supply shall be provided and sized to operate under normal load for 60 h. Codes for health care facilities require the fire alarm system to be connected to the life safety branch of the emergency system, which is supplied by the primary and secondary power sources. When this is done, batteries are not generally required. Since there is some controversy concerning the need for batteries with generators, the designer should check with the authority having jurisdiction. If batteries are required, they must have 4 h capacity.

8.13 Security systems

8.13.1 Introduction

Electrical and electronic devices that provide monitoring and security detection are used primarily to supplement passive physical and staff monitoring provisions. Intrusion devices are used to monitor the security of property within the facility in areas where high risk of theft is probable, as well as to protect from staff leaving through unmonitored exits. Current codes do not require security systems, but they may be justified for personal safety of staff, patients, and public (in parking garages for instance) and to reduce property loss.

8.13.2 Design criteria for security systems

The following devices are elements that may be combined into a hospital facility security system:

a) *Metal-detection system.* These systems are intended to prevent inadvertent or premeditated loss of valuable hardware, instrumentation, movable equipment, etc., which may be intermixed with soiled linen or with refuse that is being removed from a facility. These systems use metal detection, x-ray, or other detection systems at all loading (discharge) platforms to screen all carts or material-handling equipment leaving the facility.

b) *Intrusion-detection system.* This equipment should be considered for pharmacy dispensing areas, drug vaults, narcotic cabinets, radiology, silver recovery, bulk storage rooms, gas storage rooms, cashiers, emergency exits, and medical records. Movable protection devices can be any number and kind of security sensors that are removed from their circuit during times the protected area is occupied. This is done so that they do not constantly signal the presence of authorized personnel working in the area. Such devices may include switches on doors, relay contacts of motion detectors, capacitance detectors, photoelectric beams, or pressure mats, etc. Intrusion detectors should have the following features:

1) An internal, automatic-charging dc standby power supply with primary ac power operation.

2) A remote, key-operated activation/deactivation switch installed outside protected areas adjacent to the room entrance door frame.

3) An integral capability for the attachment of wiring for remote alarm and intrusion indicator equipment (visual or audio) to provide annunciation at a security office or central control center.

Where security systems affect personnel safety or protect valuable items or information, the engineer should specify a supervised security system. The electronics of these systems indicate trouble when shorts or open wires develop.

c) *Closed-circuit television system.* Television systems are used for monitoring and controlling access points to facilities. Security guards monitoring television systems may have an opportunity to locate or identify intruders and prevent violent or destructive activities. Television cameras are located in high-traffic areas, such as main lobbies where door switches are useless. They are commonly used in waiting areas, cashiers' counters, at loading docks, and in parking areas. Television security electronics usually provide remote control of cameras and switching control of video signals. Refer to 8.15 for design criteria.

8.13.3 Security sensor devices

A security sensor is any detection device ranging from a simple door switch to a sophisticated solid-state motion detector. Examples of security sensors are as follows:

a) *Mechanical switches.* These switches, generally with spring-loaded levers or plungers, operate when a door, window, or cabinet cover is removed or opened.

b) *Magnetic switches.* These switches supervise the position of movable openings, such as doors and windows. A magnet on the movable portion operates a switch on the fixed or frame portion.

c) *Balanced magnetic switches.* These switches utilize a bias magnet inside the switch housing on the fixed frame together with a standard magnet on the movable portion of an opening. They will respond to an excessive magnetic field imposed on them, as well as to a reduced field. They are most difficult to compromise with an external magnet, and are therefore more tamperproof than standard magnetic switches.

d) *Foil (tape) and screens.* Foil is a thin strip of low ductility tin-lead material adhered to a glass surface to detect breakage. Cracking or breakage of the glass interrupts the circuit current flowing through the foil. Screens are grids built with wooden dowels containing a groove in which a fine hard-drawn copper wire is embedded. The grids are used as an electrical barrier over openings. If a dowel is broken, the wire breaks, interrupting the circuit current in the same manner as foil.

e) *Pressure mats.* When stepped upon, these devices close an electrical contact. They make an excellent intrusion-detection device since they can be concealed under carpeting or scatter rugs. They are stable, reliable devices and, when used properly, have an extremely low false-alarm rate. They have *single-pole, single-throw* (SPST) switching action, providing only a cross (short) on the protection circuit.

f) *Beams.* These devices are beams of light (usually infrared or solid-state) to a constantly energized photocell. When the beam is interrupted, the receiver de-energizes, causing an alarm.

g) *Audio detection.* Sensitive microphones may be installed in an area to detect sounds of intrusion. Sounds that are picked up are amplified and operate an alarm relay if they are loud enough and are repetitive beyond a preset count. Audio detection operates best in quiet areas, such as vaults.

h) *Ultrasonic.* This system fills an area with high-pitched sound waves (above human hearing) and detects the disturbance of the sound pattern when motion occurs in the area.

i) *Infrared body-heat detection.* This motion detection system is basically optical since the detector "sees" a moving human source of infrared energy (98 °F) against a background at room temperature (usually around 72 °F).

8.14 Facility monitoring

8.14.1 Introduction

Health care facilities contain complex systems critical to patient care that must be monitored. Current codes require many of the following monitoring systems.

8.14.2 Medical gas alarms

NFPA 99-1996 requires hospitals to monitor the operation and condition of the source of supply, the reserve (if any), and the pressure in the main line of their nonflammable medical gas distribution systems.

The gases covered by this standard include, but are not limited to, oxygen, nitrous oxide, medical compressed air, carbon dioxide, helium, nitrogen, and mixtures of such gases. The alarm system is required to detect two classes of system problems: abnormal line pressures (high or low) and low gas supply.

Alarm equipment, such as alarm panels and actuating switches, is normally supplied as part of the medical gas distribution system (piping, manifolds, gas columns, etc.). The engineer should closely coordinate his or her work with the specifier and the supplier of the gas distribution equipment. The engineer's areas of responsibility normally include the following:

— Alarm system ac power
— Alarm panel locations
— Interconnecting alarm signal wiring

The NEC requires the ac power source for the gas alarm system to be the life safety branch of the hospital electrical system.

All medical gas alarm systems are required to include two master alarm signal panels, which will display alarms related to the source of gas supply for the entire system. One master panel shall be located in the office or principal working area of the individual responsible for the maintenance of the medical gas system such as the maintenance supervisor or hospital engineer. The second panel shall be located to ensure continuous surveillance, at the telephone switchboard, the security office, or at another suitable location. The intent of these requirements is to ensure continuous, responsible surveillance of the medical gas system, since the life of the hospital's patients may well depend on continuous delivery of the medical gases.

In larger hospitals, where medical gases are distributed to widely separated areas, area alarm panels are required. NFPA 99-1996 specifically lists the following areas where medical gas may be supplied, and where area alarm systems must likewise be installed:

— Anesthetizing locations
— Vital life support areas
— Critical care areas
— Intensive care areas
— Post-anesthesia recovery
— Coronary care units
— Operating and delivery rooms

The area alarm panel shall be installed at the nurses' station or other suitable location near the point of use that will provide responsible surveillance.

The engineer must make provisions for the signal wiring between the alarm panels and the actuating (pressure sensing) switches. The switch locations will be determined by the supplier of the gas distribution equipment. The engineer's responsibility will normally be limited to providing support and protection for the signal wiring in the form of raceways and cable trays.

NFPA 99-1996 contains these additional provisions, which should be noted by the engineer:

— Air compressors and vacuum pumps shall not be installed in rooms or enclosures used for the storage of gas cylinders.

— Electrical equipment and fixtures located in cylinder storage areas shall be located at least 5 ft (1.5 m) above the floor, to avoid damage from the cylinders.

8.14.3 Refrigeration alarms

8.14.3.1 Introduction

Hospitals frequently contain refrigeration equipment such as blood bank refrigeration, donor organ refrigeration, pharmacy refrigeration, laboratory refrigeration, kitchen refrigeration, kitchen freezer, and/or morgue refrigeration.

As effective operation of the hospital depends partly on the continuous and proper operation of these refrigerators, the installation of refrigerator alarms helps to ensure proper operation. The alarms provide an indication of loss of power, and indications for improper internal temperatures.

8.14.3.2 Design considerations for refrigeration alarms

Alarm equipment locations and power requirements should be obtained from the refrigeration equipment supplier. Each type of refrigeration equipment normally comes with its own alarm system. The master monitor station and its associated temperature sensor are normally located at the refrigeration enclosure, while remote monitors are normally located where continuous surveillance is available. The engineer should provide raceway for the multiconductor cable between the master and remote monitor stations. The NEC requires that power for these alarm systems should be derived from a life safety circuit.

8.14.4 Emergency generator monitoring

NFPA 99-1996 requires an emergency generator monitoring system. The generator annunciator shall be located at the central control center. See 5.4.5 for design criteria.

8.14.5 Energy monitoring and control systems

8.14.5.1 Introduction

Energy monitoring and control systems (EMCSs) may be used as part of an energy conservation program. Such systems, in addition to saving energy, may

— Protect and limit damage to equipment.
— Allow malfunctions to be corrected with minimal service interruption.
— Operate equipment only when necessary, thus extending equipment life.
— Cut down on the number of operating personnel required.
— Improve maintenance management.

— Combine with other systems to perform other related functions, such as fire alarm annunciation, security, life safety, and other real-time event-initiated functions.

Various levels of control are available as follows:

a) *Basic local controls.* These are equipment control systems supplied/recommended by the equipment system supplier. These systems turn equipment on or off depending on sensor-activated (temperature, humidity, pressure) messages. A larger, more sophisticated EMCS should incorporate local controls into its system.

b) *Single building system.* A microcomputer controls the independent local controls of several pieces of equipment in one building. In the event of a failure of the microcomputer, the local controls operate the equipment.

c) *Distributed processing control systems.* These systems employ a minicomputer that controls numerous limited-area systems or the single building system, or both. Mass storage of information is used to keep records and to support a sophisticated software system. In the event of minicomputer failure, the basic local controls will operate the equipment.

8.14.5.2 Design considerations for energy monitoring and control systems

Refer to IEEE Std 241-1990 for the design of EMCSs.

8.15 Television systems

8.15.1 Introduction

In its most general form, a health care television system is utilized to transmit visual and, when desired, audio data over cable circuits, rather than via antennas. In addition to the cable plant and receivers, a health care television system will usually include a master antenna or a connection to a local cable franchise to obtain commercial entertainment programming, or both. Portable video cameras and video tape recorders are occasionally used as program sources. This subclause describes a fairly simple master antenna television (MATV) system, which would be installed in a nursing home or small hospital.

Television systems in larger clinics and hospitals become more complex with the addition of specialized closed-circuit television (CCTV) systems. Such systems may include a central control and equipment room, production studio, fixed video cameras, or a satellite earth station.

Health care applications of television systems may be categorized as follows:

a) *Entertainment and education programming.* This system distributes entertainment programming from a number of sources to patient rooms and visitor areas. A secondary function is the distribution of educational programming to patients and staff.

b) *Interdepartmental communication.* There are a number of specialized CCTV systems in this category that provide two-way, audiovisual communication between physicians and support departments, such as pathology and radiology.

c) *Patient monitoring.* This category also includes several specialized CCTV systems. Such systems provide visual contact with patients in ICUs, emergency treatment rooms, and in certain areas of radiation therapy units.

d) *Security monitoring.* A CCTV system, with fixed video cameras and a central monitoring point with continuous surveillance, augments security systems.

8.15.2 Design criteria for television systems

8.15.2.1 General

No current codes require television systems. Rapid changes are taking place throughout the entire field of television that are affecting its use in health care facilities. A vast number of new program services are becoming available, not only to the general public, but also to special groups through the new technical facilities, such as satellite earth stations, microwave interconnections, and improved videotape distribution. Viewing is shifting to new program sources and to pay TV.

8.15.2.2 Entertainment and education programming

Television systems consisting of a TV signal distribution system are recommended in virtually all health care facilities. The usual programs from local broadcast systems are available.

8.15.2.3 Controlled viewing

Some form of directed programming, sometimes referred to as addressable terminals, is essential to the needs of health care facilities. The concept of individually addressable television receiving sets clearly matches the need to limit the viewing. The question is cost and the maturity of the design. The health care facility should use the channel blanking feature of the TV receivers that provide manual means to control the reception of up to 36 channels with a system of 54–300 MHz bandwidth. The active channels on television receivers can be selected at the lower front panel. This method can provide a simple and inexpensive manual selection of the channels allowed for reception at any receiver. The disadvantage is that a member of the facility's staff must go to each patient room to make the manual selection, which can be time-consuming in a 300-patient-room facility.

8.15.2.4 Computer-directed programming

This system provides a central control panel where one can direct programming to each television set in the health care facility. In addition, the system can keep track of time used and provide a printout for billing information. Patients can be billed for full-length movies and patient education programs. Computer-directed programming should be purchased when it is cost-effective. This means that it will pay for itself within three years from manpower savings and from new revenue from movies and patient education. This will happen when the designs have matured and the system costs have decreased. However, the engineer should consider specification of TV sets for near-term use, which incorporate compatibility with computerized-directed programming.

8.15.2.5 Television sets and recorders

a) *Color television systems.* Use color television systems only for broadcast systems, for hospital surgery, or where the need for color has been justified.

b) *Television projection systems.* Television projection systems are used for large group viewing for staff education. The lighting should be of a type that is adjustable. These systems will accept signals from MATV antennas or from a connected closed-circuit system.

c) *Recording equipment.* Use video tapes where instant playbacks are desired, for further studies, or permanent records. Use broadcast-type cameras or high-quality two-to-one ratio interlaced cameras to send signals to video tape recorders.

8.15.2.6 Medical staff education

The health care facility's size and teaching requirements will determine the criteria for educational television. Pictures of surgical procedures have long been an important educational tool among surgeons. In recent years live television has been a feature of national or regional meetings, by which means a large audience, usually situated in a hotel lecture room or other meeting hall, can watch a surgical procedure being carried out at a remote hospital. Modern television techniques such as split-screen, instant replay, slow motion, and added animation, enhance the educational value of these showings. With the advent of lower-priced equipment, surgical television is beginning to take a more prominent place as an intramural or institutional educational instrument. With standard equipment, operative procedures can be transmitted live or shown as taped films in the hospital auditorium, classroom, and at department meetings. Cineradiography done during surgical procedures can be shown in continuity with the operative film. Tapes of such procedures, combining views of the operation, the pathologic section, intraoperative x-rays, and noncommitant commentary of the surgeon, and his or her team and consultants comprise a record unsurpassed by any other medium. Appropriately edited, this type of audio-video record may form the basis of a teaching library, especially valuable in instances of rare or unusual cases, and possibly in medicolegal situations.

8.15.2.7 Pathology consultation

A two-way audio-video system between the frozen-section laboratory and the operating room can enable the surgeon to communicate directly with the pathologist and permit examination of a microscopic slide in consultation with the pathologist by video without leaving the operating table. It also provides the pathologist with a view of the pathologic lesion in situ without entry into the operating room. A television camera may be mounted in or on the surgical light for this purpose. With a camera situated over the cutting table, the surgeon can direct the pathologist or technician as to precisely how to section a specimen, if necessary, without leaving the operating room. In general, a two-way audio-video system between operating room and the frozen-section laboratory should eliminate the need to bring the pathologist into the operating room; it should permit the surgeon, by simply viewing the video screens in the operating room, to supervise the sectioning of a specimen and to peer into the microscope without leaving the operating room.

a) *Radiology consultation.* As an aid to diagnosis, an audio-video hook-up between the operating room and the x-ray department permits x-rays to be viewed on the television screen in the operating room. This method holds several distinct advantages over the present practice of locating the films, carrying them into the operating room, sorting out the most appropriate films to mount on the view box, and risking such annoyances as not getting a good view from the operating table, mounting the wrong films, possibly contaminating clean objects by inadvertent contact, and misplacing films in transit between the operating room and the x-ray department. Where fluoroscopy x-ray equipment containing a video camera is employed in surgical procedures, the x-ray image may be displayed on a monitor in the radiology department for interpretation.

b) *Staff bulletin board.* The hospital should first evaluate the doctor's register system as these systems overlap. The videotext concept should be considered, by which literally hundreds of pages of printed or graphic information could be called up individually at many receivers.

8.15.2.8 Patient monitoring

a) *Intensive care unit (ICU).* Hospital regulations require that each ICU patient be visible from a nursing station; however, it is possible to meet this regulation and still not have a clinically useful view of the patient. Although one can argue that there is very little useful information derived from a televised view of the patient, as compared to information provided by the physiological monitors, many nurses feel more comfortable with closed-circuit television. The video picture of the patient is a reminder that the patient is a human being, and it can be particularly useful in large units. When provided, the general room illumination should be adjustable with a dimmer control switch to enable the lighting level to be reduced at night for patient comfort.

b) *Radiation therapy.* Some radiation therapy procedures require the use of heavy shielding between the patient and the equipment operator. At the same time, it is important to position the patient precisely with respect to the radiation beam, and to ensure that the patient does not move during the exposure. This problem is often resolved with a monochrome CCTV system, installed to give the equipment operator a clear view of the patient and the beam reference marks. The video camera should be furnished with a zoom lens and with resolution adequate to allow precise determination of the patient's position. The video cable should be installed between the camera and the monitor to preserve the shielding performance of the radiation shielding.

8.15.2.9 Satellite receiving station

A satellite station may be used to generate revenue from satellite receiver programming. For example, movies could be shown to patients for a fee.

8.15.2.10 Security

The criteria for security surveillance by camera is determined by the size of the facility. See 8.13.

8.15.3 Design considerations for television systems

8.15.3.1 Cable plant

Basic community antenna television (CATV) design concepts are recommended for the television distribution system as distinguished from the somewhat simpler concepts sometimes used in small master antenna television (MATV) systems. The added costs of the CATV methods are insignificantly small because materials cost 20% more, but labor costs are less for a 10% net additional cost. The advantages are that the system can be extended or otherwise added to without redesign and with only a minimum disruption of the plant or its operation. Leakage of signals (in or about) is minimized and interaction between receiving sets is minimal.

The signal distribution system should consist of a cable network with 0.412 in (1.046 cm) trunk/feeder cable providing the main signal path. At appropriate intervals, the cable will have directional taps spliced in to provide a tap-off point for the drop cables, which are the final link to the television receiver. A distribution amplifier may be necessary to distribute the signals at the proper level. Each directional tap will require two 0.412 in (1.046 cm) connectors. The number of outlets of each tap will be determined by the location in the building. Also, the attenuation of the tap is determined by the signal level at the tap location.

The type of amplifier will be determined by the signal level that can be delivered to the central control and equipment room.

8.15.3.2 Master antenna

The engineer should make a list of signals to be received, and design accordingly. The type of antenna required is determined by the frequencies covered and their signal strength. Several antennas may be needed to cover all required frequencies.

a) *Location and orientation.* The exact location and orientation of antennas are determined by a signal strength survey.

b) *Lightning protection.* Follow requirements for lightning protection given in the NEC, Article 810, and in NFPA 780-1995. Where lightning protection must be installed, use surge arresters and ground them effectively.

8.15.3.3 Amplifiers

Use preamplifiers and amplifiers as follows:

a) *Preamplifiers.* Use preamplifiers when incoming signals are too weak to be accepted by the amplifier.

b) *Amplifiers.* Use amplifiers for signal amplification as required to overcome distribution system losses and provide suitable output. A broadband amplifier may be suitable if it can cover all incoming channels and maintain adequate signal level inputs to the distribution system; otherwise, single channel amplifiers for each input may be necessary.

8.15.3.4 CCTV camera selection

A modern camera is a small, compact unit with a minimum number of circuits and comprises a self-contained, one-package system providing the following features as appropriate:

a) *Interlace.* Interlace describes the condition where the lines in the second of two successive fields in a picture tube are spaced between the lines in the first field. Use this action where fine details are read. Use interlace wherever a system supplies standard TV receivers (antenna systems).

b) *Random interlace.* Use a random interlace camera (self-contained unit) where lines in successive fields may or may not be spaced between each other. Use the camera in all applications where detailed observation is not required or where videotape recorders will not be used.

c) *Picture details.* Picture details (resolution) are expressed in "lines." Commercial television in the U.S. uses a 525-line system, in which distinguishable details are based on 525 horizontal scans of each picture. This is the minimum amount of resolution to be provided. Provide more resolution only where required for acceptable viewing, such as the necessity of 800 lines for surgical observation.

8.15.3.5 Camera mounting

Use indoor and outdoor mountings as follows:

a) *Indoor.* Use an air-cooled housing where temperatures exceed those of camera specifications. In studios, the heat from the stage lighting makes air conditioning necessary. Use explosion-proof housings for viewing hazardous areas. Use pan and tilt mounts (manual or remote) when cameras view more than one area. Use standard tripods on cameras for portable use.

b) *Outdoor.* Always use a weatherproof housing. Never face cameras toward the sun at any time of the day. Avoid picking up reflections from glass or water, if possible.

8.15.3.6 Subject viewing

Locate a camera so that desired areas, objects, or subjects receive the maximum benefits from available lighting.

a) *Lens selection.* Choose a lens that fits the scene. A fixed lens limits the field of view to one scene. Lens turrets have the advantage of handling three or four lenses with varying focal lengths (normal view, wide angle, and varying degrees of telephoto). A zoom lens permits varying the focal length without loss of subject viewing during the change.

b)   *Operation.* Cameras that are easily accessible may be controlled manually. The more expensive remote control should be provided where local operation is not feasible. Remote control should be located and coordinated with other operating devices involved in the application being viewed on an adjacent monitor.

c)   *Video switching.* Provide video switching where more than one camera must be viewed on a monitor.

8.15.3.7 Subject lighting

Distinguishable details depend on scene contrasts, camera resolution, and monitor revolving powers. Consider ultra-low lux cameras for outside security to avoid over-lighting the area solely for the camera. Consider the use of infrared lighting and cameras for certain security uses.

a)   *Required lighting levels.* Use the same light levels needed by the human eye for clear visibility. Minimum lighting incident on the scene should be at least 20 fc (215 lx).

b)   *Additional lighting.* Plan lighting so that a minimum number of "hot spots" are seen from camera locations. Illuminate the complete scene for viewing.

c)   *Automatic iris.* An automatic iris is necessary on the camera to control the amount of light focused on the picture tube or vidicon. It automatically compensates the camera gain for illumination increases from 10–10 000 fc (107–107 600 lx).

8.15.3.8 Monitor selection

Monitors should have the same resolution and type of interlace as cameras. Locate monitors for minimum light reflections on tube faces. Avoid vertical mountings. Use circular polarized face plates where ambient lighting is high. For distances between monitors and viewers, see table 8-2. Use multiple monitors for large group viewing.

8.15.3.9 Studio

The studio layout should be arranged for efficiency and storage considerations. The studio should be large enough to show a patient in bed. The design should consider acoustical criteria. Lighting should include track lights and some floor pedestals, which will flexibly provide key, fill, and backlighting for various sets. Selective dimming will be needed on certain circuits. Special cooling will be required.

8.15.3.10 Chapel

If the camera in the chapel is to be used several times a week it should be permanently mounted with a remotely controlled zoom lens on the camera. If the camera is used in the chapel only once per week it should be easily detachable from its wall mounting so that it can be used the rest of the week in other places.

8.15.3.11 Operating room

In recent years, the camera on a floor-standing boom and the hand-held camera have been replaced by more appropriate installations. The television camera may be mounted on an extension arm attached to the stem of the surgical light and outfitted with sterilizable detachable handles. Some manufacturers of surgical lights provide a model with a television camera mounted in the center pod of the light.

Another approach for surgical suites of any size is a portable unit consisting of a console that contains a videotape recorder and a viewing screen on which is mounted an adjustable boom to hold the television camera. The camera should be remotely controllable for pan, tilt, and zoom.

8.15.3.12 Satellite receiving station

The satellite receiving station can be located either at ground level or on the building roof with a clear view of the satellite arc. Cable trays or ducts are required from central control to the roof and to a convenient outside location at ground level. If roof mounting is selected, structural reinforcement will be necessary because it weighs about one ton.

Table 8-2—Recommended minimum monitor sizes

Number of viewers	Distance ft (m)	Monitor size in (cm)
1	10 (3.0)	8 (203)
2	15 (4.6)	14 (356)
3	20 (6.1)	17 (432)
4	30 (9.1)	21 (533)
5	35 (10.7)	24–27 (610–686)

8.16 Sound reinforcement systems

8.16.1 Introduction

Sound reinforcement systems are electronic systems, providing sound pickup, processing, amplification, and reproduction, intended to reinforce an acoustic sound source within the room or space where the source is located. Many sound reinforcement systems also reproduce recorded material associated with slide or movie projection.

8.16.2 Design criteria for sound reinforcement systems

A system is required to improve signal intelligibility where distances, obstructions, or acoustical conditions limit the intelligibility of an acoustic source (e.g., speaker or performer). The sound system must maintain adequate direct sound-to-reverberant field ratio (for clarity) and improve the signal-to-noise ratio (i.e., increase volume). A good sound system should provide natural sound that seems to originate at the acoustic source.

Sound reinforcement systems are often required in auditoriums, meeting rooms, lecture rooms, and chapels. In special cases, a large space might be used for several purposes and a sound system would be required, e.g., in a cafeteria or large lobby.

8.16.3 Design considerations for sound reinforcement systems

Sound reinforcement systems consist of one or more microphones, a mixer, processing electronics, audio amplifier(s), and one or more loudspeakers. The proper operation of a sound system depends primarily on the location and specifications of the microphones and loudspeakers within the reinforced space.

8.16.3.1 Room acoustics

Small auditoriums and lecture rooms designed with acoustics in mind often do not require sound systems except to reproduce recorded material. Highly reverberant rooms and larger rooms will employ a sound system to improve intelligibility. Most gathering spaces benefit from a reinforcement system that aids the occasional quiet speaker and helps lecturers with noisy audiences. The usefulness of any sound reinforcement system, and whether it is needed, depends on the space where the system is installed.

Room finishes vary in the amount of sound energy they absorb. Hard surfaces, such as concrete, plaster and tile, reflect the majority of sound energy that reaches them. Soft surfaces, such as carpet, acoustic tile, and batt insulation behind a porous covering, absorb a large portion of the sound energy that reaches them. Sound energy in rooms with mostly hard surfaces will dissipate more slowly than sound energy in rooms with soft surfaces. Thus, rooms with low sound absorption have longer reverberation times.

The optimum reverberation time of a room varies with its size and its use. Optimum reverberation time is close to 1 s in lecture rooms and meeting rooms. Auditorium reverberation times may vary from 1-3/10 s to 1-9/10 s, depending on the primary use. Some auditoriums are equipped with movable curtains or absorptive panels so the reverberation time may be varied for different uses. Specific room conditions are a function of the architectural design.

The design (or existing conditions) of a project may result in a reverberation time longer or shorter than optimum for the project's intended use. Sometimes corrections to the room acoustics are an appropriate way to solve this problem, but often the sound system must be designed to accommodate imperfect conditions.

8.16.3.2 Loudspeaker location

When an amplified sound reaches a listener within 30–40 ms of the original sound, the sounds appear to blend and reinforce each other. Sound waves in air travel at about 1120 ft/s (341 m/s). Therefore, the best location for a central loudspeaker cluster is above the acoustic source (lecturer, etc.) such that the sound path to a listener from the acoustic source and from the loudspeaker cluster differ by less than 30 ft (9.1 m). This condition should be optimized for every listening location in the room.

The best reinforced sound is reproduced at one location. When a listener receives sound from two sources, interference patterns result, reducing its clarity. A typical auditorium stage with a loudspeaker on either side is the classic example of poor sound system design.

Sound energy should always be directed at an audience. When misdirected, it serves to increase the reverberant field or accentuate an echo in the space, thus reducing the audio intelligibility.

8.16.3.3 Centralized, distributed, and precedence systems

A centralized system reproduces sound at one location; a distributed system reproduces sound at several locations; and a precedence system utilizes a central system and a distributed system in combination. Properly employed, a precedence system seems like a central system to the listener. This is accomplished by delaying the signal to the distributed loudspeakers via a time delay unit and separate amplifiers.

Centralized systems are used in spaces where sound may be directed (line of sight) to the audience from one location. Distributed systems are used in spaces with low ceilings or where the "front" may change. Precedence systems are used in situations where the stage (or front) is permanent but a central loudspeaker cannot reach the whole audience due to either low ceilings or obstructions. Centralized and distributed systems are used more often than precedence systems.

8.16.3.4 Volume

Sound reinforcement systems must maintain sufficient volume to provide a satisfactory signal-to-noise ratio at each listener location. The amplifier power and loudspeaker ratings may be chosen to provide nearly any volume level desired, but the overall system gain will be limited by the system feedback point. The maximum system gain will be determined by the number of open microphones, their relative location to loudspeakers, the distance from the source to the microphone, the distance from the loudspeaker to the farthest listener, and the room acoustics.

Usually, the sound reinforcement system will be designed to handle much louder signals than the maximum system gain allows. This permits the presentation of movie soundtracks and other prerecorded information at higher levels than that used for sound reinforcement.

8.16.3.5 Mixers

The types of control used in an auditorium system usually depend on its size and complexity as well as its use. The simplest installation, such as a lecture room with one microphone, uses a preset mixer. It may be adjusted slightly for each lecturer but generally remains at the same setting throughout any given lecture. When several microphones are used, such as at a panel discussion in an auditorium, the relative level of each microphone can be preset, but then the system gain must be low since all microphones remain open. In situations like this, an automatic microphone mixer may be employed.

Automatic and preset mixers must be adjusted differently for each event, so the equipment rack should be readily accessible to the reinforced space. Controls for projector and auxiliary inputs should be provided at the mixer location.

8.16.3.6 Audio signal processing

Several electronic processing techniques are used to improve the sound quality of reinforcement systems. One or more of the following items are often employed:

a) *Frequency shaping.* An equalizer may be utilized to correct for microphone, loudspeaker, and room frequency responses. Historically, a real-time frequency response curve was adjusted to within 3 dB of a flat response from 125 Hz to 1000 Hz or 2000 Hz with a 6 dB per octave roll-off below 125 Hz and a 3 dB per octave roll-off above 1000 Hz or 2000 Hz. The high-frequency knee at 2000 Hz was usually used for voice reinforcing systems and the knee at 1000 Hz was used for systems where music will be reproduced by the system. The technology for testing sound systems was greatly improved by the introduction of time delay spectrometry (TDS) testing techniques. TDS technology allows a sound technician to measure the direct sound field energy produced by loudspeakers. Using this testing method, the direct sound field frequency response is adjusted for a flat response between 250 Hz and 10 000 Hz. TDS methods allow the sound technician to verify the total system polarity. The system should be connected so that a positive pressure at the microphone produces a positive pressure at the loudspeaker. These frequency response curves are subject to variations for specific jobs, especially for unusual room acoustics. Both real-time and TDS methods can help provide a natural and highly intelligible sound signal but TDS methods give the sound technician a better tool to troubleshoot problems. TDS testing methods are preferred to real-time methods for all larger sound reinforcement systems.

b) *Automatic microphone mixing.* The maximum acoustic gain of a reinforcement system is limited by the number of open microphones. Installations using several microphones often require an automatic mixer. An automatic mixer opens a microphone line when a sound source excites the microphone. Many automatic mixers reduce the overall system gain when several microphone lines are open. Automatic mixers help maximize gain while preventing feedback.

8.16.3.7 Equipment

There are many loudspeaker types available for smaller rooms and distributed sound systems. Each type is suited to a specific application and may perform poorly in other applications. In larger rooms, where long throws are required, a large cone driver in a horn or utility enclosure is used for low frequencies and a driver and horn (or several horns) are used for high frequencies. The physical dimensions of horns are determined by frequency and distribution characteristics that are selected to accommodate the shape of the space served. Sufficient mounting space must be allowed for the central loudspeaker or loudspeaker cluster. In extreme cases, long throw horns may be over 4 ft (1.2 m) long, and each cluster may contain several horns.

Cardioid (directional) microphones and omnidirectional microphones are both used in reinforcement systems. Cardioid microphones are preferred by many performers and production groups for the control they provide. Omnidirectional microphones have a smoother off-axis frequency response and are easier to equalize in permanent installations. They are preferred for most lecture and auditorium reinforcement systems. Dynamic (nonpowered) microphones are preferred since they simplify system installation.

Wiring for a reinforcement system involves separate cables to each microphone input, cables to projector and auxiliary inputs, cabling to and from a control console when required, and wiring to loudspeakers. Power is required at the control console, equipment rack, and projector locations. Wires for the inputs to the sound system are small gauge, but several pairs of #12 AWG or #10 AWG wire may be used to drive a large loudspeaker cluster.

8.16.3.8 Installation

The installation practices are crucial to good sound reinforcement system performance. All of the concerns listed in item d) of 8.6.3.2 are applicable to sound reinforcement systems. In addition, the following items are potential problems:

a) *Loudspeaker distribution.* The distribution of a low-frequency speaker (a cone driver in an enclosure) is typically 120° or more and its direction is not critical; however, each high-frequency driver-horn combination is manufactured with a specific distribution pattern and must be properly directed toward the audience if it is to serve its purpose. Typical distribution patterns include 90° by 40°, 60° by 40°, and 40° by 20°. Every listener in a space should be included within the distribution pattern of one horn, and the patterns should overlap about 20% horizontally and 10% vertically to provide even, high-frequency coverage.

b) *Loudspeaker weight.* A loudspeaker cluster for a large auditorium may be very heavy. A check with the structural consultant regarding cluster support is recommended. Secure but adjustable mounting should provide for each high-frequency horn and low-frequency driver.

8.17 Data processing systems

8.17.1 Introduction

The use of computers in medicine is growing. In the past few years, there has been a proliferation of highly sophisticated microprocessors and microcomputers enabling a wide array of patient care applications to be developed for the health care industry. Furthermore, microprocessor circuitry and microcomputers are now frequently incorporated into much of the new medical equipment.

Computers are being used for patient information management as well as accounting and inventory purposes. These systems may be connected to each other in an integrated fashion while vital patient care information is delivered to nursing areas on terminals or networked-microcomputers. For instance, a growing number of hospitals have a computer-aided laboratory information system that transmits laboratory data to appropriate nursing stations as it automatically enters charges for the procedures or tests to the accounting system.

Some hospitals have started taking advantage of the new electronic filing technology that enables a hospital to store a vast amount of patient records, such as medical charts and diagnosis reports, on a compact disk. This technology allows medical staff to gain access to electronic images of these reports on networked-microcomputers at the patient areas or off-site clinics.

The graphical user interface approach is utilized by software developers to make data processing systems more user-friendly by reducing the number of commands a user has to master in order to use the system effectively.

In a limited number of hospitals, computers are being used in the care of patients. Some of the patient care applications are found in situations such as anesthesia, in the treatment of patients in need of blood and liquids, and for patients with a variety of metabolic and endocrine disorders. Computerized diagnoses of electrocardiographs, electroencephalographs, and other graphic or numeric readouts are also in use.

For purposes of planning, it is prudent to assume that sooner or later computer terminals or networked-microcomputers will be installed in most every area of the health care facility.

8.17.2 Design considerations for data processing systems

Cable plant capabilities for present and future data processing facilities shall be provided to all central control stations, nursing stations, patient rooms, laboratories, administrative areas, and departmental offices.

Whether a particular piece of data processing equipment will cause interference with nearby medical equipment is, of course, a critical consideration.

In planning for a microcomputer-based network, the selection of hardware (such as the type of cabling, the server required, network interface cards, etc.) and software (the network operating system, application programs, etc.) should be dictated by the characteristics of the various departments in terms of reliability requirement, response time, and location.

The selection of specific data system equipment is beyond the scope of this recommended practice, but various design considerations specific to data system support are outlined in the succeeding subclauses of 8.17.

8.17.3 Data facilities

There are many parallels between data systems and telephone systems, but data systems are associated with greater complexities in system design.

A data system may consist of terminal equipment, local distribution cable, transmission equipment, long-distance transmission facilities, central communication systems, and data center equipment. It might be a collection of computing machines linked to shared resources without any central equipment. It might be a floppy storage disk carried between two personal computers. Although the expansion of telephone facilities to carry data is often very economical, it is absolutely necessary to review the owner's plans before making any assumptions about equipment locations or wiring topology of a data network.

Data networks serve user terminals. The terminals may be workstations, personal computers, video display unit (VDU) or video display terminal (VDT) (character or graphics terminals), printers, teleprinters, or facsimile machines.

Terminals may be linked to central systems via dedicated conductors or via transmission equipment. They may reside on a wide area network (often connected with telephone lines) or on a local area network (LAN). Switched networks and various network bridges and mail systems support more complex interconnections.

Data transmission equipment is much like computer equipment. It is electronic in nature and requires varying degrees of power service continuity depending on the type of traffic (information) carried. Data switching equipment has similar parallels to PBX equipment.

Data centers (i.e., computer rooms) contain both the central communications equipment and data storage and processing equipment. They are usually associated with a concentration of data cable and exhibit several special design requirements.

8.17.3.1 Data terminals

Most data terminals are based on cathode ray tube (CRT) technology. With a basic terminal or VDU, a screen is usually associated with a keyboard and connected to a CPU. Personal computers and workstations tied to a network may be used as terminals to access remote computing power. Terminals, personal computers, and workstations vary over a wide range of sizes. Their power requirements range from 40 W to several thousand watts, most often in the range of 100–300 W. Lighting for comfort at a VDT terminal requires careful engineering. A well-shielded or indirect system with a moderate illumination level, between 20–50 fc (200–500 lx) is typically employed. Refer to IESNA RP-1-1993 for additional design information.

8.17.3.2 Cable systems and support structures

Data terminals are connected via a communication cable. This cable may be a twisted pair cable (sometimes identical to telephone cable), a shielded twisted pair cable, coaxial cable, or fiber optic (glass or plastic) cable. The cable may run to a computer room or to equipment in a nearby closet. Refer to [B3] for additional information.

Cable systems for LANs may have a topology distinct from the telephone system. The classes of cable system topologies include bus, star, ring, and branching tree. These topologies resemble their names. A bus connects points along a line. A star connects points to a central location. A ring connects points on a loop. And a branching tree is a complex (maybe hierarchical) system of interconnection. Logical transmission may be different from the physical topology; for example, a logical ring may be wired as a star (back to a central closet).

It is often advantageous to enforce a star topology for terminal wiring. It allows changes to the interconnections via physical cable changes at a central closet location. With appropriate data network equipment, a star topology can limit signal loss to a single terminal when an individual cable is damaged or disconnected.

Once the topology of data wiring is defined, its support structure may be designed using the same distribution systems used for telephone wiring. Some particular concerns, beyond those for telephone wiring follow:

a) Coaxial, fiber optic and, to a lesser extent, shielded cable require greater care than telephone cable. The minimum bending radius of these cables is larger than telephone cable.

b) Space required for terminations, especially at outlet boxes, must be carefully considered for each type of cable.

c) Data cables are generally a larger diameter than telephone cables.

d) Data cables generally have more stringent distance limitations than telephone cables.

e) Data cables are more susceptible to interference than analog voice (telephone) cables.

The backbone or riser cable for data systems may take on any of several forms. The simplest approach is to route individual terminal cables to one location in a building. On the other hand, it is not unusual to collect the signals from several data sources at a closet and route a single cable to the central building location. This is accomplished by various data transmission and network equipment. In this case the backbone or riser cables may be lighter than the sum of the terminal cables they serve; the riser cables are usually coaxial or fiber optic cables.

Data cable is often terminated with modular terminal systems allowing quick cross connects. Typically data terminals require more physical space per cable than telephone cable terminals, which are quite compact. Data terminals are sensitive to moisture and dirt. Data connections must be clean and tight due to the nature of data signals. Typical terminal space dimensions may be misleading. Each project must be analyzed separately to define terminal space requirements.

8.17.3.3 Data transmission and network equipment

Data equipment locations will depend on distance limitations and the economics of the particular data system utilized. In many cases, some of the data equipment will reside in apparatus closets or communication equipment rooms (CERs) and terminal rooms associated with the telephone system.

This equipment requires ventilation or cooling, power (with consideration for continuity) and illumination between 30 and 70 fc (322 and 753 lx). The illumination is for changes and maintenance; the equipment usually operates unattended.

Data equipment is often assembled on a rack with modular cable terminations, and consideration must be given to access and floor space. It is usually appropriate to maintain data equipment adjacent to telephone facilities, but to designate separate telephone and data spaces within terminal rooms and CERs.

8.17.3.4 Data center installations

Data centers, otherwise known as data processing centers, computer centers, or computer rooms, are the hub of various data storage and processing systems. It is unusual to find a self-contained computer room.

Three classes of outside connections occur: First, to data terminals residing in the same building or on the same campus as the data center; second, to widely dispersed terminals via the public telecommunication network; and third, to other users via point-to-point radio (microwave or satellite) links. These classes of connections are associated with different approaches to data cable access. The first case requires terminations for data terminal wiring in the building. This is usually a large bundle of small cables routed to racks in the computer room. The second case requires a cable path from the computer room to the main distribution frame or utility network interface for access to the public network. The cable is usually a large multipair cable routed to terminals allowing for cross-connect to the data communications equipment. In a large facility, public network access may be via a fiber optic cable. Typical data centers utilize a mix of classes of connections.

Data equipment size and installation requirements will vary considerably, depending on the user's communication service needs. It is not unusual to have area requirements as small as 200 ft^2 or as large as tens of thousands of square feet. The specifics should be obtained from the user and the prospective equipment manufacturers, taking into consideration potential growth. Without specific data, the following typical installation requirements should be used to design facilities of any size:

a)   Average live load of communication equipment is approximately 70 lb/ft^2.

b)   Ceiling height above the finished floor is 8 ft (2.4 m) minimum.

c)   Lighting level of 70 fc (750 lx) at 30 in (76 cm) above the finished floor. A more specific lighting approach is appropriate with lower levels with well-shielded fixtures at terminals, and high levels at tape and disk drives. Dual switching with careful zoning will allow for flexible lighting response for computer equipment moves.

d) Aisle space and equipment configuration is dependent on the physical restrictions of the building, as well as interconnect cable, maintenance, supervision, and manufacturing requirements.

Most systems today have been designed for power and signal cables to enter from below. Hence, raised flooring should be installed over the structural floor, creating a space to be used as a cable raceway. In addition, the raised floor can be used as an air plenum, which will provide the necessary conditioned air directly to the equipment air intake louvers. The raised floor shall have an adequate number of floor registers or perforated panels, or both, to provide the required air flow. Cutout trims should be provided to protect against cutting of cables. Ramps should be provided to facilitate movement of equipment and test gear. The height of a raised floor is dependent on available head room, number of planned cables, and pressure restrictions affecting air conditioning. For various requirements regarding the placement of wire/cable in underfloor plenum spaces the NEC, NFPA 75-1995, and local codes should be consulted.

Consideration should be given to acoustical treatment in equipment operating areas. Noncombustible acoustical ceiling tiles, flame-retardant carpets, wall coverings, curtains, etc., provide for noise reduction and absorption. Proper design and equipment placement can reduce mechanical equipment noise. Duct lining, resilient equipment mounting, location of air handler unit, and size of dampers are some considerations.

Conditioned air should be supplied, which will limit the ambient temperature and humidity to within the limits specified by the equipment manufacturer. Much equipment today can operate without any degradation in performance at temperature levels in excess of 78 °F. For energy conservation purposes, where super-cooling is not required, the ambient should be maintained at human comfort levels. An adequately filtered backup ventilation system should be provided to limit the temperature rise to 10 °F above the outside ambient in case of main air-conditioning outage. Thermal shock, direct distribution of conditioned air to critical equipment, humidity control, and redundancy all are factors for the mechanical designer to consider.

Typical power requirements for a data facility are 25 W/ft^2 for communication and computer equipment, 2.0 W/ft^2 for lighting, and 15 W/ft^2 for the HVAC system. Service is normally 208Y/120 V, ac, three-phase, four-wire, 60 Hz. On some large computing equipment 400 Hz is required and power is furnished via a frequency converter. Steady-state voltage requirements are typically +10%, −8% with a frequency variation of 1/2%. The duration and rate-of-change of any variation must be taken into account. Generally, a 20% transient, lasting longer than 30 ms, or a voltage outage, lasting longer than 15 ms, may cause errors, loss of information, shutdowns, or equipment damage. Equipment tolerances can be exceeded by numerous events, including utility or building power system faults, large switched loads, local utilities network switching, lightning, reclosing operations, planned brownouts, or unplanned blackouts. This can occur several hundred times a year. The user has several systems available to protect his facility against voltage variation or outages or both. Constant voltage transformers, the mechanical inertia motor-generator set, power conditioning systems, and UPS systems are some types of equipment available to improve voltage regulation.

The system chosen shall be dependent on the type of operation, economics, and consequences that can develop if unregulated voltage is provided. The utilization of UPS systems for critical computer systems is increasing. Refer to 5.11 and to [B4] for additional information.

Grounding for communication equipment must be provided. An independent ground riser from the building's earth electrode network shall terminate on an isolated ground bus and be sized on at least 2 kcmil per linear foot of cable run. Single-point grounding or multipoint grounding, or both, may be used depending on the communications equipment's frequency characteristics. Refer to FIPS Pub 94-1983 for additional information.

In some installations, the impedance of the ground system and its association with power system grounding may affect data system performance, especially data transmission equipment. System suppliers usually have documentation on specific system grounding requirements.

8.18 Telewriter and facsimile systems

8.18.1 Introduction

Telewriter equipment allows transmission of handwriting to remote stations, where it appears exactly as written. Facsimile equipment offers a more powerful system for transmission of any fixed graphic material, including printed material and pictures. Both telewriter and facsimile systems are being replaced by computer-based networks.

8.18.2 Design criteria for telewriter and facsimile systems

Within hospitals, telewriter terminals are used to transmit three basic types of data: requests for information, reports, and authorizations. The terminals are commonly placed at the following locations:

— Nurses' stations
— Pharmacy
— Dietary office
— Medical records
— Laboratories
— Admitting office
— Business offices; administration offices
— Maintenance

A second category of use for telewriter equipment is communications for the deaf. A telewriter terminal may be connected to a telephone so as to answer an incoming call and provide two-way written communications with any caller equipped with similar equipment.

Facsimile equipment is used both for interdepartmental communications and for communications between hospitals. The most common interdepartmental application is the daily transmission of patient drug requirements from the nurses' stations to the pharmacy. Facsimile communication makes the best use of staff time in this situation, since the equipment operates unattended and is much quicker than batch orders conveyed by messenger. When the facsimile equipment is selected for this application, the hospital should also consider placing terminals in the dietary office and laboratory areas.

Where a hospital is a member of a hospital association, facsimile communication may be used to transmit inventory and administrative data between hospitals.

8.18.3 Design considerations for telewriter and facsimile systems

The selection and location of equipment will normally be accomplished by the architect or system supplier. The engineer should obtain the list of terminal locations with a notation as to whether the terminal is a sender, receiver, or both. At each location, a power receptacle should be provided. Dedicated telephone type cabling is required between each terminal.

8.19 Pneumatic tube systems

8.19.1 Introduction

The system consists of an interconnecting tubular network through which small-sized containers travel. The container movement is powered by compressed air. These containers, or carriers, as they are referred to, can be dispatched and received at different stations in the system automatically or semi-automatically. The system can thus transport material between points that are horizontally or vertically remote. The carriers are designed to transport items such as paperwork, pharmaceuticals and medical supplies, small tools, IV bottles or bags, production parts, sealed food items, etc. The main advantage of the pneumatic tube system is that it provides fully automated small-piece distribution for least cost when compared to other systems. It is the lowest-cost fully automated material-handling device available to a large facility that can travel vertically or horizontally and provide the fastest delivery time.

8.19.2 Design criteria for pneumatic tube systems

The system configuration including piping layout and equipment locations is usually designed by the system supplier or architect. The electrical engineer must verify equipment locations and provide power connections. Control wiring between stations is usually in the system supplier contract.

8.19.3 Design considerations for pneumatic tube systems

The engineer should verify the requirements of the system to be installed. The following are general guidelines for power requirements:

a) *Stations.* Stations require a 115 V ac power source from a dedicated circuit breaker.

b) *Diverters.* Diverters require a 115 V ac power source from a dedicated circuit breaker.

c) *Blowers.* Blowers require a three-phase, 208 V ac or 480 V ac circuit for 2–15 hp to the motor starter and connection from the starter to the motor. A manual disconnect is recommended within sight of the blower. The starter requires a 115 V ac coil, which is connected to the blower control panel.

d) *Computer control terminal.* The computer control terminal requires a 115 V ac power source from a dedicated circuit breaker.

8.20 Disaster alarm systems

8.20.1 Introduction

A disaster alarm system alerts the central control center as to the status of disasters, either natural or man-made. Signals must be coordinated with local civil defense and disaster area authorities, and design must follow their system.

8.20.2 Design criteria for disaster alarm systems

Disaster alarm systems, such as civil defense alerts and weather alerts, are required in health care facilities by civil authorities. The engineer should check local requirements.

8.20.3 Design considerations for disaster alarm systems

a) *Actuating devices.* Actuation can be local or remote. Data can be furnished directly or via telephone, radio, or microwave channels. The number of channels and their coding should meet the requirements of civil defense and local disaster area authorities. Signals are originated by remote control from the offices of civil authorities, or by local push buttons. Each coded channel requires a signal canceling button with a pilot light.

b) *Annunciator.* The annunciator shall be located at the central control center. Annunciator panels should have a circuit supervisory feature to indicate alarm, operational faults, trouble buzzers, silencing switches, and pilot lights. Test buttons are necessary to verify readiness of equipment and for use in training drills.

8.21 References

This chapter shall be used in conjunction with the following publications:

ASME A17.1-1993, Safety Code for Elevators and Escalators.[3]

---

[3]ASME publications are available from the American Society of Mechanical Engineers, 22 Law Drive, Fairfield, NJ 07007.

CABO/ANSI A117.1-1992, Accessible and Usable Buildings and Facilities.[4]

CFR (Code of Federal Regulations), Title 47: Telecommunications, published by the Office of the Federal Register (FCC Rules and Regulations are contained within this document).[5]

FIPS Pub 94-1983, Guidelines on Electrical Power for ADP Installations.[6]

IEEE Std 241-1990, IEEE Recommended Practice for Electric Power Systems in Commercial Buildings (IEEE Gray Book) (ANSI).[7]

IESNA RP-1-1993, Recommended Practice for Office Lighting.[8]

NFPA 70-1996, National Electrical Code® (NEC®).[9]

NFPA 72-1996, National Fire Alarm Code.

NFPA 75-1995, Protection of Electronic Computer/Data Processing Equipment.

NFPA 90A-1996, Installation of Air Conditioning and Ventilating Systems.

NFPA 99-1996, Health Care Facilities.

NFPA 101-1994, Life Safety Code®.

NFPA 780-1995, Lightning Protection Code.

UL 268-1989, Smoke Detectors for Fire Protective Signaling Systems.[10]

UL 1069-1989, Hospital Signaling and Nurse Call Equipment.

Uniform Building Code™, 1994.[11]

---

[4]This publication is available from the Building Officials and Code Administrators International, Inc. (BOCA), 4051 W. Flossmoor Rd., Country Club Hills, IL 60478.

[5]CFR publications are available from the Superintendent of Documents, U.S. Government Printing Office, P.O. Box 37082, Washington, DC 20013-7082.

[6]FIPS publications are available from the National Technical Information Service (NTIS), U. S. Dept. of Commerce, 5285 Port Royal Rd., Springfield, VA 22161.

[7]IEEE publications are available from the Institute of Electrical and Electronics Engineers, 445 Hoes Lane, P.O. Box 1331, Piscataway, NJ 08855-1331.

[8]IESNA publications are available from the Illuminating Engineering Society of North America, 120 Wall Street, FL 17, New York, NY 10005-4001.

[9]NFPA publications are available from Publications Sales, National Fire Protection Association, 1 Batterymarch Park, P.O. Box 9101, Quincy, MA 02269-9101.

[10]UL publications are available from Underwriters Laboratories, Inc., 333 Pfingsten Road, Northbrook, IL 60062-2096.

[11]This publication is available from the International Conference of Building Officials (ICBO), South Workman Mill Rd., Whittier, CA 90601.

8.22 Bibliography

Additional information may be found in the following sources:

[B1] Americans With Disabilities Act (ADA). 42 U.S.C. 12101 et seq.[12]

[B2] Basic National Building Code.[13]

[B3] Bernaden, J., and Neubauer, R., eds., *The Intelligent Building Sourcebook*, Johnson Controls, Inc., published by the Fairmont Press, Inc., 1988, distributed by Prentice-Hall, Inc., Englewood Cliffs, NJ.

[B4] Griffith, D. C., *Uninterruptible Power Systems*. New York: Marcel Dekker, 1989.

[B5] Kaufman, J., "Planning Communications for Modern Hospitals: A Professional Approach," *Construction Products & Technology*, Nov. 1969.

[B6] Kreager, P., *Practical Aspects of Data Communications*. New York: McGraw-Hill, 1983.

[B7] Laufman, H., *Hospital Special Care Facilities: Planning for User Needs*. New York: Academic Press, 1981.

[B8] Nash, H. O., Jr., "Fire Alarm Systems for Health Care Facilities," Conference Record, Industrial Applications Society, IEEE-IAS 1982 Annual Meeting.

[B9] Smith, J. R., "Hospital Paging Systems in the Special Emergency Radio Service," A technical and regulatory review before the American Society for Hospital Engineering of the American Hospital Association. Update on Hospital Paging Regulations Meeting, Apr. 23, 1980, Dallas, TX, Apr. 25, 1980, Chicago, IL.

[B10] Smith, J. R, "Paging System Capacity, Instructions for Estimating Channel Capacity and Delay," *Communications Magazine*, June 1980.

[B11] Southern Building Code.[14]

---

[12]CFR publications are available from the Superintendent of Documents, U.S. Government Printing Office, P.O. Box 37082, Washington, DC 20013-7082.

[13]This publication is available from the Building Officials and Code Administrators International, Inc. (BOCA), 4051 W. Flossmoor Rd., Country Club Hills, IL 60478.

[14]This publication is available from Southern Building Code Congress (SBCC), 900 Montclair Rd. Birmingham, AL 35213.

Chapter 9
Medical equipment and instrumentation

9.1 Introduction

In a modern hospital, the selection and purchase of equipment and the care and maintenance of that equipment are important tasks facing the administration and maintenance staff. In order to make proper use of today's hospital equipment, all aspects of the purchase, installation, and maintenance of the equipment should be considered. All of these items have costs associated with them, some of which may not be apparent at first glance. The purchasing process should follow a set pattern, such as described in 9.1.1 through 9.1.3.

9.1.1 Need

The department head or staff member in charge of the project or task should request purchase of a new piece of equipment after investigation into its use in the hospital. Criteria for requesting the purchase may include

a)   The purchase's ability to enhance the state of the art.
b)   Its ability to produce specified results.
c)   Its ability to reduce costs and/or save time.
d)   The length of time before the purchase is outmoded.
e)   Whether it will help patient care, or be used for diagnostic procedures.

Additionally, lease vs. purchase of the equipment should be considered.

9.1.2 Cost

In analyzing costs, the project manager should determine

a)   Whether the desired equipment needs to have more than one supplier or manufacturer.
b)   Whether the equipment cost has been checked from all suppliers.
c)   Whether the cost can be capitalized, and over what period of time. Budget constraints need to be considered.

9.1.3 Space requirements

In analyzing the space requirements for the purchase, the following should be considered:

a)   Does the institution have available space for the new piece of equipment?

b)   If new space is required, or if the area needs remodeling, will the cost of this work be prohibitive?

c)   Are all of the required utilities available at the location?

d)   Is there a clear path wide enough and high enough to actually get each piece of equipment into the desired location?

e) Will any existing structures need to be removed and replaced or repaired after bringing in the piece of equipment?

9.1.4 Utilities

Along with space requirements detailed in 9.1.3, the next most important factor to consider is whether utilities are needed to operate the equipment.

Equipment may require hot water or cold water, or both; other requirements may be air, gas, steam, exhaust ducts, special vents, and electrical service. Electrical service and availability should be checked for the following:

a) Voltage (special voltages)
b) Capacity (amperes)
c) Hertz (frequency)
d) Protection
e) Control
f) Heating or cooling
g) Humidity range
h) Special construction or systems needed to provide for proper and useful operation (such as RFI shielding, EMI shielding, special communication systems, etc.)

9.1.5 Quality of utilities required

Some modern equipment requires that the utilities be within a particular operating range for the equipment to function properly. In water supplies this would be seen as domestic water vs. hot water, or chilled water, or filtered water, or deionized water. In air systems, the requirements will appear as the need for cooling year-round, the need for a specific humidity range, and possibly even a need for a low-temperature range.

Electrical needs will be found depending on the equipment as both the quality of power provided and criteria for the characteristics of the power supply system. Since much of modern medical equipment is computer-based or computer-controlled, electrical disturbances play a large part in proper operation. Likewise, for equipment that requires a large-ampacity, short-duration power input, the impedance of the power supply system becomes important.

One standard of power quality is the Computer and Business Equipment Manufacturer's Association (CBEMA) curve. This curve represents the envelope of voltage disturbances within which typical equipment can function. The ability to function is based on the following characteristics of the power supply built into the equipment:

a) Noise filtering
b) Stored energy
c) Energy surge absorption ability
d) Voltage regulation characteristics

One final consideration is what the equipment is doing to the power supply voltage waveform and to the current waveform. Current technology sometimes chops the voltage waveform to regulate the power to the equipment. This produces a nonsinusoidal waveform on the power supply system. Whenever the power supply waveform is nonsinusoidal, the waveform can be divided into its fundamental frequency and the harmonic frequencies of the fundamental. These harmonics appear as current and impact the total system through heating losses, and possible resonance when connected to capacitive loads on the power supply line. Resonance can cause very high voltages on the supply line.

9.1.6 Definitions

9.1.6.1 dc offset: Found when the ac voltage waveform is elevated above ground by some constant voltage.

9.1.6.2 failures: Periods when the voltage drops to near zero for a prolonged period. Failures can be either momentary or outages. These two failures are differentiated by how long the voltage is unavailable.

9.1.6.3 glitch: When either a dc offset or a failure causes the reversal on 1s and 0s in computer memory or data path. A glitch is the result of a condition, rather than a condition. As computers run faster and faster, the occurrences of glitches become more frequent.

9.1.6.4 oscillation: The variation, usually with time, of the magnitude of a quantity with respect to a specified reference when the magnitude is alternately greater and smaller than the reference.

9.1.6.5 sag: The cycle-to-cycle decrease in the voltage. Sags occur at steady-state time intervals.

9.1.6.6 spikes: An impulse that is imposed on the waveform. These usually have a duration of less than 100 μs.

9.1.6.7 surge: The cycle-to-cycle rise in voltage. Surges also occur at steady-state time intervals.

9.2 Equipment selection

9.2.1 Pre-purchase evaluation form

Many hospitals use a pre-evaluation form before purchase to ensure that equipment will meet all of the institution's requirements.

9.2.2 Example of pre-purchase evaluation form

New equipment pre-purchase evaluation form. This form is to be completed by the manufacturer and returned to the Director of Purchasing with manuals and attachments as indicated below. This form should be completed by an employee of the manufacturer with sufficient technical information or knowledge to provide answers to the items below. If the manufacturer is uncertain about specific portions, it is suggested he send available material promptly so further communication, if needed, will not be delayed. Refer questions to the Director of Purchasing and/or to_____.

Information detailing specific hospital requirements is outlined in the specification requirements. Additional copies of this form are available on request from the Director of Purchasing.

1.

To: Date

Item: Project #

2. Listings:

Is unit listing with UL? Yes [ ] No [ ]

If Yes, please specify UL listing #

Is equipment listed with other certifying agencies?

Please give specific standards/listing #

3. Line-operated equipment, including battery chargers:

Line voltage limits for stable operation: Frequency limits:

From: To: V ac   From: To: Hz

Phase: Normal operating current: A

                                           Surge current: A

What are the power quality requirements: high voltage, low (sag) voltage, and voltage transients
(including duration)?

What anomalies will the equipment impose on the power supply line?

What is the requirement for supply line impedance?

How will safety and/or operation be affected if the voltage goes outside the range of 108–132 V?

4. Battery-operated equipment:

Type of batteries or packs:

Number per unit:

Recharge time (where applicable):

Discharge time (under specified load):

Can unit be line-operated when batteries are fully discharged? Yes [ ] No [ ]

Will batteries charge while unit is line-operated? Yes [ ] No [ ]

5. Power cord:

Required minimum is an 18 gauge, three-conductor industrial or hospital grade cord at least 10 ft with a NEMA locking-type or hospital grade NEMA type 5-15 or 5-20 plug.

Does your power cord meet these requirements? Yes [ ] No [ ]

If No, specify differences and indicate cost of modification in Section 13.

6. Power switch and overcurrent interrupters:

Type of power:

Switch (i.e., toggle, slide, etc.):

Type of overcurrent protection:

Ampacity:

Single pole [ ]

Double pole [ ]

Three pole   [ ]

Is power switch clearly labeled? Yes [ ] No [ ]

Is power switch in line of sight from operator position? Yes [ ] No [ ]

Enclosure: Surface [ ] Recessed class [ ]

Shall protect all line (hot conductors) to all parts of unit. Shall be easily accessible. If fuse, the rating and type shall be marked beside the holder and a clearly marked spare shall be provided. If overcurrent protection does not conform to these specifications, see Section 13.

7. Mechanical design for physical protection:

Unprotected openings on exposed horizontal surfaces are not allowed.

Other openings shall be guarded against spillage.

Small appliances used in patient's bed shall be immersible in conductive fluid without macroshock hazard. If design does not conform to these specifications, see Section 13.

8. Environmental and interface characteristics:

Temperature limits for operation:	From	To	°F
For storage:	From	To	°F
Humidity limits for operation:	From	To	% RH
For storage:	From	To	% RH

Maximum allowable storage time: Sensitive to RF interference?   Yes [ ] No [ ]

Known to generate RF interference?   Yes [ ] No [ ]

Sensitive to power line transient?   Yes [ ] No[ ]

Known to generate power line transient?   Yes [ ] No [ ]

Sensitive to power line harmonic distortion?   Yes [ ] No [ ]

Known to generate power line harmonic distortion?   Yes [ ] No [ ]

Known to require other utilities?   Yes [ ] No [ ]

Are exposed metal surfaces ungrounded?   Yes [ ] No[ ]

If answer is Yes to any of these questions, give details on separate page.

Specific sterilizing procedures to be used?   Yes [ ] No [ ]

Type of labeling for O_2 and flammable location:

      Quantity of radiation emission:

      Type of shielding:

9. Provide the following manuals and technical information:

Site planning/installation drawings

Operator's manual

Wiring diagrams

Schematic circuit diagram

Parts list

Statement of known potential hazards

Block diagrams

Preventive maintenance program

Operational tests

Performance specifications

User performance test

Service manual

One set to be provided with this form. One additional set upon delivery.

10. Warranty/guaranty:

Warranty will start after delivery and initial installation (if applicable).

If modifications are made to conform to our specifications, will warranty be violated? Yes [ ] No [ ]

Length of warranty:

11. Service and training information:

Estimated response time for service calls from time of notice: hours

Is local service available?   Yes [ ] No [ ]

Give location and working hours of nearest service facility:

A replacement unit is available in: hours

Are training programs available for service personnel?   Yes [ ] No [ ]

Are training programs available for users?   Yes [ ] No [ ]

(Give location, schedule, cost and instructor's qualifications for both types of training programs on a separate sheet.)

Manufacturer's repair depot location:

12. Leakage/risk currents:

Acceptable limits

Measurement site	Device for patients with intracardiac leads	General patient devices	Nonpatient devices	Typical device values indicate worst leakage current
Patient leads or attachments to ground	10 µA	50 µA	Not applicable	
With 120 V applied to patient leads	20 µA	Not applicable	Not applicable	
Worst case to ground	100 µA	500 µA	500 µA	

13. Modifications/comments:

Please list description and cost quotations for any modifications, accessories, or other items necessary to fulfill the requirements stated. Cost of upgrading unit will weigh heavily on our decision to purchase.

1.

2.

3.

4.

14. This form is to be completed and signed by the manufacturer's product manager or equivalent.

Completed by:

Name

Address

Address

Signature

Title

Date

Telephone number

Facsimile number

9.3 Equipment and area served

9.3.1 Patient care

9.3.1.1 Patient-connected measurement, monitoring, and data acquisition equipment

Management of patients has been significantly aided by measurement, monitoring, and data acquisition systems. These devices are located in coronary care and progressive care units, operating rooms, intensive care units (ICUs), and general care areas. Coronary care is a self-descriptive term for areas devoted to patients with heart problems. As recovery takes place, limited movement becomes beneficial, and the patients progress to a progressive care unit. Here, monitoring takes place with individually-carried telemetry units. ICUs are for patients requiring very special attention, such as recovery from surgery. These areas frequently employ extensive measuring and data acquisition equipment.

Proper care requires information about heart and lung performance, the medication provided, and any notes made by the nursing staff. There are myriad other observations and actions to be taken with all types of patients. This subclause covers that class of equipment generally known as patient monitoring equipment and the type of equipment usually found in coronary care units (CCUs), progressive care units, operating rooms, and ICUs.

Figures 9-1 through 9-4 illustrate patient monitoring systems. This equipment collects and displays information on heart and lung performance. Heart rates; systolic, diastolic, and mean pressures; cardiac outputs; respiratory wave forms; and rates and temperatures are measured and displayed. Because of the large amount of information gathered, computer systems are sometimes employed to help in the assimilation of the information.

Figure 9-1—Patient monitoring system, central station

Alarms may be provided at the bedside instruments for parameters deviating below or above certain set points. Additionally, computers can be programmed to analyze cardiac arrhythmias, the term given to significant random abnormalities of the heart waveform. Trends of events can be stored and recalled for later observation. Figures 9-5 and 9-6 illustrate instruments in operating and intensive care areas. The parameters are typically the same as for the CCUs but it is more likely that measurements will be made from transducers or electrodes

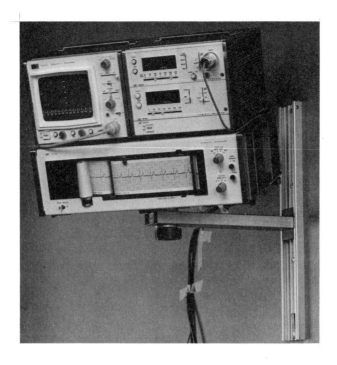

**Figure 9-2—Patient monitoring system, bedside station
with paper tape recorder**

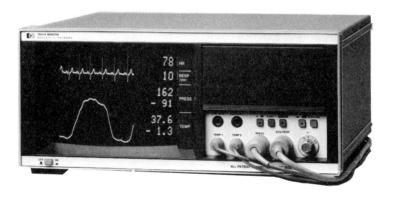

Figure 9-3—Patient monitoring system, bedside station

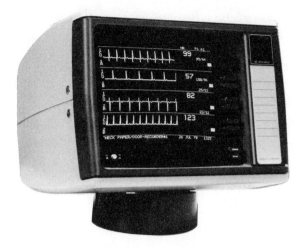

Figure 9-4—Patient monitoring system—table or console, mounted

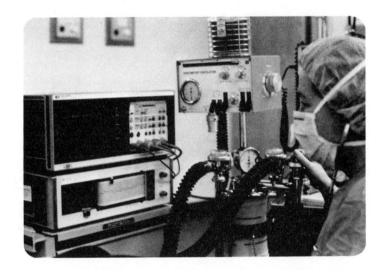

Figure 9-5—Instruments in operating and intensive care areas

placed inside the heart chambers. Because of patient status, more capability is provided in such instrumentation and it typically contains additional controls, features, precision, and accuracy. Extensive use of computer systems is made during catheterization procedures. Catheterization is the process of collecting data from inside the heart chambers for the purpose of determining the details of heart performance and whether surgery can be effective in correcting deficiencies with blood flow or other heart abnormalities. Figure 9-7 shows such a system.

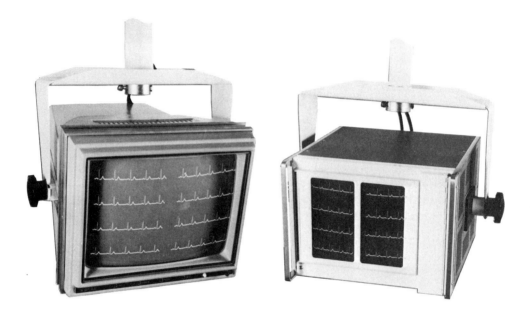

Figure 9-6—Instruments in operating and intensive care areas and catheterization labs

As heart patients regain their strength, many are allowed considerable freedom in their daily activities, but they still require close monitoring. Such patients are found in progressive care units. These units employ telemetry systems for monitoring heart rates and waveforms as the patients are allowed to walk within a prescribed area. Figure 9-8 shows this type of equipment.

9.3.1.2 How the equipment works

In the general sense, all of the equipment can be described by the aid of the block diagram in figure 9-9. A transducer, either on the surface of or inside the body, picks up the signal of interest. These signals range from a few microvolts to several millivolts, depending upon the parameter of interest. Bandwidths range from dc to approximately 100 Hz. The output of the transducer is converted to an electrical signal that undergoes certain processing that depends upon the end purpose of the data. Typically, filtering will be employed for the purpose of

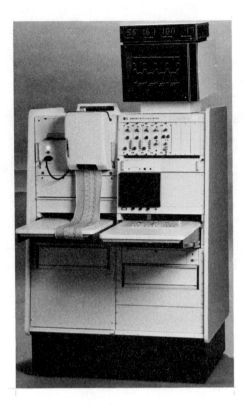

Figure 9-7—Catheterization computer system

removing as much noise and patient-induced artifact as possible. There will be processing for indicating deviations from either high- or low-alarm settings, waveform presentation, and analog-to-digital conversion for the computer data management systems.

Patients are relatively large-volume, complicated, electrical sources. The instruments connected to these patients should be able to provide acceptable information in the presence of large amounts of electrical noise and deliberately induced signals that have been applied for other reasons. Examples of large noise sources are electrosurgery, defibrillation, and pacemakers. The spectrum covers amplitudes from a few microamperes to several amperes, frequencies from a few cycles per second to many megahertz, and voltages ranging to a few kilovolts. The patient is a convenient pickup for 60 Hz and electromagnetic signals. Patient and electrode impedances are complex resistive-capacitative combinations that make the generation of unwanted signals an easy matter.

Defibrillators apply large energies, ranging up to 400 J, for the purpose of converting a fibrillating heart to normal sinus rhythm. A fibrillating heart beats in a random manner, such that the net blood flow is close to zero. Normal sinus rhythm is the rhythm of a heart that is pumping adequately. The defibrillation pulse can have durations ranging from about 3–30 ms, and the voltages reaching electrodes attached to the patient can range as high as a few kilovolts,

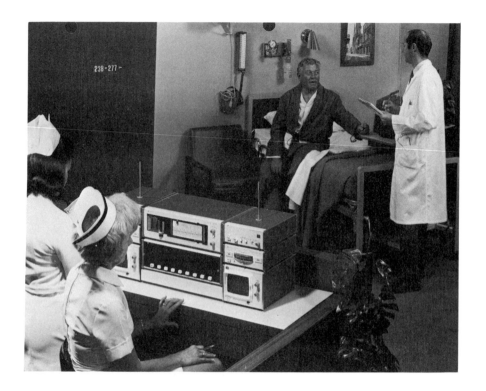

Figure 9-8—Progressive care unit

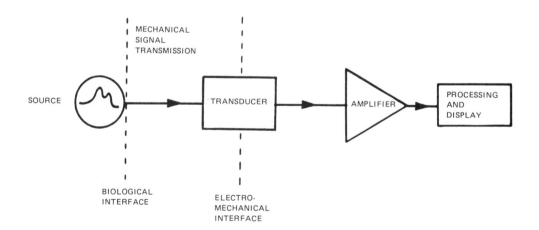

Figure 9-9—Patient measurement system

differential or common mode. Thus, adequate protection should be afforded to the monitors connected to the patients. The monitor's output may be disturbed by the large amount of energy applied but the monitor should recover quickly and not be damaged.

Pacemakers apply currents of a typically rectangular shape to the heart for the purpose of compensation for a chronic abnormality. Electrodes are embedded inside the heart and stimulated by means of pulses ranging from a fraction of a milliampere to a few milliamperes, and with durations ranging from a few tenths of a millisecond to 2 ms. Equipment used in determining and displaying heart rate is used to display these pulses in order to determine if the heart has responded properly to the stimulus but, at the same time, must not count these pulses in case the patient's heart should fail to function. Alarm circuits should be able to discriminate between the absence of a heart beat and the presence of the artificial stimulus. Since the artificial stimulus is orders of magnitude greater than the few millivolts of electrocardiograph signal, the design task is formidable. Typically, some compromise will be reached and information is provided to the user with respect to the care that will be exercised when pacemakers are involved.

Electrosurgical devices are cutting tools employing large magnitudes of high-frequency current. Kilovolts, amperes, and megahertz signals are involved. The equipment tied to the patient should not be damaged by such signals and, in the case of surgery, useful data is expected in the presence of these large disturbances.

9.3.1.3 Patient safety

Some knowledge of electrical safety considerations may be helpful when designing hospital installations. Patient safety is viewed in terms of the small amount of 60 Hz currents that, if allowed to flow through the heart, could induce fibrillation [B1], [B6].[1] This is the same condition that can occur when a person comes close to electrocution by touching a high-voltage power line. In the broad sense, patient safety also includes protection from erroneous data due to electrical noise. The lack of information due to noise conditions or the generation of erroneous data can make diagnosis difficult or impossible under critical conditions and potentially puts the patient into jeopardy. Electromagnetic interference has been reported as causing defibrillators, pacemakers, and ventilators to malfunction [B3], [B4], [B5]. It can also add noise that will either obscure data or make it difficult to interpret. High-density currents flowing through electrode or transducer sites may also injure the patient by causing serious burns.

9.3.1.4 The microshock hazard

Figure 9-10 illustrates the conditions that could arise due to the flow of 60 Hz leakage currents as a function of poor input isolation of the measuring equipment or poor grounding of the primary circuits. A fault in the ground line will allow leakage current to flow through the path indicated. One such path encompasses electrodes or transducers placed inside the heart. If the input circuits of the instruments involved are adequately isolated, the current that flows can be kept to a very low value under the worst possible case—full line voltage being the direct source, for example. The exact distribution of 60 Hz currents that will cause fibrillation with

---

[1]The numbers in brackets correspond to those of the bibliography in 9.5.

a high degree of predictability has not been determined. However, the results of various experiments have resulted in an upper limit of 20 µA, 60 Hz being considered as the threshold for fibrillation. UL 544-1993[2], CSA Std C22.2, and ANSI/AAMI ES1-1993 all require a 20 µA limitation for input circuit isolation for the condition of the direct application of 120 V.

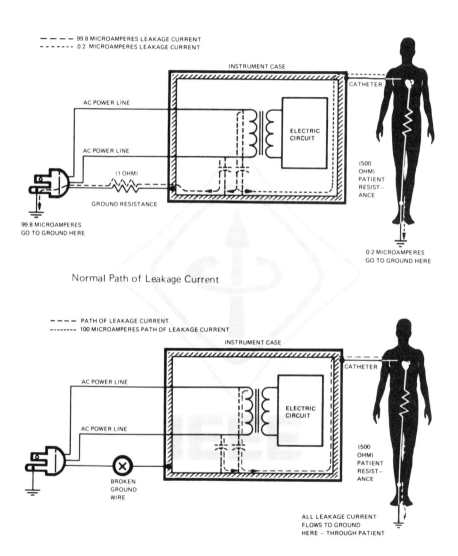

Figure 9-10—Path of leakage current with defective grounding wire

[2]Information on references can be found in 9.4.

These documents also require that the chassis leakage current in figure 9-10 be held to 100 µA or less. This limitation essentially eliminates a shock being felt by personnel caring for the patient and is a reasonable compromise between safety and the extra cost of providing unnecessarily low chassis leakage currents. Figure 9-11 illustrates a commonly used method of isolation.

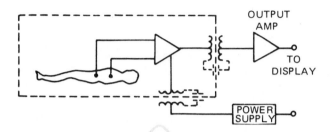

Present practice aims to isolate as much as possible the patient and instrument front-end from all external electrical sources. Thus input power and output signals are coupled with high-isolation devices (high-frequency isolation transformers or opto-couplers).

Isolated Inputs

Figure 9-11—High-frequency isolation transformers

9.3.1.5 60 Hz noise

Figure 9-12 indicates how stray currents coupled to the body generate common mode voltages that must be accommodated by the measuring instruments. Such devices must be able to effectively attenuate these signals by 100 dB or more. Levels of 10 V may exist on the body, and yet should not interfere with measurements of signals in the millivolt region.

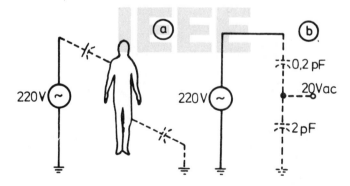

Capacitive coupling to surrounding power sources and grounds (a) causes the human body to appear electrically as a 60 Hz noise source (b).

Figure 9-12—60 Hz interference causes

Figure 9-13 illustrates the generation of differential voltages from 60 Hz electromagnetic signals. Since these signals are differential and in the passband of much of the measuring equipment, they need to be eliminated or reduced at their source. The patient environment should be one that will restrict the electromagnetic field to low levels. There will typically be an unavoidable area in the electrode system used for measuring heart rate and any signals picked up by this loop will be amplified as a normal signal.

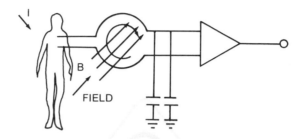

Figure 9-13—Generation of differential voltages from 60 Hz electromagnetic signals

9.3.1.6 Burns

High-density currents flowing through electrode sites can generate burns. The usual source of the energy involved is the electrosurgery equipment. Figure 9-14 illustrates the problem and shows that poor contact of the return electrode of the electrosurgical unit may cause the currents to seek an easier path to ground. This route might be through other electrode sites.

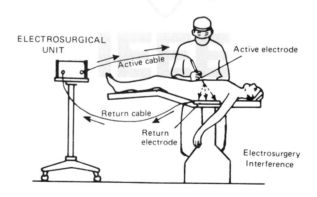

Arrows indicate flow of electrosurgical current in a complete circuit.

Figure 9-14—Electrosurgical current in a complete circuit

9.3.1.7 Electromagnetic noise

Electromagnetic interference may be caused by signals coupled to the patient from power lines and high-frequency generators such as radio and TV stations. This noise covers the spectrum from a few hertz to several gigahertz. Electrosurgical units, FM, AM, and TV transmitters, radar and communication equipment, computer systems, and electrosurgical units place noises on the power line that may be sinusoidal, pulse, impulse, as well as other types. The voltages can range from a few microvolts per meter to volts per meter for noise transmitted through the air.

Hundreds of volts to low kilovolts for sharp pulses may exist on power lines.

Transmitted interference should be handled by the measuring device involved and requires extensive detail in the design of input filters, shielding, and the bypassing of nonlinear elements. Chassis leakage current limitations prevent discriminating against arbitrary amounts of line interference by the use of power line filters. Filter sections tied to ground are generally not usable because they quickly cause the chassis leakage currents to exceed 100 μA. Series inductive elements in conjunction with stray capacities followed by attention to design detail are the methods employed to attenuate the effects of line noise. Hospital power circuits need to be carefully designed in order to avoid patient care area circuits having to accommodate the return currents of noise-producing equipment such as elevators, computers, pumps, and the like.

9.3.1.8 Environmental considerations

Although much of this equipment resides in a fairly benign environment, it may be used in a wide variety of situations. Thus, the equipment will need to operate in the following typical environments:

— Temperature: 15–45 °C
— Shock: 30 G
— Vibration: 15–30 G
— Condensation: none
— Humidity: 45 °C, 90% relative humidity
— Line voltage: 115 V ± 10%, typically

However, many areas of the country are now faced with potential brownout conditions and much equipment is designed to operate satisfactorily down to a 90 V line. Further, many hospitals routinely test their emergency generators. Depending upon how carefully such systems are energized when testing, transients may be placed upon the line that can reach levels of 200 V and more for durations of several milliseconds. The equipment involved is expected to survive such transients without any damage or permanent loss of data.

9.3.1.9 Design and installation recommendations

Planning will be a key factor in determining the effectiveness of the unit. Typically, this will include decisions as to size and location of the unit, choice of equipment, financing, selection of the staff, training, maintenance, and service. Although it is essential to consider all factors, this subclause will concentrate on the physical considerations of the unit.

Figure 9-15 illustrates a possible layout. It shows a nurses' central station, private rooms with individual bedside monitoring, and a progressive care unit with telemetry. Each hospital will have its own requirements. The operating room and intensive care areas have not been included. However, similar considerations apply. For an intensive care area, nearly all of the equipment will be bedside mounted and may have signals routed to a central station. Operating room equipment may be centrally located, analogous to a central station, or it could be mounted near the anesthesiologist, or close to the operating room table. The instruments may be in racks, consoles, or individually stacked on bench tops. During the initial planning phases, it will be necessary to work with the hospital and the equipment suppliers in order to fix the locations of the equipment, consider the power needs, evaluate potential noise sources, and consider which members of the hospital staff will be using the equipment and what access they should have, including visibility and ease of use of the controls. The cabling should be designed with respect to length, the type needed from the point of view of signal transmission, access to ceiling mounts, and any interconnecting hardware. During the planning phase, performance characteristics of different types of equipment can be matched against the desired operation in order to facilitate selection. Prior to the order being placed, the hospital representative, architect, and manufacturer's representative should meet to discuss the locations of the equipment, the power needs, and the conduit requirements. It is best to appoint a coordinator so that all involved with the installation will be kept appraised of current requirements and any changes.

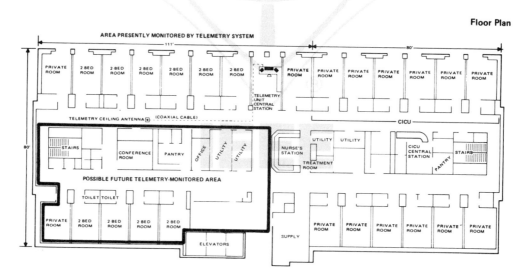

Figure 9-15—Floor plan showing telemetry system areas

During construction or renovation, the hospital and manufacturing representatives should tour the proposed equipment site in order to review equipment locations, mounting of hardware, power requirements, conduits, and the overall equipment concepts. Prior to installation of the actual electronic equipment, the hospital and manufacturer may wish the cables, wall mounts, shelves, central junction boxes, and ceiling mounts supplied in order that they might be more easily mounted before final construction has been completed.

Figure 9-16 provides an example of the considerations involved and shows the need to consider conduit length and sizes. It is preferable to have installed a conduit that may be a bit larger than needed than to find that the one in place is too small to accommodate the wires that have to be pulled.

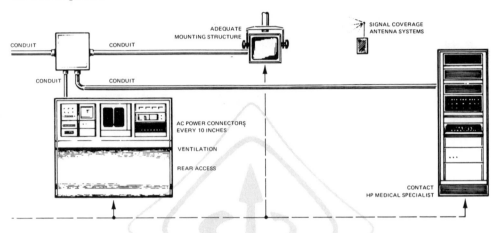

Figure 9-16—Typical conduit routing

It will be necessary to make drawings of each and every detail of the installation in order to avoid the errors and oversights that can only be remedied by added work and extra expense. Large installations can involve 200–300 separate pieces of equipment and miles of conduit and cable. From a mechanical safety point of view, adequate support should be provided for wall-mounted bedside installations and operating room or central station ceiling-mounted installations. Typically, the test conditions are four times the load weight for 1 min.

A good installation will require a considerable amount of attention to detail. Some suggestions follow:

a) *Bedside.* A typical bedside configuration is shown in figure 9-17. For beds where blood pressures will be directly monitored, include transducer mounting poles, etc.

CAUTION

If wall mounts are used to support the monitors, they shall be capable of supporting four times the specified weight capacity after they have been properly installed. When plaster walls are used, it is recommended that steel or plywood plates (as shown in figure 9-18) be employed to distribute the load over a larger section of wall. Expansion bolts are not considered adequate or safe.

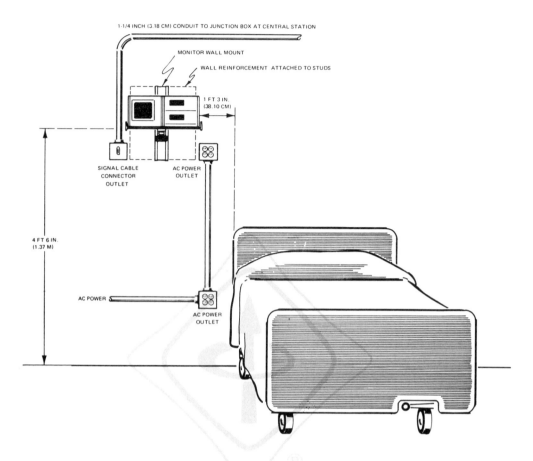

Figure 9-17—Typical bedside configuration

b) *Central station.* Central station consoles can range from simple tables on which the equipment sits, to a custom-built enclosure. Regardless of the central station console chosen, the following minimum features need to be provided:

1) AC power connectors approximately every 10 in (25.4 cm) along the console's length

2) Cable protecting conduits from central station console to central station junction box

3) A horizontal surface for mounting monitoring equipment (for special consoles, consult the supplier during planning stages)

4) A surface above and behind the monitoring equipment, to protect the equipment

5) Access to rear of monitoring equipment at the central station location without the need to move equipment

6) Adequate ventilation (cooling) for the monitoring instruments

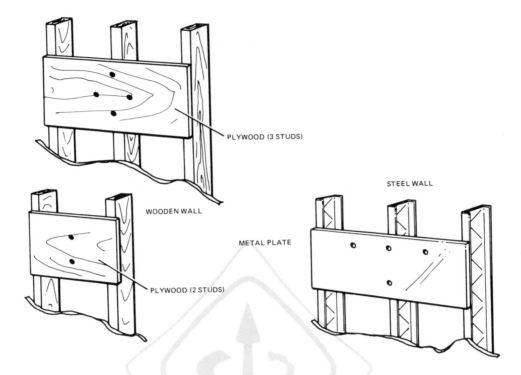

PLYWOOD (3 STUDS)

STEEL WALL

WOODEN WALL

METAL PLATE

PLYWOOD (2 STUDS)

Figure 9-18—Examples of wall reinforcing

c) *Remote areas.* Recent trends in equipping intensive care facilities indicate that remote displays at strategic locations, based upon the medical staff flow patterns, are desirable. It allows observation of the entire unit while staff members are away from the central station. Whenever displays in these areas are considered, adequate mounting facilities and power and signal distribution, which are the responsibilities of the hospital, should be considered as well. Note that memory oscilloscopes normally require coaxial cables for signal interconnection to the central station.

d) *Telemetry system.* If the hospital considers telemetry, it may be necessary for the manufacturer to make on-site field strength measurements to ensure adequate signal coverage. Because each hospital has specific details of construction, such as placement of walls, location of electrical equipment, etc., that can affect telemetry signal reception, each installation should be treated on an individual basis.

e) *Computers.* Hospitals using computer systems should make adequate signal and power arrangements during the initial stages of planning. Recommendations for computer installations vary with specific situations. Consult the equipment supplier as soon as possible in the planning stages of these installations. Figure 9-19 illustrates one type of computer system.

Note that computer system installations normally require special signal junction boxes and larger than normal diameter or additional conduits. In addition, power requirements for computer-based systems are generally higher and provisions for

363

Figure 9-19—Computer system

increased power capacity should be incorporated into the hospital ac supply lines to the proposed computer/patient monitoring areas.

f) *AC power.* A separately protected, common power source of 115 V, 60 Hz should be provided for the system, properly tied to the hospital's emergency power system. Each bed should have an individually protected, 20 A, three-wire grounded NEMA-type outlet. Thus, the system remains operative if a failure occurs at one bedside. Power wiring should never be run in the same conduit nor closely parallel to signal wiring from monitoring instruments.

1) *Voltage requirements.* Most patient monitoring equipment operates from single-phase 120 V (or 230 V in locations outside of the U.S.) ac, 50–60 Hz. Line voltage may vary as much as 10% (e.g., 108–132 V or 207–253 V) without affecting operation or accuracy of the instrument. Variations greater than 10% may have to be corrected by a regulating transformer or other means.

2) *Bedside power.* Required power level for each bedside is generally 90–200 VA.

The following recommendations for bedside stations apply:

— Use only hospital grade acceptable power connectors.

— Use a minimum of two duplex outlets on each side of the patient's bed. The outlets should be connected to and protected by breakers in accordance with the National Electric Code® (NEC®) (NFPA 70-1996).

— Use a minimum of 825 VA for each pair of outlets.

— Provide power outlets within a few feet of the junction boxes and equipment support locations.

— Provide a grounding system in accordance with NFPA 99-1996 and the NEC.

— Provide an exposed terminal connected directly to the patient common reference bus for testing purposes. These should be within 5 ft (1.52 m) of each bed and each may serve more than one bed.

— Design the system layout to keep power cables to a minimum length as this contributes both to physical and electrical safety.

— Provide for adequate ventilation in areas where the patient monitoring equipment is to be installed.

3) *Central station.* The required power level for the central station is about 80 VA for systems of eight or fewer beds. For each eight-bed system add 100 VA.

g) *Conduit and junction boxes (if needed).* Elements essential to most ICU installations are the bedside junction boxes, the signal cable conduit or carrier, and the central station junction box.

1) *Bedside junction boxes.* For a new or existing hospital building: NEMA electrical box with plaster ring for standard 1-1/2 in (3.18 cm) conduit. The junction box can be either flush- or wall-mounted. One of these junction boxes should be mounted at each bedside station in the ICU area.

2) *Central station junction box.* The central station junction boxes provide versatility for an eight-patient ICU area. These boxes will accept conduit and raceway adapters for hidden or surface-mounted building cable carriers. Note that central station junction boxes can be shipped to the building site before the monitoring equipment, if desired by the hospital contractor.

3) *Patient signal wiring from instruments.* Hidden 1-1/2 in (3.18 cm) diameter conduit between flush-mounted bedside and central station junction boxes is recommended for maximum cable protection and attractiveness of completed installation.

h) *Mounts.* Use of a wall mount, ceiling mount, or shelf to mount the bedside modules keeps the area immediately adjacent to the bed free from monitoring equipment, an important consideration when patients are in need of constant attention. The mounting brackets can be installed when the cables are being installed or at the same time as the central station, remote, and bedside junction boxes are being installed. Steel or plywood plates should be included in the wall sufficient to distribute equipment support forces over a large section of the wall as required by specific construction. In an arrangement using two wall mounts, the mounting holes between units should be 14 in (35.56 cm) apart, center-to-center. When not mounted directly on the wall surface, it is recommended that the bracket(s) be mounted on a suitably large, 3/4 in (1.91 cm) thick plywood sheet prior to wall mounting to make it easier to properly space and align brackets. Typically, two half-modules, shelf, and bracket weigh approximately 30 lb (13.6 kg), so appropriate fasteners should be used. See figures 9-20 and 9-21 for illustrations of mounts.

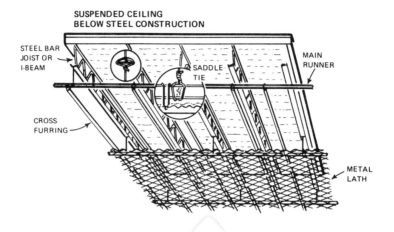

SUSPENDED CEILING
BELOW STEEL CONSTRUCTION

STEEL BAR
JOIST OR
I-BEAM

SADDLE
TIE

MAIN
RUNNER

CROSS
FURRING

METAL
LATH

CEILING SUSPENDED BELOW STEEL JOISTS

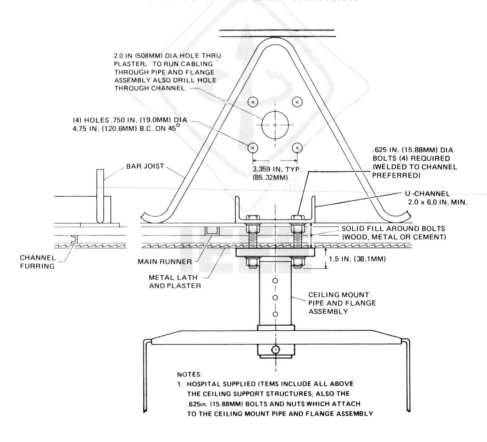

2.0 IN (508MM) DIA HOLE THRU
PLASTER. TO RUN CABLING
THROUGH PIPE AND FLANGE
ASSEMBLY ALSO DRILL HOLE
THROUGH CHANNEL

(4) HOLES .750 IN. (19.0MM) DIA
4.75 IN. (120.6MM) B.C. ON 45°

BAR JOIST

3.359 IN. TYP.
(85.32MM)

.625 IN. (15.88MM) DIA
BOLTS (4) REQUIRED
(WELDED TO CHANNEL
PREFERRED)

U -CHANNEL
2.0 x 6.0 IN. MIN.

SOLID FILL AROUND BOLTS
(WOOD, METAL OR CEMENT)

CHANNEL
FURRING

MAIN RUNNER

METAL LATH
AND PLASTER

1.5 IN. (38.1MM)

CEILING MOUNT
PIPE AND FLANGE
ASSEMBLY

NOTES:
1. HOSPITAL SUPPLIED ITEMS INCLUDE ALL ABOVE
   THE CEILING SUPPORT STRUCTURES; ALSO THE
   .625in. (15.88MM) BOLTS AND NUTS WHICH ATTACH
   TO THE CEILING MOUNT PIPE AND FLANGE ASSEMBLY

Figure 9-20—Ceiling mount supports for steel joist ceiling construction

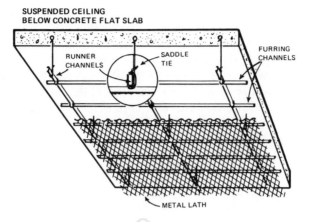

SUSPENDED CEILING
BELOW CONCRETE FLAT SLAB

RUNNER CHANNELS

SADDLE TIE

FURRING CHANNELS

METAL LATH

CEILING SUSPENDED BELOW CONCRETE SLAB

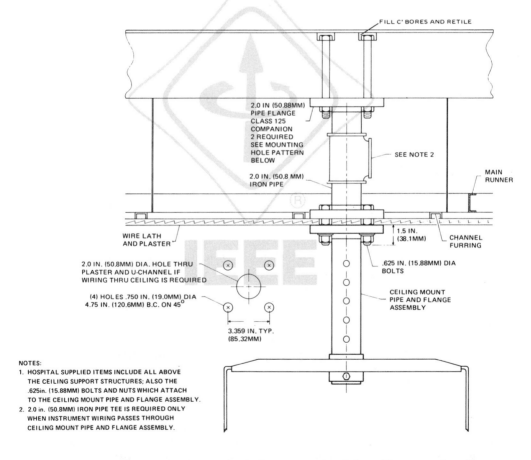

FILL C' BORES AND RETILE

2.0 IN (50.88MM) PIPE FLANGE CLASS 125 COMPANION 2 REQUIRED SEE MOUNTING HOLE PATTERN BELOW

SEE NOTE 2

MAIN RUNNER

2.0 IN. (50.8 MM) IRON PIPE

WIRE LATH AND PLASTER

1.5 IN. (38.1MM)

CHANNEL FURRING

2.0 IN. (50.8MM) DIA. HOLE THRU PLASTER AND U-CHANNEL IF WIRING THRU CEILING IS REQUIRED

.625 IN. (15.88MM) DIA BOLTS

(4) HOLES .750 IN. (19.0MM) DIA 4.75 IN. (120.6MM) B.C. ON 45°

CEILING MOUNT PIPE AND FLANGE ASSEMBLY

3.359 IN. TYP. (85.32MM)

NOTES:
1. HOSPITAL SUPPLIED ITEMS INCLUDE ALL ABOVE THE CEILING SUPPORT STRUCTURES; ALSO THE .625in. (15.88MM) BOLTS AND NUTS WHICH ATTACH TO THE CEILING MOUNT PIPE AND FLANGE ASSEMBLY.
2. 2.0 in. (50.8MM) IRON PIPE TEE IS REQUIRED ONLY WHEN INSTRUMENT WIRING PASSES THROUGH CEILING MOUNT PIPE AND FLANGE ASSEMBLY.

Figure 9-21—Ceiling mount supports for concrete slab ceiling construction

9.3.1.10 AC power and grounding

All equipment should be on a separate grounding system not used by other hospital equipment. Particular attention should be paid to x-ray equipment. X-ray equipment shall not use grounds and power lines for the patient monitoring equipment being described. It is recommended that a grounding system in accordance with NFPA 99-1996 be used. Figure 9-22 illustrates one example of grounding and ac power wiring. Care should be taken to ensure that there is no ground potential differences between grounded surfaces in the patient care area.

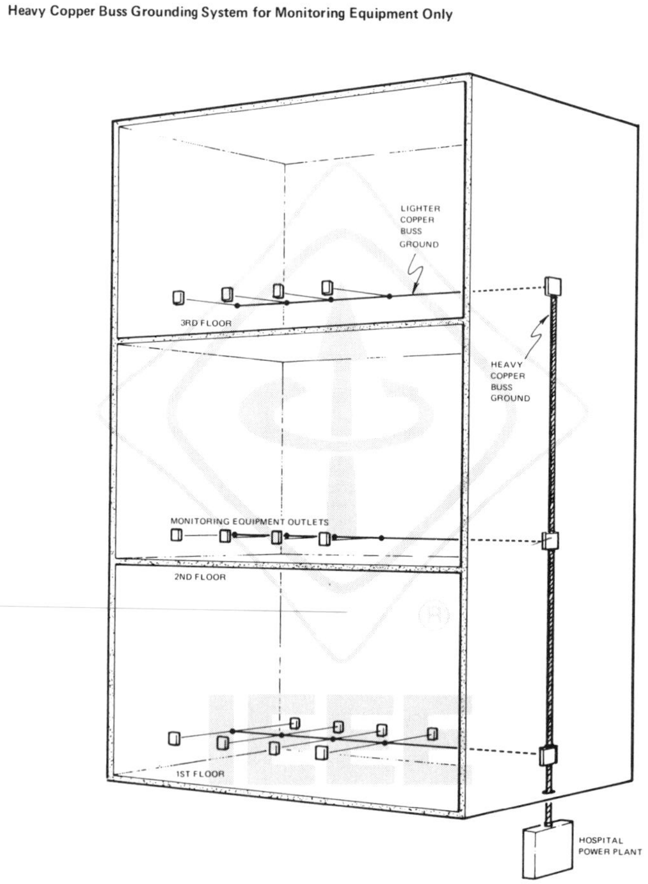

Heavy Copper Buss Grounding System for Monitoring Equipment Only

Figure 9-22—Heavy copper bus grounding system

9.3.1.11 Central station

Central stations may be fairly simple groupings of equipment or they can be quite complex involving 20–30 pieces of equipment or more. Thus, careful attention should be paid to the configuration and power and cooling requirements. To protect the hospital personnel and the patient, it is recommended that each instrument cabinet be grounded. This will typically be done through the three-wire power cord connected to a properly installed electrical system.

9.3.1.12 Checks

It is sometimes helpful to work against a checklist in order to avoid overlooking major items. Following is one set of suggested checklists that might prove helpful.

Prior to installation:

a)   Have conference with hospital personnel.

b)   Have conference with hospital architect.

c)   Note the type of patient monitors at bedside and remote areas.

d)   Note the type of central station monitors/alarms.

e)   Is the architect aware of the number of conduit runs required?

f)   Is the architect aware of recommended conduit size?

g)   Is the architect aware that no other wires should be run in same conduit with ICU signal cables?

h)   Is the architect aware that ac power, diathermy cables, etc., should be run far enough away from ICU to prevent interference?

i)   Is the architect aware that proper conduit junction boxes are included?

j)   Is the architect aware that builder supplies and installs bedside and remote junction boxes?

k)   Is the architect aware that manufacturer supplies bedside and remote junction box face plates, if required?

l)   Is the architect aware that manufacturer will supply central station junction box, if needed, that is to be installed by the builder?

m)   Is the architect aware that individual three-wire ac outlets are recommended for each bedside instrument and each central station monitor?

n)   Have cables been identified by bed number and ordered (with noted variations, if any) after cable lengths from point-to-point have been carefully measured? Order 10% longer length to prevent getting a cable too short to do the job.

o)   Confirm the day scheduled for cable and patient monitoring equipment installation with person assigned.

p)   Does the project coordinator has a move-in day assigned for the CCU/ICU equipment?

NOTE—Go over checklist and correspondence again; the effot will be worthwhile. Oversights will cause delays, and delays often run up the cost in an exponential manner.

9.3.1.13 Architect checklist prior to installation

a)   Does the builder know the number, location, and size of conduit runs?

b)   Does the builder know the location, voltage, and number of ac power outlets?

c)   Does the builder know the location and number of each type of system junction box, if used?

d)   Is the builder/electrician aware that ICU system conduit and junction boxes, if needed, must be installed?

e)   Is the builder/electrician aware that only patient monitor signal cables can be run in monitoring conduits, and that ac power, diathermy cables, etc., should not be run parallel along with ICU monitoring conduits in order to prevent interference?

f)   Is the builder/electrician aware of correct conduit junction boxes, if used?

g)   Is the builder aware that the manufacturer will apply bedside junction box face plates, if used?

h)   Is the builder aware that the manufacturer will supply central station junction box, if used?

i)   Is the electrician aware of recommended electrical requirements and location of each outlet in ICU, that is grounding system requirements, patient safe environment, etc.?

j)   Is the electrician aware of any recommended equipotential test binding post requirements at each patient bedside?

k)   Is the builder aware of mounting requirements of brackets and shelves if these are to be used?

9.3.1.14 Other important notes

Select a site for the equipment not directly adjacent to the emergency generator power plant, main power service entrance, diathermy machines, and units containing large motors. These will commonly produce extremely large amounts of electromagnetic interference and the problem of obtaining high-quality data rises exponentially with closer distances to such sources. Keep high-current feeder lines away from patient areas.

Although much of the electronic equipment used will be capable of operating over wide temperature extremes, it will be better to design the environment such that temperature variations from day to night can be minimized. This will reduce the probability of condensation forming that may interfere with the operation of some units. Also, any corrosive problems due to moisture buildup will be minimized.

Isolated power centers are not required for electrical patient safety. However, local codes or other hospital considerations may dictate their installation. If such power centers are to be used, or if their use is anticipated at a future date, allowance should be made during the initial construction or renovation. Wire lengths need to be considered as well as location. In order to minimize leakage currents, some have recommended that polyethylene insulated wire be used when isolated power centers are involved. This wire has less capacity per foot and leakage currents will be lower. Isolated power centers have received much discussion with regard to costs and benefits relative to patient safety. Proper equipment maintenance should not be overlooked. Thus, a minimal clearance is needed for cooling and for access to the sides and rear for maintenance.

9.3.1.15 Summary

Equipment used in CCUs, progressing care units, ICUs, and operating rooms has proved to be of material benefit in aiding the hospital staff to care for patients. The installation procedures recommended should be helpful in not compromising the usefulness of this equipment. The following reminders may be helpful:

a) Generators of electromagnetic and electrostatic noise should not be located near patient areas.

b) The high-current buses that supply the hospitals or large pieces of machinery should not be run through the walls, in ceilings, or under the floors of patient care areas, and should be as far from these areas as practicable.

c) Room environments should be designed to avoid temperature extremes.

d) Wall and ceiling mounts should receive special attention with respect to their load-carrying capacity.

e) Power and signal wires should be separated as far as possible.

f) Minimal clearance should be maintained around the equipment from a cooling and serviceability point of view.

g) Equipotential grounding systems should be used with impedances as low as practicable in order to minimize noise voltages building up and coupling into signal circuits. This refers to both the resistive and inductive property of the ground system.

h) The necessary amount of time should be provided for consideration of all of the details of the planning process. Problems discovered later are often rectified by spending additional sums.

i) Coordination should occur such that the builder, manufacturer, architect, and hospital administration know at all times what is taking place.

9.3.2 Pediatric and neonatal

9.3.2.1 General

The OB/GYN department in a hospital serves that branch of medicine that deals with the diseases and the normal processes of women, especially in the fields of the reproductive organs and childbearing. The department usually has space provisions for patient rooms, labor rooms, examination areas, delivery suites, and nursery, including a neonatal (newborn) section.

During the past decade, the delivery suite and its associated labor room and nursery area have been disappearing from local neighborhood hospitals.

Maternity centers have been established in central area hospitals in most major U.S. cities. The neonatal area is a principal element of all these centers.

9.3.2.2 Basic equipment in the neonatal area

a) *Incubator.* Most incubators have two functions: reverse isolation and heat balance. Some are designed only to maintain the infant's temperature (e.g., radiant warmers). It is important for nursery personnel to bear in mind that the isolation function of the usual incubator is only to protect the infant from airborne infections, because his inspired air has been filtered. An infected infant in such an incubator discharges his unfiltered expired air into the nursery, and other infants are not isolated from him unless they are also in an isolation-type incubator. Incubators that have been carefully checked and that are free from fire and electrical hazards should be available for any infant who needs supplemental heat. There should always be a standby heat incubator or radiant warmer and bassinet for unexpected deliveries or problems. Additional humidity or an oxygen-enriched environment can either be provided by the incubator or, when radiant warmers are used, delivered to the infant by means of a hood.

The incubator contains a small blower, an air filtration system, a heating rod device, and a water port for humidity control.

1) Typical electrical parameters
   i) Voltage: 120 V
   ii) Frequency: 60 Hz
   iii) Amperes: 2–5 maximum

2) Sources of electrical problems
   i) Plug and cord
   ii) Corrosion of heating device

b) *The patient monitor.* The typical patient monitor used in the neonatal nursery (or similar unit in an ICU or CCU unit) will provide measurements for the following parameters:

1) The ECG or EKG electrocardiogram (see figure 9-23) is a graphic recording or display of the time-variant voltages produced by the myocardium during the cardiac cycle. The P, QRS, and T waves reflect the rhythmic electrical depolarization and repolarization of the myocardium associated with the contractions of the atria and ventricles. The ECG is used clinically in diagnosing various diseases and conditions associated with the heart. It also serves as a timing reference for other measurements.

2) Respiration. Breaths/min in the range of 0–80.

3) Blood pressure. Utilizing a pressure transducer, a carrier amplifier, and a display utilizing two meters showing the systolic and diastolic pressure in mm/Hg.

4) Temperature is recorded from the skin, the rectum, and the ambient area. Normal temperature ranges are as follows:
   i) Oral (mouth): 98.6 °F (37 °C)
   ii) Rectal: Usually 1 ° higher than the oral reading
   iii) Skin temperature: 70 °F (21 °C)

5) Electrical parameters:
   i) Voltage: 120 V
   ii) Frequency: 60 Hz

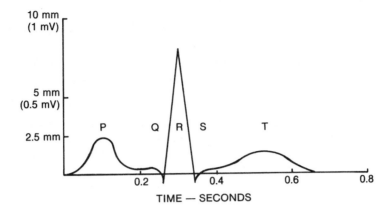

Figure 9-23—Electrocardiogram in detail

    iii)   Watts: 100–200 W

  6)   Sources of electrical problems:

    i)   Radio frequency interference
    ii)   Patient electrodes (chest, ear, and nose clips); there can be 12 electrodes
    iii) Stylus wears out; driven by servomotor
    iv) Voltage fluctuations from outside sources
    v)   Incorrect grounding

  7)   Design and installation recommendations:

    i)   Locate receptacles and patient input outlets as close to patient as possible.

    ii)   Emergency power is essential (an alternate source with adequate capacity should be provided from an independent branch for emergency use and routine maintenance).

    iii) Electrical circuits for bedside (or crib and incubator) patient monitors and central station monitors to be on same phase leg.

    iv) All receptacles should be hospital grade or equivalent.

9.3.3 Surgery

The surgical suite, whether in a small community hospital or in a major general or teaching hospital, is usually the most complicated in the facility in regard to electrical systems, equipment, patient safety considerations, and, of course, in communications.

The electrical equipment utilized in the surgical suite shall be designed for ultimate patient and staff safe use as well as for the surgical procedure in which it is involved. The electrical circuiting for the area shall be designed for the load served as well as for patient safety. See Chapter 6 for further details on the correct use of isolated power, equipotential grounding, and other special requirements.

9.3.4 Dialysis

The introduction of maintenance dialysis for the treatment of renal disease with uremia is generally acknowledged as one of the most important advances in medical treatment in the last 25 years. This procedure is used to prolong the life of thousands of patients awaiting kidney transplants, and it also extends the active life of the kidney patient.

The electrical systems within the dialysis suite shall be designed with patient safety as the foremost consideration as well as feeding the equipment utilized. The area is always suspect to moisture from patient waste, the dialysate fluid, and other fluids with a salt base. All electrical equipment needs to be grounded, and it is advisable to provide an equipotential grounding system in the suite.

All receptacles should be ground-fault interrupter-type and hospital grade or equivalent. The dialysis machine should be fed from its own independent circuit; this will provide the highest probability that a nuisance trip on another piece of equipment will not interrupt the patient treatment. Due to the length of time a dialysis patient spends on the machine, consideration should be given to electric supply system outage frequency and to the need for emergency power.

9.3.5 Radiology

9.3.5.1 Introduction

Radiology equipment refers to a wide range of diagnostic and exploratory systems. What began as a simple process using film and x-ray radiation exposures is now a real-time, computer-based industry. The uses of radiology equipment are many, ranging from simple x-ray films that locate broken bones to computer aided tomography units that provide digitally-enhanced section views through the patient. Likewise, as the number of different units has grown, the areas in a medical facility where they might be found has also grown. The problems that were once centralized in one location are now scattered throughout practically every area of a medical facility. Due to this scattering of units, the once simple solutions to x-ray unit power distribution may no longer be as economically feasible. This requires detailed study in each instance of not only the specific equipment, but also the specific electrical power distribution system.

9.3.5.2 Theory

9.3.5.2.1 X-rays and their production

The term *radiograph* requires definition. It is a visible photographic record—an x-ray picture—produced by the passage of x-rays through an object or body and then recorded on a special film. In medicine, it enables the radiologist to study the inner structures of the human body as an aid to diagnosis. How a radiograph is produced—what physical and chemical reactions take place—is the subject of this subclause.

The first question that naturally arises is: What are x-rays, and how do they behave? They have two aspects of behavior—as rays and as particles. A ray can be defined as a beam of light or radiant energy. (Energy simply means the capacity for performing work.) Light or radiant energy travels as a wave motion and hence one measurable characteristic is its wavelength.

To understand the concept of waves and wavelength, think of the disturbance created in a quiet pond when a pebble is tossed into it. As the pebble strikes the water, some of its energy produces waves that travel outward in ever-widening circles. Although the water is in motion, it does not travel forward progressively. This can be seen by the motion of a floating chip of wood, or of a leaf that rises and falls with the waves but does not progress from its original location. The energy of the waves proceeds outward from the center. The wavelength of the water waves is the distance from crest-to-crest or trough-to-trough. In any system of waves, the distance between two successive corresponding locations in the moving energy pattern is the wavelength.

Light, radio waves, x-rays, and so forth are energy waves of electric and magnetic influence. They are appropriately called electromagnetic waves and travel at tremendous speed—about 3×10^8 m/s (186 000 mi/s). All these forms of electromagnetic radiation are grouped according to their wavelengths in what is called the electromagnetic spectrum. The following examples will provide some comparison of waves and wavelength.

The length of 60 Hz ac waves is about the distance as from coast to coast of the U.S. The wavelength of short radio waves is about 2 m. Medical x-rays—only about 1/10 000 the wavelength of visible light—have a wavelength of about one billionth of an inch. The useful range in medical radiography comprises wavelengths approximately 0.01–0.05 nm.[3]

As mentioned earlier, x-rays also act as if they consisted of small, separate bundles of energy called quanta (singular: quantum), or photons. Under certain circumstances the action of a beam of x-rays can be better understood if it is considered not as a succession of waves, but rather as a shower of particles. This does not imply that a beam of radiation changes erratically from particles to waves and back again. Instead, the aspect that is most apparent depends upon the way the radiation is being used, or on the method being used to detect or record it.

The two natures of x-rays are inseparable. For instance, to know the energy in a single quantum (i.e., in one of the small separate bundles of energy), it is necessary to know the wavelength of the radiation. But wavelength is a wave characteristic and must be determined from a consideration of the wavelike nature of radiation.

The experimental facts that prove radiation to be both wavelike and particle-like are well established. Radiation has a dual nature, not in the sense that it behaves unpredictably, but in the sense that one aspect will predominate under one set of circumstances, the other aspect under another.

Fundamentally, x-rays obey all the laws of light, but among their special properties certain ones are of interest to the x-ray technician, as follows:

---

[3]The wavelength of visible light at the center of the visible spectrum is about 5.5×10^{-5} cm, while the x-rays used for radiograph—those in the center of the medical x-ray spectrum—have a wavelength of approximately 5.5×10^{-9} cm. Therefore, the wavelength of the x-rays is only about 1/10 000 that of visible light.

a)   Their extremely short wavelength enables them to penetrate materials that absorb or reflect visible light.

b)   They cause certain substances to fluoresce; that is, to emit radiation in the longer wavelengths, i.e., visible and ultraviolet radiation.

c)   They affect photographic film, producing a record made visible by development.

d)   They cause biologic changes (somatic and genetic), a fact that permits their use in therapy but also necessitates caution in using x-radiation.

These special properties have application in medical and industrial radiography, therapy, and research.

9.3.5.2.2 The x-ray tube

X-rays are created when fast-moving electrons (minute particles, each bearing a negative electrical charge) collide with matter in any form, with the result being x-radiation. The most efficient means of generating x-rays is an x-ray tube. This is an electronic device that is considerably larger but actually less intricate than the electronic tubes in a radio. In an x-ray tube, x-rays are produced by directing a stream of electrons at high velocity against a metal target. In striking the atoms of the target, electrons are stopped. Most of their energy is transformed into heat, but a small proportion (about 1%) is transformed into x-rays.

The simplest form of x-ray tube is a sealed glass envelope (from which the air has been pumped) containing two important parts: the anode and the cathode. The anode is usually formed of copper and extends from one end of the tube to the center. A block of tungsten about 1/2 in square is set in the anode face at the center of the tube. This is called the target. Tungsten has been found to be the most efficient target material for two reasons: first, its high melting point withstands the extreme heat to which it is subjected, and second, it has a high atomic number, making it a more efficient producer of x-radiation than materials of lower atomic number. The small area of the target that the electrons strike is called the focal spot; it is the source of the x-rays. There are two types of anode—the stationary and the rotating—more will be said about them presently.

The cathode contains a tungsten wire (filament) wound in the form of a spiral about 1/8 in diameter and 1/2 in long; it is set in a cup-shaped holder (called the focusing cup) an inch or so away from the anode. The support for the focusing cup extends outside the tube so that appropriate electrical connections can be made.

The cathode filament is heated to a glow (incandescence) in just the same way as the filament is in an ordinary light bulb. However, the filament is not heated to produce light, but rather to act as a source of electrons that are emitted from the hot wire. The cathode is so designed and located within the tube that the electrons form a stream, beamed in the right direction, and of the exact size and shape to produce the desired focal spot on the target of the anode.

When a very high potential (thousands of volts) is applied to these two x-ray tube components (the cathode and the anode), the available electrons are attracted to the anode in such a manner that they strike the focal spot with tremendous force. The higher the potential (voltage) the greater the speed of these electrons. This results in x-rays that are of shorter wavelength and greater penetrating power and intensity.

As has been mentioned, the focal spot is the area of the target that is bombarded by the electrons from the cathode. The shape and size of the focusing cup of the cathode, the length and diameter of the coil (filament), and the dimensions of the focusing cup in which the coil rests all determine the size and shape of the focal spot.

Heat as well as x-rays are generated by the impact of the electrons. Only a small part (about 1%) of the energy resulting from this impact is emitted from the focal spot in the form of x-rays. Most of the energy is wasted by heating the target. This heat should be conducted away from the focal spot as efficiently as possible. Otherwise, the metal would melt and the tube would be destroyed. Tube manufacturers use a variety of methods for carrying the heat away from the focal spot. The simplest method is to back up the target with a good heat-conducting metal, such as copper, and to extend the copper outside the glass bulb to a fin radiator. In some tubes, water or oil is pumped through internal holes in the copper so as to dissipate the heat more effectively.

The size of the focal spot has a very important effect upon the quality of the x-ray image. The smaller the focal spot, the better the detail of the image. But because a large spot can tolerate more heat than a small one, some method of obtaining a practical size of focal spot that would provide good image detail had to be found. These methods are: utilizing the line-focus principle and rotating the anode.

The line-focus principle refers to the fact that the electron stream is focused in a narrow rectangle on the anode target. The target face is made at an angle of about 20° to the cathode. When the rectangular focal spot is viewed from below—in the position of the film—it appears more nearly a small square. Thus, the effective area of the focal spot is only a fraction of its actual area. By using the x-rays that emerge at this angle, radiographic definition is improved while the heat capacity of the anode is increased because the electron stream is spread over a greater area. [4]

To increase further the capacity of the anode to withstand heat, the rotating-anode tube was developed. As the name implies, the disk-shaped anode rotates on an axis through the center of the tube during the period of operation. The filament is so arranged as to direct the electron stream against the beveled area of the tungsten disk. Thus, the position of the focal spot (the area of the target the electrons strike) remains fixed in space while the circular anode rotates rapidly during the exposure, continually providing a cooler surface for reception of electron stream. In this way the heat is distributed over the area of a broad ring, and for the same exposure conditions, the focal spot area can be made one-sixth or less that required in stationary-anode tubes.

Some tubes contain two separate filaments and focusing cups that provide focal spots of different size and capacity.

---

[4]In designating tube size, manufacturers use a dimension that is the effective focus size. That is, a so-called 1.0 mm tube has a projected focus of 1 by 1 mm.

Manufacturers furnish charts will all types of x-ray tubes to indicate the limits of safe operation—the maximum factors of kilovoltage, milliamperage, and time that can safely be used for a single exposure. Some manufacturers also give cooling charts that indicate how rapidly exposures may be repeated. Thus, a tube can always be operated within its rated capacity.

9.3.5.2.3 Operation of the x-ray tube

The electrical apparatus that permits the control and operation of the tube consists of a number of basic components, as follows:

a)   A high-voltage transformer
b)   An autotransformer
c)   A rectifier
d)   A power supply for the filament of the x-ray tube
e)   A choke coil to adjust the current supply to the filament

The circuits involving the x-ray tube, rectifier, and high-voltage transformer are arranged so that high-positive voltage is applied at the anode end of the tube, with the high-negative voltage applied at the cathode. The electrons from the hot cathode filament are negative charges and thus are attracted with great force to the positive anode. This high voltage is usually expressed in terms of peak kilovolts (1 kV = 1000 V).

It is well to understand that kilovoltage has nothing to do with the manner of electrons that compose the stream flowing from cathode to anode. Kilovoltage controls the speed of each electron, which in turn has very important effects upon the x-rays produced at the focal spot.

The number of electrons is controlled by the temperature (the degree of incandescence) of the cathode filament. This control is accomplished by adjusting the filament current through its own low-voltage electric circuit. The hotter the filament, the more electrons that are emitted and become available to form the electron stream—that is, the x-ray tube current. In the x-ray tube the number of electrons flowing per second is measured in milliamperes (1 mA = 0.001 A). The quantity of x-rays produced at a particular kilovoltage depends upon this number. For example, when the number of electrons per second doubles, the current (milliamperage) doubles, and the x-rays produced double in number. Note that setting the x-ray machine for a specific milliamperage actually means adjusting the filament temperature to yield the current flow (milliamperage) indicated.

Perhaps it will be easier to understand what takes place inside an x-ray tube if its operation is compared to that of a conveyer system at a sand pit. Suppose that above one end of the conveyer belt there is a hopper full of sand that runs out the bottom through an adjustable opening onto the moving belt. Assume that the grains of sand are the electrons. The number of grains available to be carried away each second by the belt depends on the size of the outlet opening of the hopper, which can be compared to the degree of incandescence of the cathode filament. The moving belt will carry away all of the sand just as the kilovoltage will move all of the electrons available at the filament that comprise the electron stream.

Now, suppose the belt is speeded up. This is like increasing the kilovoltage. The number of grains of sand (electrons) traveling per second remains unchanged. Only so many get through the opening (the cathode incandescence) regardless of the belt speed (kilovoltage). Those that are available just travel faster. Again, suppose that the hopper hole is opened wider (filament incandescence is increased). More grains of sand (electrons) per second fall on the belt. The belt carries a bigger load—more grains per second (greater milliamperage)—but the belt speed (kilovoltage) is the same. As the effects of milliamperage and kilovoltage are discussed in the following subclauses, it may be helpful to refer again to this "conveyer" discussion. This should help to explain how these two factors affect the x-ray beam.

9.3.5.2.4 The x-ray beam and image formation

What happens when the x-ray beam leaves the focal spot?

Most diagrams of the x-ray tube show x-rays as forming a neat triangular pattern as they are produced at the focal spot. This serves a good purpose in emphasizing the action of x-radiation outside the tube. However, the radiation does not behave in that way. Actually, x-rays are like visible light in that they radiate from the source in straight lines in all directions unless they are stopped by an absorber. For that reason, the x-ray tube is enclosed in a metal housing that stops most of the x-radiation; only the useful rays are permitted to have the tube through a window or port. These useful rays are called the primary beam. That pencil of radiation at the geometric center of the primary beam is called the central ray.

A high voltage is applied to the x-ray tube in order to produce x-rays. The electrical apparatus is such that the kilovoltage can be changed over a rather wide range, usually 30–100 kV or more. When the lower range of kilovoltages is used, the x-rays have a longer wavelength and are easily absorbed. They are termed soft x-rays. Radiation produced in the higher kilovoltage range has greater energy and a shorter wavelength. Such x-rays are much more penetrating and are called hard. It should be understood that the x-ray beam consists of rays of different wavelengths and penetrating power.

9.3.5.2.4.1 X-ray absorption

In listing the important properties of x-rays, it was noted that they are able to penetrate matter. That generality must be qualified, because not all the x-rays that enter an object penetrate it. Some are absorbed. Those that do get through form the image, or shadow, as it is frequently called.

The extent to which x-rays are absorbed by a material depends on the following three factors:

a)   The wavelength of the x-rays
b)   The composition of the object in the path of the x-ray beam
c)   The thickness and density of the object

The long wavelength x-rays—i.e., those produced at lower kilovoltages—are easily absorbed. The shorter wavelength x-rays—i.e., those produced in the higher kilovoltage range—penetrate materials more readily.

How does the composition of the object have a bearing on x-ray absorption? This depends on the atomic number of the material. For example, a sheet of aluminum, being of lower atomic number than copper, absorbs a lesser amount of x-rays than does a sheet of copper of the same area and weight. Lead (of still greater atomic number) is a great absorber of x-rays. For this reason it is used in the tube housing and for protective devices, for instance, in the walls of the x-ray room and in the special gloves and aprons used during fluoroscopy.

The relation of x-ray absorption to thickness is simple; a thick piece of any material absorbs more x-radiation than a thin piece of the same material. The density of a material has a similar effect. For instance, an inch of water will absorb more x-rays than an inch of ice.

In considering the medical uses of x-rays, it is important to understand that the human body is a complex structure made up not only of different thicknesses but of different materials. These absorb x-rays in different degrees. Thus, bone absorbs more x-rays than flesh does; flesh, more than air (in the lungs, for instance). Furthermore, diseased structures often absorb x-rays differently than do normal flesh and bones. The age of a patient also has a bearing on absorption. For example, in the elderly, the bones have less calcium content and hence less x-ray absorption than do the bones of younger people.

The relationship among x-ray intensities in different parts of the image is defined as subject contrast. Subject contrast depends upon the nature of the subject, the radiation quality used, and the intensity and distribution of the scattered radiation, but it is independent of time, milliamperage, and distance, and of the characteristics or treatment of the film used.

9.3.5.2.4.2 Factors affecting the image

The image can be affected by three factors: milliamperage, distance, and kilovoltage.

a) *Effect of milliamperage.* Increasing the milliamperage increases the quantity of x-rays, and decreasing the milliamperage decreases the quantity. All the x-ray intensities of this leg pattern, or the brightness of the image, will increase as the amount (quantity) of x-radiation from the focal spot increases. Therefore, this brightness can be readily controlled by changing the milliamperage. However, it should be understood that the various x-ray intensities will continue to bear the same relation to each other.

b) *Effect of distance.* Again, the x-ray intensities of the pattern can be altered uniformly by an entirely different, nonelectrical means—by moving the tube from or toward the object. In other words, the distance of the tube from the object has an effect on the intensity of the image. Thus, as the distance from the object to the source of radiation is decreased, the x-ray intensity at the object increases; as the distance is increased, the radiation intensity at the object decreases. This all results from the fact that both x-rays and light travel in diverging straight lines.

A change in distance is very similar to a change in milliamperage in its effect upon the overall intensity of the image. The amount by which the overall image intensity is changed when milliamperage or distance is changed is a matter of simple arithmetic.

c) *Effect of kilovoltage.* A change in kilovoltage causes a number of effects. The first to be considered here is the fact that a change in kilovoltage results in a change in the penetrating power of the x-rays. Another fundamental rule of all x-ray technique is that increasing kilovoltage reduces subject contrast; decreasing kilovoltage increases subject contrast.

A second effect of increase in kilovoltage is that not only are new, more penetrating x-rays produced, but so are more of the less penetrating rays, which were also produced at the lower kilovoltage. This occurs with no change in tube current.

The combination of these two effects of increase in kilovoltage is to modify the pattern so that a pronounced increase in overall intensity of the pattern would have been noted, in addition to the differences in intensity having been leveled out.

d) *Summary.* From the discussion thus far, the following conclusions can be drawn: Overall intensity of the image can be controlled by the three factors—milliamperage, distance, and kilovoltage. When millamperage or distance is used as a factor for control of intensity, subject contrast is not affected. However, when kilovoltage is used as a control of intensity, a change of subject contrast always occurs in conjunction with the change in intensity.

9.3.5.2.4.3 Heel effect

For simplicity's sake, it has been assumed that the intensity of radiation over the entire area covered by the primary beam is constant. This is not quite correct. Actually, there is a variation in intensity due to the angle at which the x-rays are emitted from the focal spot. This is called the heel effect. The following is a description of this effect and the way in which it may be used to advantage.

This so-called heel effect is the variation in intensity of the x-ray output with the angle of x-ray emission from the focal spot. The intensity of the beam diminishes fairly rapidly from the central ray toward the anode side and increases slightly toward the cathode side. This phenomenon can be made good use of in obtaining balanced densities in radiographs of heavier parts of the body. To do so, arrange the patient relative to the tube so that the long axis of the tube is parallel to that of the body part, with the anode toward the more easily penetrated area. For example, in radiography of the thoracic vertebrae, the neck should receive the less intense rays from the anode portion of the beam, while the heavier chest area should be exposed by the more intense rays from the cathode portion of the beam.

The heel effect is less noticeable in closely coned projections where the x-ray beam is fairly restricted. Where a long area, such as the thoracic vertebrae must be included, it is important.

9.3.5.2.4.4 Geometry of image formation

The purpose of radiography is to obtain as accurate an image as possible. Two factors that contribute to this accuracy are the sharpness and size of the shadow. A demonstration that can be made with light bulbs will make clear how these factors are applied in radiography.

Get a small, clear lamp, such as is used in a nightlight. Set it up about 3 ft from a wall, turn it on, and place your hand an inch or two from the wall. Notice that the shadow produced by this small light source is nearly the same size as your hand, and that the edges are quite sharp. Now move your hand away from the wall—toward the light—and watch how the shadow grows larger, and fuzzier along the edges. Next, substitute a large, frosted bulb and notice that the edge of the shadow is a little fuzzy even when your hand is close to the wall. The unsharpness is caused by the larger light source. Again, move your hand toward the lamp and see how the shadow enlarges and the unsharpness increases.

So it is with x-rays. The smaller the source of radiation (focal spot) and the nearer the object is to the recording plane (film), the sharper and more accurate the image. Conversely, the larger the source of radiation and the farther the object is from the recording plane, the greater the unsharpness and magnification. In addition, not only the shadow of the edge of the object but all of the shadows of the structures within it are involved in radiography, because x-rays penetrate the object whereas light does not. The same laws apply to the shadows of the internal structures as apply to the edges. If one of these structures is farther away from the recording plane than another, the structure farther away will be magnified more, which will result in unequal magnification. This variation from the actual proportions of the object is known as distortion. (Distortion and magnification are not necessarily bad things. Sometimes this is deliberately done in order to permit diagnosis of an otherwise obscured part.)

All the foregoing may be summed up in five rules for accurate image formation:

a) The x-rays should proceed from as small a focal spot as other considerations will allow.

b) The distance between the tube and the object to be examined should always be as great as is practical. At maximum distances, radiographic definition is improved and the image is more nearly the actual size of the object.

c) The film should be as close as possible to the object being radiographed.

d) Generally speaking, the central ray should be as nearly perpendicular to the film as possible to record adjacent structures in their true spatial relationships.

e) As far as is practical, the plane of interest should be parallel to the film.

9.3.5.2.4.5 Scattered radiation

In discussing x-ray absorption and shadow formation, when x-rays strike an object, some rays pass through and some are absorbed. In other words, it is implied that all of the rays that come out of the object have come straight from the focal spot (primary beam) and have traveled through the part to form a well-defined, clear-cut image, and that all of the rays that did not penetrate were absorbed and could be forgotten. Unfortunately, this is not the case. Some of the radiation is scattered in all directions by the atoms of the object struck, very much as light is dispersed by a fog. The secondary rays thus produced are known as scattered radiation or scattered x-rays.

Because of this scattering, the object is a source of photographically-effective but unwanted radiation. It is unwanted because it does not contribute to the information of the useful image. On the contrary, it produces an overall exposure superimposed on the useful image. The effect of this overlying uniform intensity is to reduce contrast, and hence to decrease the visibility of gradations in the image when viewed on the fluoroscope or recorded on film.

Other sources of scattered radiation are materials beyond the image plane—the table top, for instance. Radiation arising from such sources may be scattered back to the image.

9.3.5.2.4.6 Recurring scattered radiation

Obviously, it is advisable to minimize scattered radiation. Back-scatter is readily controlled by placing a sheet of lead immediately behind the film. Another important way to reduce scattered radiation is to confine the primary beam to a size and shape that will just cover the region to be x-rayed. This is done by attaching to the x-ray tube a cone or aperture diaphragm.

Cones are metal tubes of various shapes and sizes—some provide circular fields and others, rectangular. Aperture diaphragms consist of sheets of lead with circular, rectangular, or square openings. When these are properly used, the part of the object not x-rayed does not contribute appreciably to scattered radiation. Hence, an overall improvement in image quality is obtained. It is important to know what area a diaphragm or a cone of given size will encompass at a certain distance. If the cone is too large, it serves no purpose. Some manufacturers specify the projected diameter of their cones at given focus-film distances. For cones that do not carry this information, it can also be determined with test films and the results then marked on the cones.

Another way to determine the projected field is to use the following formula:

$$(A \times B)/C = X$$

where

A	is the distance from focal spot to film plane
B	is the aperture of diaphragm or diameter of cone
C	is the distance from focal spot to diaphragm or lower rim of cone
X	is the diameter of projected field at film plane

As an example, the focus-film distance A is 36 in; the diameter of the cone B is 4 in; the distance from focal spot to lower edge of cone C is 12 in. What amount of film X would be encompassed by the x-ray beam? Using the formula above, we have:

$(36 \times 4)/12 = 12$ in, diameter of projected field

It should be remembered that the smallest cone that will provide adequate coverage should always be used, and that care should be exercised in centering the tube so that cutoff of the image will not occur.

Thick, heavy parts of the body, such as the abdomen, produce a much higher proportion of scattered radiation than does a thin part, such as the hand. Therefore, when radiographing the heavier body parts, an additional means of controlling scattered radiation is necessary. A device called a grid is introduced. This apparatus is composed of alternating strips of lead and radiotransparent material, such as wood or aluminum, so arranged that when the focal spot is centered over the grid, the plane of each lead strip is in line with the primary beam. The lead strips absorb a considerable amount of the oblique scattered radiation (that is, the rays not traveling in the direction of the primary beam). The radiotransparent strips allow most of the primary rays to pass through to the film.

The relation of the depth to the width of the radiotransparent strips represents the grid ratio. To illustrate, if the depth of the transparent strip is eight times its width, the grid ratio is eight to one (8:1); if the depth is six times the width, the ratio is 6:1, etc. The greater the ratio, the more efficiently will the grid absorb scattered radiation.

When a stationary grid is used, the shadows of the lead strips are superimposed on the useful image. This can be tolerated when a grid with very thin, uniformly spaced strips is used. The very fine lines are not objectionable in the image. To eliminate the grid pattern, however, it is merely necessary to move the grid at right angles to the strips during the exposure; in this way the grid lines are blurred and not distinguishable. A device comprising a grid and the mechanism for moving it is called a Potter-Bucky diaphragm, or sometimes simply a Bucky. The grid absorbs a large part of the secondary radiation and even some of the primary radiation. It is obvious, therefore, that the exposure needs to be increased to compensate for this loss. The necessary increase in exposure should be determined by trial with the particular equipment. It depends on the grid ratio; the more efficient the grid in absorbing scattered radiation, the greater the exposure increase must be. As a guide for experimenting, a factor of three is suggested.

Regardless of the efficiency of the grid in removing scattered radiation, a cone diaphragm should always be used with the Bucky to restrict the primary beam properly. Here again, it is well to realize that with this combination, care should be exercised in aligning the tube so that image cutoff will not occur.

In passing, the use of filters must be mentioned. Filters are thin sheets of metal (generally aluminum) inserted at the tube portal to absorb the longer wavelength rays that do not contribute to the image. This is a safety device for protection of the patient.

9.3.5.2.4.8 X-ray generating apparatus

To complete the discussion of the production of x-rays, a brief description of the generating apparatus is needed. As has been mentioned, the principal devices, aside from the x-ray tube, are an autotransformer, a high-voltage transformer, a rectifier circuit and valve tubes (when necessary), and a low-voltage transformer for the filament of the x-ray tube.

a) *Transformer.* A transformer is a device used to transfer ac electrical energy from one circuit to another and from one voltage level to another. In the simplest form it consists of two coils of insulated wire wound on an iron core without having any electrical connection between them. The coil connected to the source of power is called the primary winding, the other the secondary winding. Voltage is induced in the secondary when energy is applied to the primary. The voltages in the two coils are directly proportional to the number of turns of wire in each, assuming a theoretical 100% efficiency. For example, if the primary has relatively few turns, say 100, and the secondary has many, say 100 000, the voltage in the secondary is 1000 times higher than that in the primary. Since the voltage is increased, this type of transformer is called a step-up transformer. At the same time, the current in the coils is decreased in the same proportion as the voltage is increased. In the example given, the current in the secondary is only 1/1000 of that in the primary. A transformer of this type is used to supply the high voltage to the x-ray tube.

b) *Action of ac.* Voltage can be described in the form of a graph that represents the action of an imaginary voltmeter—if such a very fast-acting one could be built—connected to the transformer terminals. When 60-cycle ac is used, the needle of the voltmeter would move from zero to a maximum (peak or crest) and back to zero again in 1/120 s. It would immediately start off in the opposite or inverse direction, reach a peak, and return to zero in another 1/120 s. This action is called a full cycle and requires 1/60 s. Sixty of these cycles are accomplished in 1 s, hence, the term 60 Hz ac. For x-ray purposes, the tube voltage is almost always expressed in terms of the peak or crest value (which is abbreviated krp). The x-ray tube receives a series of voltage pulses, one for each useful peak, and therefore produces x-rays in pulses or bursts.

c) *Autotransformer.* The usual line voltage supplied for x-ray equipment is 220 V ac. X-ray techniques, however, require a wide variety of kilovoltages. Therefore, the line voltage is adjusted by a special type of transformer—an autotransformer—so that the primary of the high-voltage transformer has a variable and predetermined supply. The result then, is that the high voltage to the x-ray tube can be preselected at the autotransformer before the x-ray exposure is actually made. The device is called an autotransformer because the primary and secondary are combined in one winding.

d) *Low-voltage transformer for filament.* Some means needs to be furnished not only to light the filament of the x-ray tube but to control the degree of incandescence. The requirements for this are a few amperes at 4–12 V that are provided by a step-down or low-voltage transformer. The secondary winding of the step-down transformer is heavily insulated from the primary and the iron core so that the high voltage to the x-ray tube shall not get back into the supply lines of the x-ray machine.

e) *Tracing the generator circuit.* There are a number of auxiliary devices that go to complete the x-ray generating apparatus, such as meters, fuses, and circuit breakers. Tracing the circuit will help to make clear the action of the various parts of the apparatus. Fuses are placed in the incoming line as in all electrical apparatus. The current passes through the switch to the autotransformer. A line voltage compensator at 3 A can be adjusted so that the correct input voltage is applied to the autotransformer. A prereading (ac) voltmeter in the autotransformer circuit indicates the voltage applied to the primary of the high-voltage transformer by means of the variable control. A circuit breaker acts when the high-voltage transformer is overloaded. A switch with automatic timer is closed to make the x-ray exposure. The high-voltage x-ray tube current is indicated by the mA.

The low-voltage transformer for the filament of the x-ray tube is supplied from a fixed position on the autotransformer. An ammeter permits the proper setting of the filament voltage control for the transformer. The secondary of the filament transformer is connected directly to the tube filament in the cathode of the x-ray tube. The terminals of the secondary of the high-voltage transformer are connected in various ways to the x-ray tube, depending on the rectification method.

Modern equipment is so constructed that all parts exposed to high voltage are especially insulated. This includes the high-voltage transformer, the rectifier system, valve-tube and x-ray tube filament transformers, cables, and the x-ray tube.

f) *Power requirements.* X-ray machines produce momentary high-power factor loads of 20–160 kVA. The momentary load usually has a duration of less than 2 s, but 6 s or 7 s exposures are not uncommon. In order to perform properly, x-ray machines operate within a certain voltage range, which is sometimes called the absolute line voltage span. Within this range, voltage regulation can not exceed a certain value (usually in the 3–10% range). A typical 95 kVA (480 V nominal) unit will have a steady-state voltage requirement of from 360 V to 507 V. During the x-ray exposure, the voltage should not dip more than 6%, and under no circumstances may it dip below 360 V. Some x-ray machines have undervoltage relays that will automatically cut them off if voltage swings outside of the prescribed tolerance. In other instances, the x-ray unit may remain on-line, but yield exposures of poor quality.

X-ray manufacturers normally specify minimum feeder sizes for given increments of feeder length. They will also specify minimum transformer sizes and minimum circuit impedance. Because of the high-power factor (usually about 95%), x-ray machines do not create great voltage drops across inductive reactances such as do transformer and generator windings. However, the resistance of the supply circuit will bear heavily on the total voltage drop. Because of the high-power factor, generator loads create heavy real power requirements on standby generators. Because of the high real power requirements for x-ray machines, x-ray exposures can cause slowing of standby generators, reducing the frequency of the supply. Reduced frequency can be a problem for x-ray generators, because some units operate on a resonance principle. Sophisticated x-ray machines, such as computer aided tomography (C.A.T., or simply, CT) scanners, and special procedures equipment with microprocessors, can require surge suppressors or other power conditioners. However, the designer should always consult the vendor before applying a power conditioner.

g) *Radiography equipment*—power distribution and grounding

   1) System capacity (voltage sags)

   2) System impedance. The constraining factor for most radiographic equipment is the impedance of the supply system, not the current capacity. Radiographic units do not draw their normal discharge current for long periods. However, when they fire, they need to have the voltage and current available in order to properly excite the x-ray tube. A power supply impedance that is too high will have an I^2R loss (heating loss) in the system, which will reduce the voltage available during firing the tube.

h) High-speed CT scanner

   1) Power distribution and grounding

      i) Transients and duration acceptable

      ii) Supply line variations

          iii) Emergency power

    2) Power conditioning

    3) Air conditioning

i) Conventional CT scanner

    1) Power distribution and grounding

          i) Transients and duration acceptable

          ii) Supply line variations

          iii) Emergency power

    2) Power conditioning

    3) Air conditioning needs (minimal)

j) MRI scanner

    1) Power distribution and grounding

          i) Transients and duration acceptable

          ii) Supply line variations

          iii) Emergency power

    2) Power conditioning (sometime supplied with system)

    3) Air conditioning

    4) Cryogen and venting requirements

    5) RF filtering, shielding, and waveguides

    6) Magnetic shielding requirements

    7) Patient comfort considerations

          i) Communication to the scanner operator

          ii) Music system for patient listening

k) PET (positron emission) scanner

    1) Power distribution and grounding

          i) Transients and duration acceptable

          ii) Supply line variations

    2) Power conditioning (sometimes supplied with system)

    3) Air conditioning

    4) Communication system to radio-pharmacy

9.3.6 Physical therapy

9.3.6.1 General

The physical therapy department is usually the prime element of the rehabilitation wing of a hospital. The department provides for the patient who has suffered injury to his motor system, or who has had a major or minor stroke affecting use of arms or legs, requiring the re-educating of affected muscles or systems. The department also retrains patients in speech therapy for those patients who have had damage in that communication sense.

9.3.6.2 Basic equipment in the physical therapy department

9.3.6.2.1 Partial immersion baths

a)   *Whirlpool bath*

This bath is given in a metal tub filled with water that is kept in constant agitation. It thus provides both water temperature control plus the mechanical effects of water in motion.

The water is kept in agitation by an ejector, a turbine, or compressed air. The bath provides heat, gentle massage, debridement (the excision of contused and devitalized tissue from the surface of the wound), relief from pain, and muscle relaxation. It also permits active or assistive exercise of the part that is immersed in the tub.

The tub's temperature is maintained by a thermostat. Typical temperature settings are 90–100 °F for the entire body, 100–102 °F for the legs, and 105 °F for the upper extremities. Often, temperature settings of 110–115 °F are used for therapeutic effects. When the patient has impaired circulation, temperature should not exceed 105 °F. Treatment usually is of 20 min duration.

Whirlpool baths are employed in the treatment of chronic traumatic disorders, inflammatory conditions, joint stiffness, pain, adhesions, neuritis, tenosynovitis, sprains, strains, and painful stumps following amputations. Adding a small amount of sodium sulfathiazole to the water hastens the healing of infections. The bath may be used preceding, or instead of, massage or other mechanical applications to injured extremities.

b)   *Contrast baths*

Contrast baths involve sudden, alternate immersions of upper or lower extremities in hot and then cold water. They increase circulation because of the contraction and relaxation of the blood vessels as a result of the alternating temperature extremes. One bath container is filled with water at a temperature of 100–110 °F, and the other holds water of 50–65 °F.

The body part being treated is immersed in the baths in a definite, systematic manner. While authorities differ slightly on the actual length of time a limb should be immersed in each tub, there is still fair general agreement. A typical contact sequence might be as follows:

— Hot for 4–10 min, cold for 1–2 min
— Hot for 4 min, cold for 1 min
— Hot for 4 min, cold for 1 min
— Hot for 4 min, cold for 1 min
— Hot for 5 min

Treatment always begins and ends with immersion in hot water.

Contrast baths are therapeutically effective for headaches, arthritis, fractures, peripheral vascular disease, and as a precedent to massage and exercise in cases of sprains and contusions. When treating patients with peripheral vascular disease, care should be taken to avoid great extremes of temperature.

In addition to the above, there are a variety of other partial immersion or localized baths. These are as follows: The hot full wetpack, in which the patient is wrapped from neck to feet in a sheet that has been immersed in water of about 80–90 °F and wrung out; cold, hot or neutral baths for the extremities, which vary by temperature; douches and showers, in which streams of water at controlled pressure and temperature are directed at the surface of the body; ablutions, or sponge baths; leg, foot, arm, and hand baths, which require immersion of the involved body part in small baths of controlled temperature; half-baths, in which the patient sits, the water level being at about the level of the navel; affusions, where the water is poured on the patient from a basin or a pitcher at approximately 60–80 °F of temperature; sitz baths, in which the torso, but not the extremities, is immersed in water; Hauffe baths, which provide a constantly increasing water temperature; and a number of other kinds. The particular form of a bath employed depends upon the disorder being treated, the body part or parts involved, the patient's physical condition, and the purposes of the hydrotherapy.

9.3.6.2.2 Full immersion baths

a) *Hubbard tank.* The Hubbard tank is a full-body therapeutic pool with a water temperature of 98–104 °F. The water is usually agitated and aerated, providing both heat and gentle massage. The patient lies on a canvas plinth and is lifted to and from the pool by means of electrically-driven overhead cranes. Some tanks have a grating on the floor which permits the able patient to stand. Partial weight-bearing and ambulation can be initiated in the pool, which may be prescribed when gait exercises are indicated, but the stress of weight is contraindicated.

The Hubbard tank is useful where the patient's disease or disability is manifest in many joints, such as in chronic arthritis, or in burn cases when debridement and active exercise are desirable.

Exercise in water is indicated for the following conditions: spastic paralysis, as in paraplegia; marked muscle weakness with the possibility of increasing strength through voluntary motion, such as in partial peripheral nerve lesions (for example, polyneuritis); poliomyelitis; following amputation when muscle strengthening and stretching of contractures in the involved extremity are indicated; chronic arthritis; following joint injuries; for mobilization in the aftercare of plastic and joint operations and tendon transplants; after abdominal fascial transplants; in certain cases of cerebral palsy; extensive skin burns; muscular incoordination; some neurologic disorders; and disorders requiring metabolic stimulation.

Water activities are contraindicated for cases of acute joint inflammation or other acute infections, febrile disease, acute neuritis, active pulmonary tuberculosis, and the acute stage of poliomyelitis.

b) *Other types.* Other types of full immersion hot baths include: Full-body hot baths, with water temperature at 96–105 °F, used for brief periods of time in treating chronic, rheumatic joint manifestations, and for the relief of muscle spasm and colic; chemical baths, usually involving the introduction of carbon dioxide gas into the water for therapy with patients suffering from chronic heart disease; oxygen baths, which pump oxygen into water of about 90–95 °F, used for hypertensive and advanced cardiac disease cases; brine or salt baths, using sodium chloride, primarily for treatment in cases of osteomyelitis, fractures, dislocations, arthritis, myositis, fibrositosis, gout, and chronic sciatica; foam baths; and sponge baths.

9.3.6.2.3 Electrical parameters

— Voltage: smaller units: 120 V, one-phase; larger units: 208/220 V, one-phase or three-phase
— Frequency: 60 Hz
— Amperes: Varies

9.3.6.2.4 Sources of electrical problems

— Improper grounding
— Corrosion of electrical components
— Portable electrical cords

9.3.6.2.5 Design and installation recommendations

a) Receptacles (or outlets) should be as close to units as possible. Provide rough-in as per manufacturer's recommendation.

b) All circuits to be ground fault protected.

c) Ground all equipment and adjacent metallic surfaces.

d) For all large tanks and spas, furnish and install outlet in ceiling for patient lift.

9.3.7 Neurophysiological department

9.3.7.1 General

The neurophysiological department in the medium or larger medical center deals primarily in established knowledge and in new research in the field of brain physiology. The department deals in the areas of brain disorders and in such diverse activities and states of the nervous system as waking, sleeping, dreaming, consciousness, speech, learning, and memory. The electroencephalogram (EEG) is the primary tool utilized by the neurophysiologist and surgeon. The electrical activity of the brain is used to determine brain death in accident cases, and in certain circumstances can be used as an electrical parameter check in organ transplants.

9.3.7.2 Basic equipment in the neurophysiological department

9.3.7.2.1 Electroencephalogram (EEG) measurements

Electroencephalography is the measurement of the electrical activity of the brain. Since clinical EEG measurements are obtained from electrodes placed on the surface of the scalp, these waveforms represent a very gross type of summation of potentials that originate from an extremely large number of neurons in the vicinity of the electrodes.

The electrical patterns obtained from the scalp are the result of the graded potentials on the dendrites or neurons in the cerebral cortex and other parts of the brain, as they are influenced by the firing of other neurons that impinge on these dendrites.

EEG potentials have random-appearing waveforms with peak-to-peak amplitudes ranging from less than 10 µV to over 100 µV. Required bandwidth for adequately handling the EEG signal is from below 1 Hz to over 100 Hz.

For clinical measurements, surface or subdermal needle electrodes are used. The ground reference electrode is often a metal clip on the earlobe. A suitable electrolyte paste or jelly is used in conjunction with the electrodes to enhance coupling of the ionic potentials to the input of the measuring device. To reduce interference and minimize the effect of electrode movement, the resistance of the path through the scalp between electrodes should be kept as low as possible. Generally this resistance ranges from a few thousand ohms to nearly 100 kΩ, depending on the type of electrodes used.

Placement of electrodes on the scalp is commonly dictated by the requirements of the measurement to be made. In clinical practice, a standard pattern called the "10 to 20 Electrode Placement System" is generally used. This system, devised by a committee of the International Federation of Societies for Electroencephalography, is so named because electrode spacing is based on intervals of 10–20% of the distance between specified points on the scale.

In addition to the electrodes, the measurement of the EEG requires a readout or recording device and sufficient amplification to drive the readout device from the millivolt-level signals obtained from the electrodes. Most clinical electroencephalographs provide the capability of simultaneous recording EEG signals from several regions of the brain. For each signal, a complete channel of instrumentation is required. Thus, electroencephalographs having as many as 16 channels are available.

Because of the low-level input signals, the electroencephalograph should have high-quality differential amplifiers with good common-mode rejection. The differential preamplifier is generally followed by a power amplifier to drive the pen mechanism for each channel. In nearly all clinical instruments, the amplifiers are ac coupled with low-frequency cutoff below 1 Hz and a bandwidth extending to somewhere between 50 Hz and 100 Hz. Stable dc amplifiers can be used, but possible variations in the dc electrode potentials are often bothersome. Most modern electroencephalographs include adjustable upper- and lower-frequency limits to allow the operator to select a bandwidth suitable for the conditions of the measurement. In addition, some instruments include a fixed 60 Hz rejection filter to reduce power line interference.

In order to reduce the effect of electrode resistance changes, the input impedance of the EEG amplifier should be as high as possible. For this reason, most modern electroencephalographs have input impedances greater than 10 MΩ.

Perhaps the most distinguishing feature of an electroencephalograph is the rather elaborate lead selector panel, which in most cases permits any two electrodes to be connected to any channel of the instrument. Either a bank of rotary switches or a panel of push buttons is used.

The switch panel also permits one of several calibration signals to be applied to any desired channel for calibration of the entire instrument. The calibration signal is usually an offset of a known number of microvolts, which, because of capacitive coupling, results in a step followed by an exponential return to baseline.

The readout in a clinical electroencephalograph is a multichannel pen recorder with a pen for each channel. The standard chart speed is 30 mm/s, but most electroencephalographs also provide a speed of 60 mm/s for improved detail of higher-frequency signals. Some have a third speed of 15 mm/s to conserve paper during setup time. An oscilloscope readout for the EEG is also possible, but it does not provide a permanent record. In some cases, particularly in research applications, the oscilloscope is used in conjunction with the pen recorder to edit the signal until a particular feature or characteristic of the waveform is observed. In this way, only the portions of interest are recorded. Many electroencephalographs also have provisions for interfacing with an analog tape recorder to permit recording and playback of the EEG signal.

9.3.7.2.2 Electrical parameters

— Voltage: 120 V
— Frequency: 60 Hz
— Amperes: One 20 A circuit

9.3.7.2.3 Sources of electrical problems

— Radio frequency interference
— Patient lead connections
— Multichannel pen recorder with chart speed of 30 mm/s
— Interconnections to VDT or analog-type recorder

9.3.7.2.4 Design and installation recommendations

a) Circuit feeding unit should be clear of any other loads.
b) A filtered circuit may be desirable.
c) All fluorescent fixtures in the immediate area may be required to be equipped with RFI filters and low-leakage ballasts.
d) The room housing the unit may require shielding in walls.

9.3.8 Pulmonary function laboratory (ICU/neonatal)

9.3.8.1 General

The practice of rhythmically inflating the lungs by artificial means has been found to be of great value in the treatment of respiratory failure, the causes of which can be induced by many conditions and/or injuries. Since it is not practical to do this by hand for any length of time, there are machines that have been designed for the purpose. This does not include machines that exert negative pressure externally on the chest, as they are not used much these days. Only intermittent positive pressure machines will be described. The enormous number of such machines available indicates that there are few that suit every possible purpose. There are even fewer that are satisfactory for the special problems presented by infants or for adults with small chest cavities.

9.3.8.2 Equipment

a) *Ventilator.* A ventilator for an ICU should be able to ventilate any patient from birth to adult size, and should be able to work equally well in the presence of normal lungs or highly abnormal ones. Humidification is essential, but apparatus dead space should be kept to a minimum. The dead space in some humidifiers is far too large for use with infants. It must also be remembered that water overload in infants is a real hazard. Accurate control of inspired oxygen concentration is important, because there is evidence to suggest that high oxygen concentrations, combined with pressure on the lungs, may contribute to death from "ventilator lung" (a condition characterized by decreasing compliance of the lungs, visible as increasing opacity on x-rays, associated with small translucent areas, and an air bronchogram-microscopy will show hyaline membranes in the alveoli).

Since ICUs tend to be places of stress for both patients and nursing staff, it is helpful if a ventilator is fairly quiet in operation—on the other hand, an alteration in noise may serve as an alarm to warn of machine failure. Ease of sterilization is important, as patients on ventilators are very susceptible to infection.

To summarize, some desirable features of a ventilator for use in this type of unit are:

— Ability to deliver accurately a tidal volume of 15–1000 ml
— Ability to deliver this volume against high resistance and/or low compliance
— Ability to deliver low flow rates
— Rate control from 15/min to 40/min
— Accurate control of inspired oxygen concentration
— A variable inspiratory-expiratory ratio (I:E ratio)
— Good humidification for all tidal volumes
— Ease of sterilization
— Quietness of operation
— Ability to apply a variable expiratory resistance

The type or types of machine chosen for an individual unit depend on personal preference and also on the conditions treated. Some units may prefer to have all of one type—this certainly ensures that the staff becomes familiar with its operation. It is preferable to have two or three different types, to cope with various problems. A greater variety could become unwieldy.

b) *Monitoring of ventilation.* It is essential to have some method of ensuring adequate ventilation of the patient at all times. For this purpose several devices are used. Most machines incorporate a pressure manometer that reads airway pressure at the mouth, or at the machine; this is connected to the patient by a wide-bore tubing of low resistance. Due to resistance in the airways, the pressure in the alveoli may be very different from that at the mouth. Many machines have a blow-off valve preset at, for example, 70 mmHg, to protect the lungs from excessive pressure.

9.4 References

This chapter shall be used in conjunction with the following publications:

ANSI/AAMI ES1-1993, Safe Current Limits for Electromedical Apparatus.[5]

CSA Std C22.2 No. 125-M1984 (Reaff 1992), Electromedical Equipment.[6]

NFPA 70-1996, National Electrical Code®(NEC®).[7]

NFPA 99-1996, Health Care Facilities.

UL 544-1993, Medical and Dental Equipment.[8]

9.5 Bibliography

Additional information may be found in the following sources:

[B1] Bruner, J. M. R., MD, "Hazards of Electrical Apparatus." *Anesthesiology,* no. 2, Mar.–Apr. 1967.

[B2] FIPS Pub 94-1983, Guidelines on Electrical Power for ADP Installations.[9]

[B3] *Health Devices,* vol. 5, no. 8, pp. 194–195, June 1976.

[B4] Leeds, C. J., RN, CCRN; Okhtar, M., MD; and Damato, A. N., MD; "Fluoroscope-Generated Electromagnetic Interference in an External Demand Pacemaker." *Circulation,* vol. 55, no. 3, Mar. 1977.

[B5] Lehnert, B. E., "A hazard of magnetic interference with normal cycling of the Boums Infant Ventilator," *Respiratory Care,* vol. 21, no. 7, pp. 576–578, July 1976.

[B6] Starmer, C. F.; Whalen, R. E.; and McIntosh, H. D.; *American Journal of Cardiology,* vol. 14, pp. 537-546, Oct. 1964.

---

[5]ANSI publications are available from the Sales Department, American National Standards Institute, 11 West 42nd Street, 13th Floor, New York, NY 10036.

[6]CSA publications are available from the Canadian Standards Association (Standards Sales), 178 Rexdale Blvd., Rexdale, Ontario, Canada M9W 193.

[7]NFPA publications are available from Publications Sales, National Fire Protection Association, 1 Batterymarch Park, P.O. Box 9101, Quincy, MA 02269-9101.

[8]UL publications are available from Underwriters Laboratories, Inc., 333 Pfingsten Road, Northbrook, IL 60062-2096.

[9]FIPS publications are available from the National Technical Information Service (NTIS), U. S. Dept. of Commerce, 5285 Port Royal Rd., Springfield, VA 22161.

Chapter 10
Health care renovations

10.1 General discussion

The one constant in a hospital is change—change in personnel, change in technology, change in treatment methods, and change in space demands. Unfortunately, most codes and the design standards written for health care professionals often neglect the upgrade and renovation of existing facilities that are necessary to meet these changing needs. This neglect stems in part from a number of factors that seriously complicate renovation projects and that often render the projects works more of art than of science. A functioning hospital is a facility that is extremely sensitive to disruptions of any sort. Renovations are therefore especially tricky, as they often disrupt not only the immediate area but also other areas.

These renovation difficulties are usually exacerbated by changing code requirements. Indeed, recognizing the growing need for direction, codes are beginning to specifically address renovation in a number of instances. Several model building codes contain provisions for bringing the entire facility up to current codes in the event of renovation above a certain percentage of facility floor space. NFPA 99-1996[1] includes sections dealing with both new and renovated buildings. Other codes provide installation guidelines for performing certain portions of a renovation. Engineers should in all cases familiarize themselves with the codes that pertain to the particular renovation, noting carefully the provisions therein for renovation projects.

More problems develop from a lack of drawings that accurately reflect existing conditions, physical structures that may not accommodate building systems (such as air conditioning systems and sprinklers), and a lack of space for electrical equipment above ceilings. Figure 10-1 illustrates examples of some of the renovation problems in typical existing conditions. All of these problems become even more difficult in the current environment of health care cost-containment and the resulting construction budget constraints. Indeed, the successful renovation of any health care space requires a delicate balance of all of these various elements and a tremendous amount of cooperation between all of the involved parties.

Despite their inherent difficulties, renovation projects are becoming more and more common, and, therefore, are more and more deserving of specific attention. Recent reports show that hospitals now overwhelmingly choose renovation projects over new construction for modernizing their facilities, or for providing new services. The U.S. Commerce Department's *1990 Industrial Outlook Handbook* [B1][2], for instance, indicated that during 1990, 70% of health care construction spending was for additions and modernization, while the remaining 30% was spent for new construction. The U.S. Commerce Department has predicted this trend to continue through the decade.

---

[1]Information on references can be found in 10.8.

[2]The numbers in brackets correspond to those of the bibliography in 10.9.

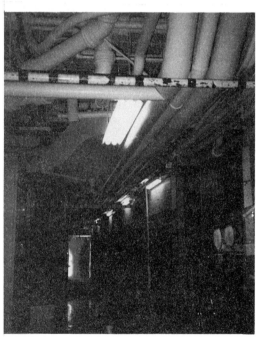

Figure 10-1—Existing conditions

Moreover, during recent years, many hospital infrastructures have been neglected as hospitals have spent their resources expanding their facilities. Many of these facilities now contain utility systems that have reached their limits in terms of both age and capacity. *Health Facilities Management* [B5] reports that hospital buildings and equipment are aging faster than those of other industries. They report that the average age of hospitals' physical plants are more than 40% older than the average age of Standard & Poor's industrial firms' physical plants. Moreover, rural hospitals average 24% older than the average age for all hospitals, and 70% older than the typical Standard & Poor's industrial firm.

This infrastructure neglect has involved

a)   Additional connections/increases in demand with no concurrent addition to system capacity.

b)   Deferral of needed maintenance.

c)   Successive remodeling/revisions to areas and systems without the benefit of a comprehensive facility design.

d)   Failure to replace outdated systems.

e)   A tendency to minimize capital costs at the expense of increased operating costs.

Hospital industry experts predict that hospitals will begin to be forced to upgrade and modernize their infrastructures whether or not they continue to grow. Indeed, a small proposed expansion often precipitates a comprehensive upgrade of one or more systems.

This chapter seeks to deal as comprehensively as possible with the issues involved in the renovation process for health care facilities. As renovations come in infinite shapes and sizes, no such treatment can cover every case. The authors have assumed a good working knowledge of the proper design for health care facilities, and have here tried to formulate a set of guidelines that will assist the engineer engaged in a renovation to ask the questions that are appropriate for such an endeavor.

10.2 Coordination

10.2.1 Coordination with users

In addition to the more detailed technical issues discussed below, a renovation project requires, most of all, coordination. The most important people in this process are the users of the space to be renovated, of the adjacent spaces, and/or of otherwise affected spaces. Such interruptions may be caused by

a)   Temporarily (or accidentally) shutting down existing services.
b)   The need to relocate personnel; by the disruption of traffic flows.
c)   The affecting of sterile environments; by noise and vibration.
d)   The need to haul debris out of the affected space or new materials into the project site.

The engineering, maintenance, and planning departments of the hospital can often assist in the coordination efforts with the various users.

A common design practice from the past, for instance, was the subfeeding of several panels from the same riser (see figure 10-2). Such a situation inevitably causes problems when a shutdown of one floor results in the shutdown of other floors. Similarly, risers through floors, both of power and of communications systems, should be accounted for in the design of a project, and either built around or relocated. The engineer should carefully locate all such risers affecting other areas and coordinate their final disposition with both the architect and the various owners' parties. Often, feeders for a particular renovation project will need to run through other occupied spaces, perhaps even patient care areas.

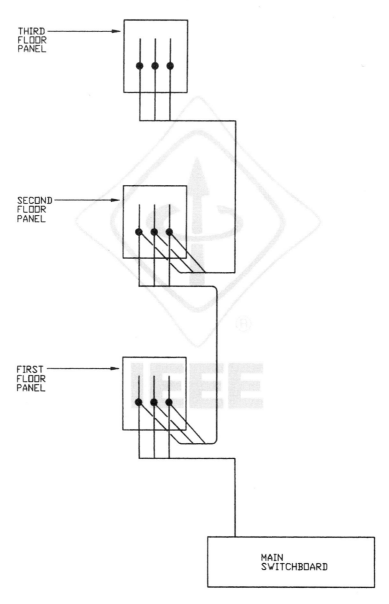

Figure 10-2—Subfeeding of several panels from the same riser

All such work should be coordinated in detail with the users of those spaces to minimize disruptions, and with the other trades (for cutting and patching, for instance). Much work may be performed after hours to minimize disruptions. Note, however, that requiring a contractor to perform such work outside normal business hours in order to accommodate users will inevitably result in overtime premiums. The operational benefits of such work should be carefully evaluated in light of these costs, and the options should be reviewed with all parties.

One approach to some of these problems that is often found extremely useful is the early demolition of the space to be renovated. The careful demolition will uncover unexpected difficulties and will allow the design to incorporate the solutions into the final plans. Such an approach can be especially useful, as even the most careful design cannot account for all of the peculiarities of a given area, nor for all of the conduits that pass through the proposed renovation space. Early demolition will ultimately save headaches, money, and often time. The problem with such an approach, of course, is the increased disruption and the loss of revenue from the additional time the space is not useful.

Another user very concerned with renovation projects is the hospital engineer. This individual is responsible for the continued proper operation and maintenance of the system after it is placed into operation, and the engineer designing a renovation will do well to coordinate with the hospital engineer. Indeed, in designing a renovation project, the electrical engineer should become something of a spokesperson for the hospital engineer; i.e., the engineer's mission is partly to educate all parties, thus resulting in an intelligent allocation of resources. Designs should be carefully thought out, and well integrated with the balance of the existing system, rather than being just another patch in a quilt of overlapping, disjointed designs.

10.2.2 Coordination with other trades

Equally as important as coordination with the user is coordination of the electrical work with the other building trades. Such coordination can take many forms. Many older buildings, designed using air induction unit ventilating systems, suffer from a lack of above-ceiling space. Column spacing may be irregular, and various structures will further constrict above-ceiling space. The building may include "choke points," or situations such as deep beams around the shafts in the core, which render a design impracticable or impossible.

Construction crews inevitably encounter situations in which the duct work conflicts with the cable tray, which conflicts with the sprinkler piping, which conflicts with the electrical feeders, and so on. Similarly, the other trades will have risers of their own that must be relocated or built around. Therefore, any renovation design should be carefully coordinated with the designers of the other trades to eliminate or to deal with all such areas of conflict. Compromises are often necessary and may include reduced ceiling heights, surface-mounted luminaries, or the rerouting of lines. Each proposed compromise should be carefully considered in terms of cost, future flexibility, integrity of design, and aesthetics. The engineer should therefore communicate the implications of each such accommodation to all involved parties during the design of the project.

Similarly, work between the trades should be sequenced so as to minimize disruptions, and to maximize ease of installation. This work sequence needs to be carefully considered during the design phase of a project to minimize delays and rework. Such care will, in turn, result in a better job at a lower cost and/or earlier completion.

A final area of coordination with other trades is the specification of equipment. Very often, the existing electrical system will contain only 240 V three-phase power, or 120/240 V single-phase power. In such cases, the engineer should coordinate the specification of any equipment outside of the electrical division specification with the available electrical characteristics. Similarly, older systems can be noisy (i.e., prone to spikes and surges as a result of a motor starting, or of x-ray loads), overloaded, divided incorrectly in terms of the essential loads, or poorly grounded, all of which should be considered in the specification of other equipment. Such requirements and the condition of existing equipment need to be discussed among all users, vendors, and other designers.

10.2.3 Coordination with code officials

The third major group that ought to be consulted in a renovation project is the various code officials that have jurisdiction over the project. When a specific project requires, for instance, implementation of a system in phases, the inspectors and codes administrators should become part of the design process to ensure that all of the various phases can be accomplished safely, and with as little difficulty as possible. Some renovations and upgrades are performed largely to meet updated codes and to placate the various inspectors, and thus their input is essential.

Some particular installations may not be able to meet the letter of the code as a result of existing conditions. A good example of this problem is the need to locate electrical equipment under existing waste risers that cannot be moved. In such a situation, the officials may allow drip-pans to be built under and around the pipes to protect the equipment. In all such situations where the letter of the code cannot be met, it is crucial to work with the senior code authorities to define an installation that is safe, that meets the needs of the owner, and that meets the intent of the codes. Design professionals need to recognize that such compromises and judgements make them particularly vulnerable to liability claims should something go wrong. Clear, written confirmations from the owner and from code officials are imperative. Finally, the design should, if possible, incorporate provisions that allow full compliance at a later time.

Similarly, many older systems do not particularly lend themselves to renovation based upon current codes. The most notable example of such a situation is that of a hospital with only one grouping of essential loads (or one grouping per area), i.e., those areas not served by life safety, critical, and equipment branches. Older hospitals tend to have been provided with one emergency panelboard that now serves a variety of loads, both essential and nonessential. Very often, trying to correct such an installation in a particular area being renovated to comply in all respects with current codes is virtually impossible without a full-scale upgrading of the entire system—a solution that can be extremely costly, inconvenient, and of marginal value. Indeed, such an upgrade can often be more disruptive than helpful in advancing overall system reliability.

In such regulatory compliance cases, the engineer and owners should carefully study the facility for overall safety and reliability of service to patients. A comprehensive plan should be carefully formulated, so that individual renovation projects, as they occur, may be designed in accordance with the general trend toward overall facility code compliance. Each step in this procedure should be carefully coordinated with the authorities having jurisdiction, for each installation will necessarily be a compromise approach. If properly planned and implemented, the sum of the compromises should provide a system of overall reliability and safety, and one that largely complies with the letter, as well as the spirit, of applicable codes and standards.

10.2.4 Coordination with existing physical conditions

The final, most obvious problem that makes renovations difficult is the set of physical limitations of the space to be renovated. The building structure usually severely limits the above-ceiling space, making coordination with the other trades especially difficult, and especially important. The routing of conduits and feeders through existing spaces can be equally difficult. The engineer should be careful in such cases to consider the types of conduits specified, as electrical metallic tubing (EMT) with set-screw fittings may be much more practical to install than intermediate metallic conduit (IMC) or rigid conduit that requires threaded connections. Frequently, abandoned chases, chimneys, or laundry chutes can be convenient avenues to spaces requiring renovation. More often, however, the feeders should be routed through occupied spaces; all options must be carefully investigated, discussed with all of the interested parties, and designed with sensitivity to their requirements. Similarly, existing switchgear may not be able to accept new breakers or switches. The system may not contain adequate spares/spaces, or may not have sufficient capacity to accept additional loading. In such cases, not only the branch circuit wiring but also the distribution system itself must be renovated, as discussed in 10.3. If the power source is upgraded, the available fault current may be increased beyond the short-circuit rating of the equipment.

10.3 Safety and reliability of existing systems

For a health care facility, the twin issues of personnel safety and system reliability are inextricably wound together, as very often a patient's life might depend upon the reliability of the building electrical system. Changes in current codes, such as the division of essential loads, largely represent a response to these concerns. Any construction involved in the renovation of a health care facility should be performed in strict accordance with all current codes to ensure a facility without inherent risks to its future occupants (however, see 10.2.3). Similarly, the designer should take care to correct any safety defects that may be uncovered in the course of the renovation.

One obvious safety issue in the renovation of an existing facility is the age of the various system components. For instance, older conductors represent a potential hazard both to individuals contacting them and to those depending upon them for continued operation of utilization equipment. The engineer needs to examine the existing site to determine if existing switchgear, panelboards, and/or feeders may be reused by splicing into existing conductors; however, it is a practice that should be avoided. Similarly, component capacities and coordination characteristics should be verified for proper operation of the proposed system. Feeders and large branch circuit conductors should be tested, and connections should be checked with temperature detectors.

The prudent engineer will also spend time examining the site for other electrical hazards. Some such hazards include the following:

a)   Branch circuit neutral wire shared by circuits from two panels
b)   Circuit breakers that are double-lugged
c)   Bare neutral feeder conductors
d)   Missing junction-box covers
e)   Poor splices
f)   Wires not properly protected by overcurrent devices
g)   Medium-voltage cables glowing with corona-halos

This list is not intended to be exhaustive; it merely reflects some of the more interesting situations experienced by the authors of this chapter. All such problems should be identified and corrected as quickly as possible. Where large nonlinear loads are being added to existing systems, the neutral conductors may not be of sufficient size.

10.4 Updating power distribution systems

10.4.1 General discussion

Current trends in hospital equipment, and in its power consumption, are moving in two opposite directions—while users are using more and more equipment, thus increasing demands of the electrical system, technology is allowing for equipment to accomplish the same tasks with less and less power. Today's chillers, for instance, use fewer kilowatts per ton than those chillers of 10 years ago. The net overall affect of a renovation, though, tends to be an increase in electrical loads. Accordingly, a hospital addition will clearly add load to the electrical system, and a hospital renovation will impose a new use profile onto the existing electrical system. The decision of whether to add on, rework, or simply reuse, should be carefully considered in terms of its impact on the balance of the existing system.

The engineer planning a modification to an existing electrical system needs to carefully evaluate the system configuration of the essential systems, and whether it has the three separate essential system branches required by the National Electrical Code® (NEC®) (NFPA 70-1996). If not, the engineer must determine

a)   Whether such a division should be imposed on the system.

b)   The types of loads.

c)   How the loads will cycle on and off, and how that use-profile will affect the balance of the system.

In addition, the engineer should assess the current-carrying capacity of elements to be reused, all the way to the service entrance switchboard, and should obtain actual field-measured loading information for these devices. With this information, the engineer can define the steps necessary to graft the proposed system onto the existing system without significant disruption.

10.4.2 Essential system plant

Of critical importance to the proper operation of a health care facility is its standby genera-tion system. Chapter 5 should be consulted for guidelines for the proper design of such a system. However, several modifications may be made relatively easily to an existing system to enhance overall plant reliability and to respond to new demands imposed by proposed load additions/modifications. A frequently encountered problem is the need for additional capacity in the generator plant. Past studies done by the American Hospital Association indicate that overloading the generator is one of the principal reasons for failure of the emergency power system during an emergency. A system currently employing two or more generators is already using some sort of paralleling, lead-lag, or other load-sharing scheme, and should be relatively easy to modify. A one-generator system, though, may be more difficult to modify. This problem too, can be attacked from a number of different directions.

The simplest approach to solving generator loading problems is the replacement of the existing generator with a larger unit. This approach, though, is limited in that it may force replacement of the distribution equipment that was presumably sized to service the smaller generator. Moreover, reliance upon a single generator is never as reliable as serving the same system from two or more units. Finally, such replacement of an existing generator will be tantamount to discarding the balance of the older generator's remaining useful life. Accord-ingly, addition of a second generator to the existing plant is usually the preferred approach.

A simple and relatively low-cost method for adding this additional generator is to add a single-engine generator set and associated transfer switch(es) remote from the existing gener-ators(s), but near to the end-use loads, and dedicated to serving those loads. Locating the new generator close to the new loads will reduce initial costs by eliminating load feeders. However, fueling the new generator from the existing bulk storage fuel tank could be expen-sive and/or difficult, depending on the site layout. Second, the remote generator makes main-tenance, operation, and testing more time-consuming than for a centrally located common plant. A third disadvantage is the lack of redundancy that could be realized when paralleling or interconnecting two or more generator sets. Finally, the building cost for the new generator space (if the generator is located indoors), the noise, the exhaust, the accessibility to the unit, and the unit's heat rejection should be all be considered before selecting this option.

A second approach to adding a generator onto an existing plant is to introduce it in a primary-secondary set-up. For example, if the existing system uses a 350 kW generator to serve 300 kW of essential loads (see figure 10-3), and if plans call for the addition of 100 kW of essential load, the existing generator could be supplemented by a 500 kW unit and transfer mechanism (see figure 10-4). In this approach, the 500 kW generator normally carries all of the load, with the older 350 kW unit acting as a standby. Then, should the 500 kW generator fail, the standby unit will come on line, shed the 100 kW of load, and carry the balance. Such an approach should also involve a redistribution of the essential loads so that all critical/life safety loads are not "dumped" when the smaller generator dumps a portion of the load. This scheme offers a comparable cost to the replacement of an older generator by a larger genera-tor; dramatically improves system reliability; offers capacity for future expansion; and uses, rather than discards, the capacity of the existing generator.

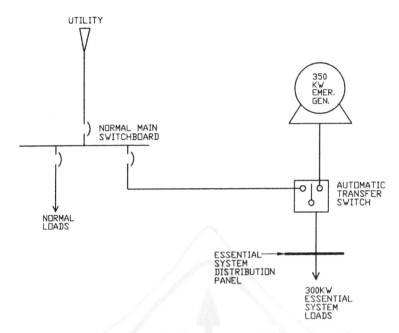

Figure 10-3—Hypothetical system before renovation

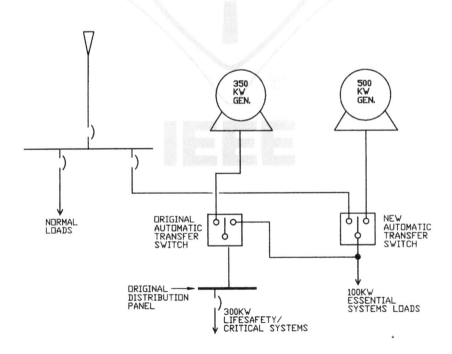

Figure 10-4—Hypothetical system after renovation

A final approach to adding a generator, and one virtually necessitated by a system of three or more generators, is to add a new generator and parallel it with the existing generator system. This arrangement provides the ultimate in reliability for essential system loads. In this scheme, some lower priority loads can be shed to balance load on the remaining generator(s). The disadvantages of paralleling generators are the cost of the system; the physical limitations of generator room expansion; the ability of the fuel, cooling, and exhaust systems to handle the additional generator; and the new short-circuit duty on the switchboard that may impact the overcurrent devices.

10.4.3 Proper division of loads

10.4.3.1 Essential distribution system

When renovating a hospital the engineer should determine if the existing essential electrical distribution system meets the requirements of the currently enforced edition of the NFPA codes (the NEC, NFPA 99-1996, and NFPA 101-1994), as discussed previously. If the system is deficient, and the renovations affect a significant portion of the building, plans for system upgrade should be formulated. If, however, the renovation affects only a small portion of the facility, the authorities having jurisdiction may be willing to issue a variance for the design.

One approach to the renovation of an essential system that utilizes only one emergency branch is, in some ways, less complicated than renovating a multiple-branch system. The most widely adopted codes (the NEC, NFPA 99-1996, and NFPA 101-1994) require that a minimum of two branches be added (note that for essential systems with a load of only 150 kVA, only one switch is required). The addition of branches to the existing system can help to facilitate construction phasing. If the existing distribution and branch circuit panelboards on the load side of the existing distribution equipment are properly subdivided, the existing distribution feeders can be rerouted and served from the new automatic transfer switches, creating the three distinct branches. However, if the load-side distribution and branch circuit panels serve a conglomeration of loads from each type of essential system load, three branches, consisting of transfer mechanisms and distribution apparatus, should be added. In essence, this approach provides an additional, properly designed infrastructure for the eventual support of the entire facility. This approach allows the future transfer of loads from the existing system to the new system as renovation projects occur.

Renovating essential systems with multiple branches, each serving a variety of essential system loads, potentially makes the construction phasing of the project much more complicated. The most effective solution in most cases is to create three entirely new branches, and to phase the renovations as described above. Alternatively, the existing branches could be designated to each serve a different one of the essential system loads. Then, as renovations proceed, the loads for those renovations can be strictly divided among the various branches until all of the facility loads are properly divided.

10.4.3.2 Area renovation

Presumably, the engineer undertaking the renovation of a particular area will be working in accordance with a cohesive system renovation/expansion vision as discussed above.

However, in rare cases such an approach may not be possible, and existing system infrastructure may not allow proper division of loads. In this event, the renovation design can reuse existing system components, relying on upstream modifications to provide suitable reliability of service to the renovated project. Alternatively, essential loads for the area to be renovated may be properly divided onto a set of panels that, in turn, are served from the one branch of the existing system, relying on future system renovations to properly reconnect these loads. Such an approach should only be used, though, as a last resort and after careful consultation with appropriate authorities.

10.4.4 Dealing with nonstandard voltages

When renovating existing facilities, the engineer may encounter nonstandard voltages. A relatively common nonstandard system found in existing facilities is 240 V (ground delta) or 120/240 V (open delta). Today it is common to install 120/208 V, three-phase, four-wire (grounded wye) systems in lieu of 240 V systems. Therefore, when renovating a health care facility, the engineer may encounter an existing piece of equipment rated for 240 V that must be served by a 120/208 V, three-phase, four-wire panel. The opposite situation may occur where a new piece of equipment rated for 208 V must be served by a 240 V or 120/240 V panel (replacing the old 240 V equipment, with attendant gains in efficiency and reliability, may also be an option). In both cases, buck-boost transformers may be used to step the voltage up or down as needed.

In many instances, existing 120/240 V panels serve only single-phase loads, and may be reconnected to a 120/208 V system. If several such panels are reconnected, the engineer should be careful to coordinate the phases the loads are reconnected to, or the phases may become highly unbalanced. Finally, other transformers may be used to serve loads of various voltages. Transformers of 480–240 V are available, as are 240–208 V transformers. Also, the transformers may be connected reversed, or 208–240 V, if required for selective loads.

10.4.5 Grounding

10.4.5.1 Introduction

The engineer should also carefully examine the existing grounding system. Elements to be checked (depending upon the particular renovation) include the system ground, the emergency generator neutral, the ground-bus bond between critical and normal branch circuit panels, and whether branch circuits serving patient care areas contain a green grounding conductor. A properly grounded system is important not only to patient and staff safety, but also to effective operation of today's electronic equipment.

10.4.5.2 System grounding

To determine if the system ground at the main switchboard is adequate, the designer should test the impedance of the ground path using a method equivalent to the "Biddle" test (see IEEE Std 142-1991). The impedance of the ground path should not exceed 10 Ω; 5 Ω or less are preferable for larger systems. If the impedance exceeds 10 Ω, additional ground rods may have to be driven to lower the impedance. Similarly, secondary grounds for transformers serving areas to be renovated should be checked, as should continuity of grounding conductors and bonding jumpers from the grounding electrode to the last existing panel to be reused.

10.4.5.3 Area renovation

When renovating patient care areas, the engineer should determine if the receptacles and fixed electrical equipment serving the area are grounded by an insulated copper conductor in a metallic conduit. In older installations, the raceway was commonly used as the bonding connection. Affected branch circuits must be rewired from the panel with a circuit containing an equipment grounding conductor. The engineer should also verify that the ground bus of the critical branch circuit panel and the ground bus of the normal branch circuit panel are properly bonded together with an insulated copper conductor #10 AWG or larger, as now required by the NEC.

10.4.6 Impact of changes on integrity of system

Obviously, any modification to an existing electrical system will have repercussions that extend far beyond the area being renovated. In particular, the engineer should check the time-current characteristics of devices to be added against those of existing devices. This crucial element of renovation design is often overlooked, but should be carefully considered so as not to compromise system selection coordination. Similarly, addition of motor loads to an existing system may put short-circuited currents onto a system incapable of withstanding these stresses. Transformer replacement will affect the maximum available fault currents to portions of the system. Other electrical characteristics, such as loads cycling on and off, loads generating harmonics that disrupt other devices elsewhere on the system, and transformer inrushes, all may result in further changes in the final system design. Accordingly the engineer needs to consider carefully the impact the loads and system design will impose upon the existing system, and take the necessary steps to mitigate those effects. The engineer should conduct a complete short-circuit and protective device coordination analysis to determine required protective device upgrades, and system withstand capabilities.

10.4.7 Operating room electrical systems

Operating rooms (ORs) are areas of much concern in the renovation process as a result of several factors. First, the overriding concern is for the patient's safety during the treatment. Second, the declining use of flammable anesthetics and changing code regulations regarding isolated power in ORs continue to cause much confusion. Finally, ORs are not immune to the proliferation of technology, and specifically, to technology that requires an outlet. A perfect example of this sort is the addition of a three-phase laser to an existing operating room now served by a single-phase isolation system.

Chapter 6 describes the reasons that an isolated power system is recommended in ORs, despite the recent dropping of the requirement for such systems by the NEC. Isolated power systems are still highly recommended (and required by some local codes), and the engineer considering the renovation of an OR will do well to consider the advantages of such a system carefully. Such consideration becomes especially important when new equipment and services are introduced into an existing OR. Generally speaking, if a particular OR already contains an isolated power system, any addition to that room's electrical system should derive from that isolated power system. If the existing system is at capacity, a second system, complete with its own alarms, can be added to accommodate the new requirements. The second system could serve several rooms, as in the case of a three-phase system serving lasers in two or three rooms. In this case, each room served should have remote annunciators located in each room, and all devices should be carefully labelled in the room to indicate the correct panel. On balance, then, using isolated power systems in ORs that are to be renovated is strongly recommended, and maintaining the use of isolated power in a room already containing an isolated power system is even more strongly recommended.

A final question often encountered in the renovation of an operating room or suite is that of receptacles to be used. At one time, ORs were equipped with NEMA locking-type receptacles under the theory that if a careless person were to trip over a cord, it should stay plugged in. Less and less equipment is now being made (or purchased) with plugs to fit these receptacles. Straight-blade receptacles are becoming more and more prevalent under the theory that the clumsy person is better off unplugging the cord, rather than ripping the device out of the patient. The engineer planning an OR renovation should be careful to coordinate the receptacle type with the needs of the staff.

10.5 Lighting renovated spaces

Properly lighting a hospital renovation project poses several unique challenges. The original lighting design relied on older technologies and on older standards that used footcandles as the sole design criterion to achieve its lighted environment. The aesthetic sought was probably the institutional-look seen in so many older hospitals, rather than today's more home-like approach. Applying current technologies and current methods for design of lighting and its control, however, can be especially difficult as a result of the physical limitations noted earlier. Proper amounts of daylight may be difficult to achieve through existing window openings. Most of the principles of good lighting for hospitals found in Chapter 7 can be achieved through careful coordination with the users, the architect, and the other trades.

The patient room is central to a hospital, and its design serves to highlight some of the creativity that should be used in renovation design. A patient room may be occupied by various people performing various sorts of tasks as described in Chapter 7. Older designs did not necessarily cater to all of these needs, but instead tried to achieve a certain footcandle level. In attempting to achieve the lighting required for all of the required functions, the engineer should incorporate the design principles and new technologies of Chapter 7 while adapting to the existing conditions. In patient rooms the problems of space above the ceiling are minimal, as most of the task-specific lighting for the space can be mounted on the walls (i.e., over-bed lights and nightlights), or may be table lamps specific for visitors, or may be located so that they are in some far away corner (such as down-lights for visitors), so as not to interfere with the other trades. Such a combination of methods and fixtures not only provides task-specific light for each of the individual room functions, but also does so in a manner that avoids some of the potential coordination problems.

Of course, the engineer should take care not to "over-engineer" the space (i.e., to not provide such a profusion of varied lights and switches that operation becomes similar to operating a 747 airplane).

Another portion of the hospital with challenges unique to renovation are laboratories. In the past, laboratories were planned by the architect and lighted to the proper footcandle level by the engineer. Newer technologies and methods emphasizing the proper lighting at the task surface can both hinder and help the engineer. The new technologies include the use of lamps with proper color rendering indices and color temperatures making the visual tasks required in the laboratory easier to achieve. However, the physical limitations of the space, as well as the fume hood and other duct work of the mechanical engineer, can make the proper arrangement of luminaires installed overhead within the ceiling extremely difficult to achieve. In such cases, the laboratory arrangements may be rearranged to best accommodate both the above conditions as well as the user's traffic and use patterns. Permanently installed or portable task-lighting may be used to provide the higher levels required for certain tasks. Again, each of these options should be carefully coordinated with the various parties to the project.

Another lighting application that causes problems in renovations are the corridors and the nurses' stations. Corridors typically have the worst space congestion above the ceiling, making wall-sconce, linear surface-mounted sources, or down-lights in soffits especially useful. Figure 10-5 illustrates one potential solution. The space above ceilings in corridors, and over and around the nurses' stations, is usually filled with equipment, making lighting particularly difficult. In addition, nurses' stations are being equipped more and more with video display terminals (VDTs) and with monitoring screens that increase the lighting and glare problems associated with these areas. Dropped areas at the perimeters of the stations afford good opportunities for fixture placement, as well as help to emphasize the nurses' station as a separate space within the larger space. Efficient use of task and undercounter lighting may also be useful in these spaces.

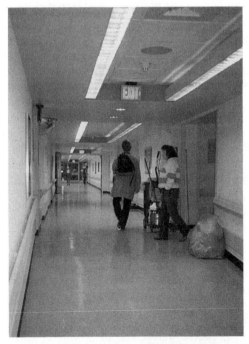

Figure 10-5—Alternate corridor lighting design

In each of the cases mentioned, the engineer should first carefully assess the lighting requirements of the space to be renovated, and then the existing conditions that will affect the lighting design. Then the engineer should design the lighting system in accordance with the principles in Chapter 7, while coordinating carefully with the architect, the other trades, and the staff to ensure the proper installation.

10.6 Working with existing communications systems

10.6.1 Fire alarm systems

Fire alarm systems seem to cause more problems in the renovation of a health care facility than any other system. They are crucial to the safety of building occupants, yet they seem to have an aura of mystery surrounding them. The fire alarm system is also highly integrated into the building as a whole.

Fire alarm technology and codes have both changed significantly and quickly, so that older buildings now tend to have some sort of combination of systems of different vintages somehow rigged together into a single precarious system. Maintenance is inevitably laborious and expensive, and failures of these systems are common.

Most older facilities were built with mechanically-coded systems. Such systems typically consist of pull-station risers located near exits with a coded pull-station at each level. Detectors (where present) are typically circuited by floor and zone to a central junction-box at a riser emanating from the control panel. Coders for the detector circuits, as well as power supplies and drivers for diagnostic and control functions, are located in the control panel. Alarm bell circuits rise up from the control panel through the building, often sharing conduit risers with the pull-stations. Annunciators tended to be back-lit panels, usually located in a telephone operator's room, maintenance shops, or the main entrance. Many older systems do not have visual fire alarm devices, and most do not have flashing exit signs as is now required by the Americans with Disabilities Act.

With the introduction of solid-state electronics some years ago, the mechanical systems began to be phased out and electronically-coded systems began to take their place. In facilities having the older mechanical systems, the newer systems were often piggy-backed onto the existing system, usually through a single mechanical coder. Such combining of systems often causes resetting problems, as well as problems with alarm location.

Manufacturers have recently begun introducing a new generation of fire alarm systems using microprocessor technology (see Chapter 8). These systems typically are noncoded, with visual annunciation via flashing lights and exit lights, and audio annunciation via march-time chimes or bells with voice indications of zone of alarm. Such systems may be either hard-wired or multiplexed, and are much more flexible than the older systems. Despite these improvements, however, interfacing these systems with older systems still causes problems that are similar to those mentioned in the preceding paragraph.

The engineer facing the project of renovation of a hospital space will do well to devote considerable time to the fire alarm system. Very often, it is deceptive to consider the needs of the space to be renovated alone; the fire alarm system should be considered as a whole. Patchwork solutions for defined spaces tend to exacerbate existing system problems. Where older systems are present, devices may not be available that will work with the system. Control panels are often extended to the point of capacity, rendering the addition of devices required by current codes impossible. Required control functions may be impossible to achieve. Risers may be old, unreliable, or located in the wrong places.

The engineer planning a space renovation should first define the fire alarm requirements for the proposed project. The engineer should then become intimate with the existing system, and accurately assess its capacity to support the required functions without major modifications. Any deficiency that requires an upgrade to support the proposed renovation needs to be carefully coordinated with the regulatory officials. Very often, a lack in the existing system will precipitate an upgrade of the entire system. Engineers should be careful that in adding onto an existing system, their addition is not merely a patchwork addition, but a functional, reliable design that does not cause additional problems to the hospital staff. Similarly, when renovation of an area of the facility requires reworking portions of the existing system, the entire system in that area should be replaced (i.e., old and new system functions should not be mixed in one area).

Two approaches are possible in the replacement of an existing fire alarm system. First, the system can be replaced in total, and all facets can be brought up to code throughout the facility. While this is logically the simpler approach, it can be logistically the most difficult, as operations in every space will be disrupted by the work. Cost is a further disadvantage of this approach.

The second, less drastic, approach is to merely replace the central equipment (and that of the space to be renovated) with the new microprocessor-based generation of equipment. This equipment will then tie into the existing system, and allow for future expansion of the system using the inherent flexibility of this type of system. This approach, while attractive from both the cost and disruption standpoints, may still pose many operational problems. In essence, it is repeating the piggy-backing of systems, with all of the attendant problems. Having different areas of the hospital on different fire alarm systems, tied together tenuously at best, can cause severe problems. One compromise solution to this problem is to completely replace the existing control boards with the new system, and terminate all of the old risers directly into the new system. This approach will not solve all of the reliability problems of the remote devices, nor will it immediately solve all of the code-violation problems, but it will be fairly inexpensive, and will solve, to a great extent, the problem of tying several generations of alarm control systems together. All aspects of the fire alarm system must be carefully coordinated with the facility administration, engineering, and fire and security departments, as well as regulatory agents.

Very often, a renovation project can reuse existing central equipment, adding or reusing existing devices, control sequences, and zoning. In such cases, however, the engineer should be careful to check the capacities of door holder circuits and audio, visual, and audio/visual circuits that are to be reused or extended. Alarm system zoning also needs to be reviewed and modified as required.

10.6.2 Sound/paging systems

Often overlooked, the public address (PA) systems in health care facilities deserve special attention in the renovation of an existing space. As technology drives fire alarm systems in the direction of noncoded voice systems, the PA system becomes a central element in the fire safety systems of the facility; therefore, it must be of supreme reliability. "Code blue" functions are often performed over the PA system, so patients' lives are often at stake. Yet in the face of these emerging demands for system performance, amplifiers are often overloaded, circuits are tapped into unknown points, volume is gradually lost by continuing additions, wiring is strung above ceilings instead of in conduits or trays, and speaker placement and settings are random at best.

In planning the renovation of a particular space within a facility, then, the prudent engineer should closely examine both the central system and the circuits in that space, if possible. Load readings at the amplifiers should be recorded to ensure that the addition of the proposed speakers can be accommodated. As much as possible, the existing circuits that will be used should be traced, and their capacity assessed, as well as their condition. If possible, the vendor who supplied the system should be consulted in assessing the system's capacity to support the proposed renovation. Within the renovated space, the cabling should be run in conduits or in cable trays provided for the purpose. Speaker placement should be planned carefully to provide the required personnel (fire response teams or "code blue" teams, for instance) the ability to hear any announcements. If the system is integrated with the telephone system and provided by the telephone vendor, the design should be coordinated with the vendor. The potential to "quiet" the hospital ambiance by using alternates, such as radio pagers, or local area paging in lieu of overhead paging, should also be explored.

Very often, a close examination of the overhead paging system will lead to the realization that it is inadequate. In that event, new amplifiers or speaker circuits may need to be provided as part of the project. It is better to discover such a problem while planning the renovation, rather than blowing an amplifier when the project is complete.

10.6.3 Nurse-call systems

Nurse-call systems tend to be easier to deal with in renovating a space than the previous systems, as they tend to be much more localized. Again, because of the rapid changes in technologies and manufacturers, obtaining replacement parts for an existing system may be extremely difficult. Sometimes the maintenance personnel of a hospital may have some extra parts in stock, or a manufacturer may be able to supply parts to make the system work. With larger renovations—because of shifting usages and needs by the staff, maintenance, reliability, and sheer availability reasons—the engineer should replace the entire nurse-call system for that area.

10.6.4 Clock systems

Clock systems come in three varieties: battery-powered individual clocks, synchronous (hardwired), or electronic (line-powered or frequency-corrected). The concern here is with only the last two, but the engineer should determine the system that the owner uses and/or prefers. Clock systems seem to have long lifetimes and to be prone to fewer failures than the systems previously discussed. For that reason, existing systems may typically be reused. Again, however, the engineer should determine the feeder circuit to be used and ensure that it can support the proposed renovation. The engineer should determine (synchronous system) which branch of the circuit carries the clock signal, and also determine if it is the appropriate system. The engineer should avoid placing capacitors onto the same branch of the electrical system, as capacitors will divert the carrier current signal to ground and will render the system useless. Finally, some of the newer generations of fire alarm systems can act as signal generators to local areas. So, small clock systems using the fire alarm system as the master clock may be created for the renovations of particular spaces. Such an approach can help to overcome capacity application problems, as well as any other systemic problems posed by the existing installation.

10.6.5 Miscellaneous systems

Hospitals contain examples of every other type of system, including observational video, patient television, building management systems, data processing, narcotics alarms, telephones, intercoms, patient monitoring, security, and dictation. There are no firm rules in extending these systems into a renovated area, but extensive coordination, discovering user needs early, installing sufficient raceways, and providing room for central equipment is necessary. These systems are all very user-intensive, and require power, wiring, and cooling. The engineer should, in all cases, talk to the users, maintainers, and to the vendors who provided and/or serviced the system to investigate the best ways to extend the systems. The needs of the space to be renovated should be carefully determined from the future users, and any impact to other spaces should be dealt with. The engineer should carefully plan all required risers for the various systems, and should coordinate their routing with the various owners' parties. Finally, if the engineer needs to provide central equipment for any of these systems, the power quality at the proposed location should be checked, and the appropriate filtering and battery backup should be checked, to ensure that proper system operation is provided.

One excellent system for distribution of the growing masses of communications wiring is cable trays. The trays run throughout the corridors to gather cabling from the individual devices and carry it to the central equipment/riser location(s). Such a system can be extremely useful in keeping the areas above ceilings free of clutter and tends to be less expensive than all-conduit systems. Even this system should be coordinated, as some communications systems require a divider in such a tray to isolate their cables, or they may require shielded or plenum-listed conductors, or low-smoke combustion conductors. The location of the tray in the ceiling should be carefully coordinated with the other trades to ensure access to it.

10.7 Preparing for future renovations

The final consideration in a renovation project, and indeed in any project, is the preparation for the future renovation. Small, simple elements of a design can help facilitate future renovations without greatly increasing the project cost and should be incorporated. Besides the obvious provision of physical spaces for future equipment, other such elements might include stubbing spare conduits up from flush-mounted panel boards; providing spare conduits between electrical rooms; and providing spare risers with junction boxes at each floor location. Circuits (both power and communications) can be moderately loaded so as to afford easy expansion; cable trays can be installed to facilitate addition of communications wiring; spare capacity, both in terms of load capacity and spare/space capacity in switchgear. The system itself should be designed to be as flexible as possible, including liberal use of main breakers, especially on panels served by feeders with several panel loads. Many microprocessor-based communication systems are tremendously flexible in their expansion/reconfiguration capability. The last and perhaps most important preparation for future renovation is proper documentation and preparation of record drawings. Planning for any future renovation is greatly facilitated by accurate, complete drawings of the project, both in terms of locating potential difficulties, and in locating areas of the design that lend themselves to easy expansion.

10.8 References

This chapter shall be used in conjunction with the following publications:

IEEE Std 142-1991, IEEE Recommended Practice for Grounding of Industrial and Commercial Power Systems (IEEE Green Book) (ANSI).[3]

NFPA 70-1996, National Electrical Code® (NEC®).[4]

NFPA 99-1996, Health Care Facilities.

NFPA 101-1994, Life Safety Code®.

10.9 Bibliography

Additional information may be found in the following sources:

[B1] *1990 Industrial Outlook Handbook.* U.S. Commerce Department. Available from Bernan Associates, 4611-M Assembly Drive, Lanham, MD 20706.

[B2] Bacon, Kenneth H., "Medical Waste; Hospital Construction Booms, Driving Cost of Health Care Up," *The Wall Street Journal,* col. 1, p. A1, Jan. 10, 1990.

[B3] "Health Care Physical Plants Worse Off than Those in Industry," *Health Facilities Management,* Mar. 1990.

---

[3]IEEE publications are available from the Institute of Electrical and Electronics Engineers, 445 Hoes Lane, P.O. Box 1331, Piscataway, NJ 08855-1331.

[4]NFPA publications are available from Publications Sales, National Fire Protection Association, 1 Batterymarch Park, P.O. Box 9101, Quincy, MA 02269-9101.

[B4] Kubal, Joseph, "Health Care Construction Boom to Continue in '90s," *Health Facilities Management,* Mar. 1990.

[B5] Martinsons, Jane, "New Construction to Overtake Renovation in '90s," *Health Facilities Management,* June 1990.

[B6] Nash, Hugh, "Application of National Electrical Code® to Renovation of Existing Buildings," Joint Session of the Health Care and Electrical Sections, NFPA Annual Convention, May 22, 1984.

[B7] Nash, Hugh, "How Healthy is Your Hospital Standby System?" *Specifying Engineer,* Mar. 1986.

[B8] Souhrada, Laura, "A-1 Renovation: Planning for the Future," *Hospitals,* Feb. 20, 1990.

INDEX

A

ground-fault protection, 59–60
  equipment selection, 59, 202, 208–210
  preventing ground currents, 60
  types of ground currents, 59–60
low-voltage systems, 64–69
medium-voltage systems, 62–64
overview, 57, 61
protection requirements, 57–58
types of faults, 58–59

T

Talk-back (voice paging systems), 276
Tandem switching (telephone systems), 253
Tape (security sensor), 315
Telemetry systems, 31, 296, 363
Telephone systems, 114, 248–257. See also
    Communication and signal systems
code blue call system, 273–274
design criteria, 249
features, 250–253
  automatic route selection, 252
  direct inward dialing (DID), 252
  integrated services digital network (ISDN)
    compatibility, 252
  intercom, 251
  multiple-attendant answering, 251
  remote diagnostics, 253
  speed dialing, 251
      station message detail accounting
      (SMDA), 252
  station message detail recording (SMDR),
    252
  system interconnection, 251
  tandem switching, 253
  voice mail, 252
overview, 248–249
telephone cable plant and support structure,
    253–257
  apparatus closets, 256
  equipment rooms, 257
  main terminal room, 254–255
  public telephones, 257
  riser systems, 255–256
  satellite closets, 257
  service entrance cables, 253–254

types of, 249–250
  central office, 250
  electronic key telephone system (EKTS),
    249, 251, 256, 258
  hybrid systems, 249–250
  instrumentation, 250
  private branch exchange (PBX), 250–253,
    255, 257
Television systems, 318–325. See also Com-
    munication and signal systems
  amplifiers, 322–323
  cable plant, 322
  cameras, 323
  chapel, 324
  computer-directed programming, 319–320
  controlled viewing, 319
  entertainment and educational program-
    ming, 319
  master antenna, 322
  medical staff education, 320
  monitor selection, 324
  operating room, 325
  overview, 318–319
  pathology consultation, 320–321
  patient monitoring, 321
  satellite receiving stations, 321, 325
  security, 314, 322
  studio, 324
  subject lighting, 324
  subject viewing, 323–324
  television sets and recorders, 320
Telewriters, 335–336
Temperature, generator sets, 128–129
Testing, electrical equipment, 70–77, 217–
    219. See also Electrical power distribu-
    tion systems
Thermal storage, 34
Three-phase isolated system, 215
Timed center-off position transfer switch,
    145–146
Tissue reaction to heat, 199
Tissue resistance, 199
Toilet emergency station, nurse call systems,
    264, 266, 272
Totalized metering, 30
Transfer switches, 72, 74, 147
  automatic. See automatic transfer switches